6 Tanyin Alley

6
Tanyin Alley

by LIU ZONGREN

CHINA
BOOKS
& Periodicals, Inc.
San Francisco

Cover illustration and design by Jos Sances
Book design by Laurie Anderson

Copyright © 1989 by China Books & Periodicals, Inc. All rights reserved.

No part of this book may be used or reproduced in any manner whatsoever without permission in writing from the publisher. Address inquiries to China Books, 2929 24th Street, San Francisco, CA 94110

Library of Congress Catalog Card Number: 89-60226
ISBN 0-8351-2146-1

Printed in the United States of America by CHINA BOOKS
& Periodicals, Inc.

"This is the story of my time, not of my life."
—Liu Zongren

Contents

Editor's Note   ix

A Few Cross-Cultural Notes   xiii

Map   xiv

1. Home from the Service   1
2. Dian Wen Becomes My Mentor   8
3. I Go for Vulgar Tastes   14
4. I Suspect Dian Wen Is Chasing Shalin   22
5. I Get Shalin when She Is Ill   30
6. We Court without Romance   37
7. The Great White Pagoda   43
8. Marriage Depends on a Room   48
9. A Sweet and Horrible Night   53
10. We Build a Love Nest on a Mousehole   61
11. Mr. Yin Is Not Content with Life   66
12. Wise Granny Yin   73
13. Patriarch Tong and His Family   78
14. Driver Wong and His Queer Wife   82
15. My Other Neighbors   86
16. Worshipers of Mao Zedong   93
17. Beijing Is Getting Hot   99
18. I Witness a Brutal Beating   105
19. The Glorious Red Terrorists   112
20. A Mountain Harvest   118

21. Dian Wen Gets Married   125

22. The Yus' House Is Rebuilt   136

23. Shalin Gives Birth to a Son   145

24. Death Jumpers   149

25. Dian Wen Is Detained   154

26. I Am Detained for Investigation   162

27. Mother Dies   172

28. A New Wave of Deaths   177

29. Shalin Is Sent to the Farm   182

30. Two Adulteresses   189

31. Shalin Comes Home for Spring Festival   195

32. I Walk out on a Limb   204

33. The Courtyard Is Falling Apart   210

34. I Am Sent to a Labor Farm   215

35. The Labor Reform Farm   219

36. The Girls Have Grown up   226

37. The Tongs' First Visit to My Room   231

38. Tong Chu Breaks His Neck   237

39. Tong Hua Returns Home; Tong Chu Leaves   241

40. It Snows on a Sunday   249

41. Pretty Kang Ping Changes—for the Worse   255

42. Premier Zhou Enlai Is Dead   263

43. Tong Yi Is Arrested at Tiananmen Square   269

44. Granny Yin Is Dead   275

45. An Earthquake   281

46. Chairman Mao Passes Away   288

47. Shalin and I Celebrate the Downfall of Jiang Qing   293

48. Winter Comes, the Thaw Begins   301

49. I Am Cleared   306

Glossary   311

Editor's Note

Liu Zongren has given us one of the most intimate looks at life in modern China yet published in the West. He depicts in detail the daily lives of ordinary people, from the establishment of the People's Republic in 1949 through the upheavals of the Cultural Revolution, and into the 1980s.

He takes us to the back alleys of Beijing slums, to government offices and to a labor reform farm reminiscent of one where he was sentenced for three years.

Unsparing in his honesty, he paints touching and frightening pictures of the poverty of the Beijing of his boyhood and the struggles of the People's Republic to rebuild a nation. He speaks frankly of China's problems: the harsh legacy of the Cultural Revolution, corruption in government, and traditional authoritarianism. That so much of the action here takes place among the poor in the shadow of the Great Pagoda is an indication of the contrasts he is able to make so vivid.

In Beijing, during the experiments of resocialization in the period of Mao Zedong's leadership, millions of people were pushed through changes so rapid that no cultural safety net was available to catch them as they tried to adjust to the high-wire act of the Cultural Revolution.

Liu develops the story of ten families as they cope with this turbulent era. Some characters tell of the ancient rules of conduct which they were asked to abandon instantly. Others speak of their anger and distrust and cynicism. Others simply show a remarkable capacity to endure physical hardship. Liu observes them all, with both compassion and objectivity.

This is a witness to the effect of a great social experiment on the individual psyche, a history fleshed in with the daily life details of Beijing: coping with the extremes of the climate, courting, shopping, burying the dead, washing diapers, airing bedding and passing the time. It is contemporary anthropology, done with a novelist's eye, producing a gallery of memorable characters. More than anything else, Liu's book serves to demystify China, introducing us to real characters rather than exotic stereotypes, and showing the best and worst in people, be it joy, anger, tenderness, lust, ego, heroism, hypocrisy, kindness, greed or sheer indifference.

At times, Liu comes close to despair and cynicism when reflecting on the suffering in his own era and in China's 3600 years of recorded history. But beneath it is the warm optimism of the gentle being that Liu Zongren is. In the background of his writing is always this long history of China, to which he so often refers. His optimism perhaps stems from the feeling that, despite the trials of its past and present, the nation has both the wisdom and the stamina to endure and to forge a better life for its people. After all, China's traditions are both a burden and a blessing. They can foster oppression, elitism and stifling paternalism, but they are also a source of great spiritual strength, confidence and consolation. The Cultural Revolution, vividly recalled here by Liu, was in part China's traumatic reckoning with its own traditions. China's future will be determined by how successfully the nation blends its mighty past with new philosophies, new values and new techniques.

My role in this book has been a modest one, a journey of editing, trying to preserve the personal style of a native Chinese speaker who learned English as an adult, as much through the works of our literature as in class and in the company of his American friends and colleagues. But it has been an honor to help prepare it for publication.

Liu works as a writer for the English edition of the monthly magazine, *China Reconstructs*. He is already writing his third book after hours at the office, on a word processor, which he appreciates as keenly as do his fellow writers in the West.

"Do not stand on ceremony," as Liu says, inviting me to the table. Reading Liu, you become part of the vast family which comprises contemporary China.

David Carr
San Francisco,
November 1988

A Few Cross-Cultural Notes

A glossary is appended to this book to help the reader understand terms from Chinese culture, historical events, dynasties, phrases used during the Cultural Revolution, and so forth.

For the sake of simplicity, most measurements have been rendered in American equivalents.

Transliteration from a tonal language like Chinese to a nontonal language is simply difficult. The current *pinyin* spelling system is employed for most Chinese words here, although some names have been left in more traditional spellings. Mr. Zongren himself does not spell his name in *pinyin*, which would require him to use *Zh* instead of *Z*. Two letters in *pinyin*, *Q* and *X* can be rather troublesome for the English reader. The *Q* should be pronounced *ch*, as in the word *ch*eer. The *X* is pronounced *sh*, as in *sh*ell.

Some words which have been regularly translated from the Chinese since the revolution have a doctrinaire quality which does not convey their meaning in common American usage. They have been reinterpreted here for clarity.

Only the word "cadre" (pronounced *cad-ray*) has been retained, for its use has been inherited from Soviet Communism and has a specific meaning relative to that culture. It refers to all government office workers, in an attempt to avoid the "bourgeois" connotations of words like "bureaucrat" or "official." To distinguish the very highest echelon of government employees and leaders, the word "official" is used.

THE COURTYARD

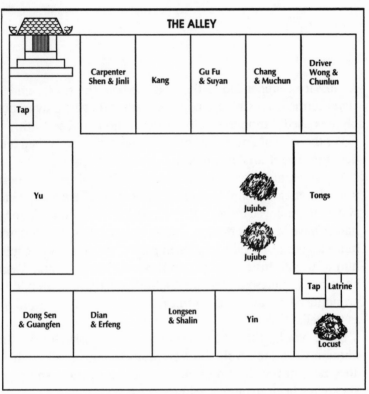

THE ALLEY

Tap

Carpenter Shen & Jinli

Kang

Gu Fu & Suyan

Chang & Muchun

Driver Wong & Chunlun

Yu

Jujube

Jujube

Tongs

Tap | Latrine

Dong Sen & Guangfen

Dian & Erfeng

Longsen & Shalin

Yin

Locust

N

W — E

S

1 · Home from the Service

"Do you remember Shalin?" Mother asked me.

I didn't. I looked up from the book in my hand, annoyed by the interruption.

I was reading *Outlaws of the Marsh*, a popular Qing dynasty novel of the exploits of a Robin Hood type band against the gentry and government officials. I had already read it four times, first as a children's picture book. One of the outlaws, Yang Shiong, was about to gouge out the heart of his wife for her adultery with a monk. The young woman, tied to a tree, was pleading for mercy.

"It seems to me you remember nothing of the neighbors," Mother looked at me over the rim of her glasses. She was shortening an old shirt of Father's for my second younger brother. I wanted to say I didn't give a damn about the old neighbors. One day I would get out of this raw, coarse alley.

"We called her Yellow-Haired Kid when she was small."

Oh, her, that tiny girl as wild as any boy in the neighborhood. She could run very fast, never falling behind when we raced from our alley through the open lot to the garbage dump to the south. She would climb the old city wall with us to pick wild jujube fruit and steal eggs from the nests of pigeons on the West Gate tower.

The ancient city of Beijing was a walled square with nine gates. Between the two western gates a gap had been cut out when the Communists took over Beijing in 1948, to make traffic flow more conveniently. What did it matter? The walls were no defense against modern cannons and bombers. The moat re-

1

mained; and across the wooden bridge which spanned it were vegetable fields. Then beyond the railroad tracks lay the graveyard. Beginning in mid-August, we would sneak out of the city at dawn to catch crickets there. After school started on September first, we would go out earlier, to be back in time for class, and sit with our trouser legs damp half the day.

One morning just at daybreak we found Shalin at the alley entrance. She wanted to catch crickets too. No other girl would dare to go near the city wall, much less beyond it. Along the wall wild grasses grew waist high, matted with garbage, human waste, dead cats and dogs, and abandoned infants. A hundred and fifty feet inside it, sheds and houses built of broken brick and mud began. Our alley was a five minute walk from this rim of human habitation. Grown-ups in our alley had decent jobs as small shopkeepers, bus conductors, carpenters and factory workers. Our mothers warned us to stay away from the rough kids who lived near the wall. So we resorted to lies and tricks to go out of the city.

That morning we had bad luck. We saw a mutilated body by the railway tracks and didn't catch a single cricket worth grading. I blamed Shalin. Catching crickets was a man's job—no women should be involved.

"I heard she joined the army," I said, feeling obliged to respond, but keeping my mind and eyes on the book. Yang Shiong refused to hear his wife's plea and ripped the blouse open to bare her breasts, a glistening knife poised in his hand.

"Yes. She joined three years after you left, in '61. She was discharged this year, too. She came back last week. Ah, a pretty, grown-up woman now. I didn't recognize her when she started talking to me at the tap. She must be twenty this year. You're twenty-four. That's right, she's twenty."

Home two weeks from my service in the air force, I still had a month before reporting to the Beijing Foreign Trade Bureau's job training school in the Western Hills. I wanted to relax after that strenuous, regimented life. I felt impatient with Mother's pestering. She had nothing but girls to talk about. Five had already been recommended. I was in no hurry to find a girlfriend, for that would mean an obligation to marry her later. Though I'd had only nine years of school before I enlisted, I wanted a well-educated woman as my wife. During the six years in the air force, I had taught myself all the high school courses. Otherwise I would not have been qualified for the training school. In two years I would have a nice office job. The girls in our poor neighborhood were no match for that.

"She's no longer the naughty Yellow-Haired Kid." Mother seemed to have made up her mind this time to talk seriously. She snapped the thread with her teeth and put down the shirt. I hurriedly finished the chapter. The outlaw had slit open his wife's chest and taken out the heart. It still throbbed in his hand.

I looked up at Mother. "Yes?"

"She's become well-mannered. And nice looking. The saying is true, 'A girl grows prettier as she grows up.' It's a pity her mother died when she was so young. Poor girl, her stepmother has never been good to her. At twenty she doesn't have a decent set of clothes."

Mother looked at me. "I want to ask her if she is willing to be your friend."

I smiled. Mother had only four boys, no girls. She yearned for the intimate warmth a daughter gives a mother. That was one reason she was eager to find me a girlfriend. Another was that I was her oldest son. Although she was forty-six and strong, she already dreamed of a grandson to ensure that the family tree would continue and thrive. I couldn't understand why she worried about family continuity so much. Perhaps it was one of her backward village concepts.

The job training school wouldn't begin until March. I had a whole month off, with no worry about finding work, as other demobilized veterans had. I knew I was the envy of the alley. No young man or girl among the neighbors would have a job as respectable as mine.

Winter had not relinquished its severe grip on Beijing. Our three rooms formed the south side of a square courtyard toward which all the windows faced. No sunshine ever came in. The edge of the alley had been bermed with a layer of coal ash to prevent rain water from accumulating and flowing into the courtyard. So the floor in our rooms was several inches below the alley level. Furthermore, a tap near our back wall provided drinking water to the seventy-some families in eight courtyards that curved along the northern edge of the open lot. Water spilled at the tap sank into the loose ground and seeped through the floor into our rooms, keeping them sodden and chilly. And the stove in the middle room gave off just enough heat to warm the three feet near it.

When the northwesterly was not strong and the sun warm, I would sit on a stool in the alley against our back wall to read a novel, casually exchanging greetings and small talk with neighbors who came with buckets and basins to fetch water from the tap.

The great stretch of vacant land across the alley had long gone and the garbage dumps had been moved out of the city. An anti-aircraft unit took over the space in 1956 and then the city government decided to build a stadium there, tearing down the concrete artillery ramparts.

To the east of our courtyard there had been a dairy farm owned by a Russian big landowner who had fled when the Czar fell. In 1956 the Soviet government called him back with his wife and two daughters. We heard that they had been sent directly to a labor camp. The dairy farm was run by the government when I went into the service. Now it was a park, framed by a wall following the curve of the alley, leaving us barely six feet to come and go.

When there was nothing except the garbage dump to the south, I could see the Great White Pagoda in its full magnificence, glistening in the sunshine. Now only the spire and half the crown emerged above the trees inside the park. I could no longer hear the ringing of its bronze bells for all the din which accompanied these changes.

While I was reading *Outlaws of the Marsh*, a quilted jacket wrapped around my lap, I found my mind often wandering away from the book to girls. I had never gotten used to them, having attended Beijing No. 3 Boys Middle School. In the army there were a few precious girl nurses at the clinic, but they looked beyond me at the young officers. Now at home, constantly pecked at by Mother, I began to be interested. Descriptions in the novel about outlaws in the mountain fortress drinking wine from large bowls, eating huge chunks of meat, killing, looting and dividing gold became less appealing. I sought those sections describing beautiful women having affairs with gallant young men.

I wondered if Shalin was really as nice as Mother claimed.

Shalin came to fetch water. I would not have recognized her if Mother had not spoken about her. She was nicely filled out and gracefully proportioned, the way an athlete should be. Her round face had a seriousness which I found incompatible with her young features. Her hair was short and tied up with a piece of red wool. She wore a well-shaped uniform. Two darker green patches on the collar marked where the badges had been. She didn't have the showiness of other girls from our neighborhood.

"Hi," I stood up and greeted her. "Do you remember Longsen?"

She looked at me for a moment and said, "Your mother said you were home." She set the bucket down.

"When did they turn the dairy into a park?" I asked.

My brothers had told me, but I had to find something to begin a conversation.

"They built it in 1962," she answered. "After they moved the cows out of the city limits."

"It's very quiet here," I said. "I mean without all those cows mooing day and night."

"They never mooed at night," Shalin corrected me. She had not learned a gentle way of speaking—but I liked her voice, soft, a little husky, and sweet.

"That's right. I forgot. It has been a long time since then. Oh, think of those calves. How lovely they were. And that huge black bull."

Shalin's face flushed. I felt a tingle at the base of my ear. Why should I have mentioned the bull? Shalin was a young lady now, not that wild kid.

Our mothers never allowed us to watch the bull mounting cows. But they watched. They would stand outside the barbed wire fence, hooting at us till we left, pretending to play with our marbles. When the huge black bull was led out of the shed, the grown-ups would become excited and forget us. Then we would swarm back.

A cow would be restrained in a frame made of thick wooden poles driven into the ground. Seeing the cow, the bull would rush over to her, but with ropes was dragged backward by the men. The excitement mounted and the women concentrated on the scene. We would edge closer and closer to where they stood. Shalin was the only girl who squeezed in and yelled amongst the grown-ups. No one scolded her or chased her away. We were jealous of her freedom. Then the bull would mount viciously, the cow shaking and twisting. In a second or two, the bull was pulled down again with great force, his huge head twisted back by the ring through his nose. He would be paraded around the grounds, his rod throbbing and ejecting spurts of liquid. After several minutes, he was allowed to mount again.

The scene was over. The boys made faces and laughed. Shalin would shout as loudly as we did. The women folk laughed and went back home to make lunch.

Shalin turned on the faucet and stared at the water splashing into the bucket. I hastily said, "It's a pity they enclosed so much of the open space. Now we can't see the Great White Pagoda. Remember how we raced out to the garbage dump to play? The pagoda looked very tall then."

"It's still tall," Shalin said quietly, not very enthusiastic about my nostalgic reminiscences.

6

I wanted to carry the bucket. Her expression told me I'd better not offer. She lifted the heavy bucket and carried it with both hands, swinging sideways slightly. Her legs were strong, bulging at the thighs.

I went off to learn English at the training school in the Western Hills. Studying was intense, leaving me exhausted at the end of every day. I came home only on Sundays. Mother seemed herself to have fallen in love with Shalin, talking about her whenever she had a chance. "She's started working. At the same place as yours, the Foreign Trade Bureau. Is it a coincidence or an auspicious omen?"

I occasionally came across Shalin on the street. Her energetic gait, athletic limbs and simple dress attracted me. She was aloof, defying my promising future at a prestigious job in a top floor office. Yet instead of my dignity being hurt, I was drawn toward her. But class work was too demanding for me to indulge much in thoughts of girls.

2 · Dian Wen
Becomes My Mentor

On a cold, dusty November day in 1951, Mother, my two brothers, eight and six, and I, eleven, arrived in Beijing. We were a bunch of bumpkins from a village on the southern edge of Tangshan, a coal mining center one hundred and fifty miles to the east. We were joining father who had found work as a carpenter.

We emerged from the railway station onto the bustling and rumbling Qianmen Street, which I later came to know as the most crowded commercial area in Beijing. Trams clanged on narrow tracks, their wands hissing and sparking as they quivered against the overhead electric lines cantilevered from concrete poles along the streets. Though dusty, the air here was cleaner and fresher than in Tangshan, where a pall of coal dust hung perpetually.

Lo, the magnificent Qianmen Gate. It soared to the sky where flocks of wild and domestic pigeons wheeled and shot back and forth, while sparrows chirped noisily. Wild berry bushes grew out of crevices in the massive wall which seemed to stretch infinitely west and east.

Although the dominant colors of Beijing clothes were still dark, the quality of fabric and the cut were very distinct from those in Tangshan. And there were more solemn-looking people in uniform-style dress, the cadres of the new government offices.

We huddled around Mother who looked about bewildered. She was an illiterate country woman who had toiled in the corn field and vegetable garden and cooked for a family of thirteen until the very day we left. In fact, she'd worked that last morning with her two younger sisters-in-law, shucking the last of the corn ears on the threshing ground.

Father called over two rickshaws—one for our luggage and one for Mother and the two younger boys. "I'll take Longsen with me on the tram," Father said. He wanted to save money by hiring one less rickshaw. "I've given the address to the pullers, so don't worry about being lost."

My brothers wanted to take the tram cars, too. But Father said we would have to walk a long way at the end of the line.

The tram was full. We stood in the front corner by the driver. Its wheels rolled, clank-clanking in a pleasant rhythm. The driver, standing like a helmsman at the gear box, tapped a musical pattern on the bell with his foot. He twitched the shiny copper steering handle playfully. When he steered into a turn, the handle creaked like a farm cart's wooden axle in need of oiling. The car rumbled through a breach in the city wall and crawled northward.

Then I saw the Tiananmen Gate rising on the far side of a flagstone-paved square. In the middle of the lower part of the gate tower was a huge portrait of Chairman Mao Zedong.

The car creaked for a long moment as it turned into Chang'an Boulevard. We went on west along the crimson palace wall. I saw a wooden archway with floral paintings, which reminded me of a smaller one at the graveyard of a landlord family in the village. We passed on, then under the archway at Xisi.

After that stores were fewer along the street and the houses became lower and shabbier. We got off at Huguosi Monastery and walked half an hour through a labyrinth of side streets and alleys to reach our new home.

Three rows of three rooms each were set on the north, south and west, and a high wall on the east defined a tiny square courtyard. In the village, our front yard alone could hold fifty people. There were a set of millstones, the vegetable cellar and an ancient grape vine spread over the front gate. The back yard was even larger with the pigsty, barn, a vegetable plot and several peach trees.

"This is the best I can afford," Father said to Mother apologetically. "And this courtyard is much better than any other around this area."

I had noticed that the other houses had only wooden planks as their street gates while ours had two panels finely finished in black lacquer bearing a couplet in a beautiful hand.

Loyalty and benevolence are the family heritage;
Poetry and books carry the generations.

Our courtyard had paths of brick while the road and other courtyards were dirt and ash.

Mrs. Chang was the landlady. She was dressed in a brocade *qipao* and embroidered silk shoes, and she wore make-up. Mother looked shabby in her country clothes, and old, though they were both thirty-four. Mrs. Chang and her mother had the northern three rooms. The sun on their windows was bright and warm. Through the glass I saw scrolls of ink paintings and calligraphy on the wall, and hardwood beds, tables, chairs and wardrobe. They must have been very expensive.

Mother didn't allow me to enter their rooms. "You might break a piece of the precious porcelain." She would politely decline Mrs. Chang's frequent invitations to come to their rooms for a chat. Perhaps Mother felt too humble to go into their nice place.

The western row was occupied by the Bais. Their rooms were stuffed with books and antiques and they had both a violin and a piano. Mrs. Chang told Mother that both husband and wife had been to Japan and now taught at middle school. The Bais did not talk to us. They would nod politely to Mother and Father in the courtyard.

"Don't let your Longsen play with the boys in the street," Mrs. Chang warned Mother. They are wild. There are no decent boys around. Our three families are the only decent people in the whole alley. So don't let your children wander out after school to learn bad manners."

10

I didn't know by what criteria she put us as her kind. We were not much better off than the rickshaw pullers, porters, vegetable vendors and scavengers who lived in the seven other courtyards on our short alley.

Mother did come to believe that we were different from the lowly neighbors. So I was confined to the courtyard after school. All of us in the alley drew water from a pump in the courtyard next door. It was in a small room squeezed into a corner where two wings met. The tiny, dark room was the home of Dian Wen, a boy my age, and his elder sister and brother and their parents. Wooden boards serving as a bed took up all the space in the room except for a three foot square around the pump. All their belongings were either hung from the ceiling or tucked under the boards.

Mrs. Chang and the Bais hired Dian Wen to fetch water for them. When I was sick he carried water for us as well. Mother paid him one fen for two buckets, the fee set by Mrs. Chang.

Dian Wen was tall and lean. I envied him for his freedom. His parents didn't stop him from going fishing or swimming in the moat or catching crickets in the vegetable fields along the railway tracks. He could play in the street all the hours after school once he had delivered his water. His mother needed the dozen fen he earned to buy flour.

His father, a rickshaw puller, didn't put much heart into the business. He had several time-consuming hobbies: birds, crickets and teahouses. He would forget to solicit customers once he began talking with other bird and cricket fanciers in the street, or when he sat in a teahouse listening to a storyteller. I often saw Dian Wen's mother standing at the gate waiting for her husband to return, so she could buy corn flour for supper. She would carry it in an earthenware pot with a chipped rim. We used cloth bags and could afford rice and wheat flour.

The alley had houses only on the north side. To the south was a great stretch of wasteland bordered on its west by shacks, the ring of ghettoes at the foot of the city wall. On the south was the garbage dump. Women from those hovels swarmed over it scavenging rags, scrap metal, coal cinders, waste paper, anything they could use in their homes or sell to junk collectors. Dian Wen's brother and sister and several other older children raked the debris as well.

The boys would play soccer in the afternoon, marking the goal with schoolbags or broken bricks. They would play cards or marbles when there weren't enough of them for a soccer game. I longed to join them. Playing with my kid brothers was boring.

My backwater country accent sounded awful and I felt ashamed of it. I was ashamed of Mother too. She had bound feet and could not read. Fortunately, Dian Wen's mother and most of the grown-ups in the neighborhood could not read either. But other women had natural feet and that was more apparent.

The boys ridiculed me and refused to let me join their games. They played a game using small cards with colored pictures. They would put a pile of them on the ground and slap one palm very hard next to it, to cause the jet of air to blow the pictures over. The winner got all the overturned cards. I bought a huge pile of pictures. Still they would not let me play. "Get out of here," Erhu waved his hand which was covered with dirt. "You country rat!"

"Who is a country rat?" I demanded.

"Who?" Erhu stood up, half a head taller than I. "You are!"

I smashed his nose with all my force and threw myself on top of him. He staggered and fell. I was on top for only a second. He grabbed my hair and knocked my head against the ground. "One, two, three," he counted. Tears welled up in my eyes; tears not of pain, but of shame.

"That's enough," I heard Dian Wen say. I stood up, looking around for a brick.

"All right," he said to me, his hands inside the pockets of his tattered jacket. "You may join us now." I saw that he must enjoy great prestige in the alley. Erhu even gave me a smile of conciliation.

Dian Wen and I became great friends. He took me along when they went to swim or catch crickets or climb the old gate. He even introduced me to a ghetto gang and allowed me to go with him to watch a fight between two gangs behind the Zoo.

3 · I Go for Vulgar Tastes

In 1644, nomadic Manchu tribes broke through the formidable Shanhaiguan Pass in the Great Wall and took over Beijing, then moved south, permeating all of China, establishing the Qing Dynasty. Each bannerman, as the Manchu conquerors were called, received a living allowance from the imperial court from the day he was born to his death. They did not have to work for a living. Every day, bannermen would sit in a teahouse gossiping, listening to storytellers and fabricating their own stories. When tired of staying there, they would go to the moat to walk their birds, swinging the cages with their stride, which forced the birds to exercise their wings. In autumn they would fight the crickets they bought at the temple fairs.

During his reign from 1736 to 1796, Emperor Qian Long launched a campaign to promote the culture of the Hans, those Chinese who had inhabited Central China for many centuries. The Manchus, barbarians, wanted to refine the royal family by learning ancient rites. They studied the old books and followed rites to the letter. They even picked up customs long abandoned by the Han. Their mannerisms became more meticulous than the Han they emulated.

Pu Yi, the last emperor of the Qing Dynasty, was dethroned and China became a republic in 1911. The Manchus lost their privileges, including the annual stipend. But they retained much of the ritual protocol.

In our alley there were two banner families: the Bais and the Dians.

The Bais looked like bannermen. They were stiffly polite to

the neighbors, addressing Father "Sir" and Mrs. Chang and Mother "Madame." Mr. Bai called me "Little Brother." They used silver and richly decorated porcelain table articles.

"When they have only brined turnips to eat," Mrs. Chang explained to Mother about the Manchus' formalized behavior, "they cut it into four different shapes and make four dishes out of it, purely for show. You see, they close their door to eat so outsiders won't know what they really have in their expensive bowls and platters."

But to me, whatever the content of the Bais' plates, it must be more tasteful than Mrs. Chang's powdered face. Such make-up always reminded me of a shriveled eggplant covered with frost in the vegetable garden of my village.

The Dians did not look like bannermen at all. They were too poor to keep up appearances. They did not even have a dinner table. Each of them would shovel a portion of whatever was in the cooking pot into a big bowl with a coarse blue line around the rim and take two steamed corn buns, squatting on their haunches. The only vestige of banner family traits was the four bird cages hanging from the eaves on warm days or inside their dark room in winter.

Rickshaw Puller Dian spent a lot of time catching grasshoppers and cicadas to feed the birds. Even when the family had no money to buy corn flour, he would spend the several dozen fen he earned to buy millet for the birds. He had not been born at a time when his family was still enjoying Imperial privilege and his father must have been the lazy type of bannerman who did not care to accumulate family wealth. He lived happily, however, letting his wife and daughter worry about the family's liveli-hood. Dian Wen did not know his ancestors had once been glorious bannermen.

"Were you looking for me?" Dian Wen asked. He had re-turned from the garbage dump with his sister, a bundle of scrap cement bags under his left arm.

"Our water ran out and I went to your room to fetch a bucket," I said. "Could you carry some for me?"

I could have fetched more than one bucket. I didn't because I wanted him to earn a couple of fen. I had convinced Mother that it would be more profitable if I spent the time on my schoolwork.

"Did you hear anything when you went to my house?" he asked, a sly grin on his face. "That little fox," Dian Wen laughed, using our nickname for Shalin. "Yesterday she came to fetch water. There was no one in the yard. Even before I could touch her, she yelled and ran out. Her father threatened to kill me."

Now I knew why he had gone out to the garbage dump early in the morning. He reached his hand into his pocket and pulled out a sheet from a book. He gave it to me and said, "Look at this. I wanted to try it on that little fox."

The drawing had a naked woman straddling a man whose huge cock was standing straight up. I pushed the sheet back to Dian Wen and said hurriedly, "Would you get the water for us right now? Mother is waiting to cook lunch."

He laughed and folded the sheet, stuffed it back in his pocket and went through the broken gate of their courtyard.

Dian Wen was popular among the big boys who were envied throughout this whole district of Beijing. The Terror of Western District was nineteen, tall and handsome. Around him were many teenage boys. Girls would steal glances as he and his entourage practiced martial arts and gymnastics in a flat spot under an old locust tree near the dump. Father had strict words about my ever being seen with them. Yet I wanted to be included. I asked Dian Wen if he would introduce me to them. My excuse was to learn some martial art routines.

"Why?" Dian Wen slapped his palm on the dirt, a puff of dust exploding, a thick pile of picture cards turning upside down. He snatched the overturned sheets and counted them intently while the other gamblers watched. He had an elegant habit of licking his thumb to help the count. Dian Wen won.

His face broke into a gleeful smile and he turned to me. "Eh?"

"I want to learn martial arts."

"You? Forget it. You were not born to fight. Furthermore your father will give you a beating if he knows you are mixed up with us."

He put a lot of stress on the "us," and laughed dry and sharp. I was hurt. "All right. Don't bother, I said."

He stood up and motioned me aside with a tilt of his head. "They are having a fight this afternoon. Do you want to watch?"

Street roughs in that neighborhood usually held their gang fights behind the back wall of the Zoo. All around were fields and wasteland. The only building nearby was the Temple of Five Pagodas. Dian Wen, several others and I had once gone there to steal apricots. I had been scared away by the many snakes along the foot of the wall and inside the passageway beneath the pagodas.

I was elated to be invited. Common people would not watch a gang fight. Beijing residents were known for their love of gossip and their curiosity. They would stop everything to watch two women fight, shouting and calling dirty names. But they would never get close to a gang fight. The ruffians always chose a secluded spot to settle accounts. If Dian Wen would not take me, I would not dare to go. Even if I dared, the fighters would not tolerate a small boy gawking at them.

I liked the way street gangs fought. When two rival gangs would meet to settle a territorial incursion or to avenge a member's humiliation, the leaders would negotiate for a date, place, and the number of people each side could bring. They might choose to fight in a martial arts form, western-style boxing, or bicycle competition. Such a fight was always a performance. In a passionate case, they would meet with fists and knives.

Dian Wen was the pet of Terror of Western District. Members of other gangs understood that the chieftain would retaliate brutally if anyone harmed Dian Wen. He himself would not take sides in fights, so was harmless. He won patronage among them through his daring and expertise in martial arts, gymnastics and soccer. Sometimes he played the role of buffer among the gangs.

"Are you sure your mother won't find out?" Dian Wen asked. I had never known him to worry about anything.

"She won't find out," I assured him.

We didn't take the regular route to the West Gate. Instead we went west, passed the slums along the wall until we reached the gap. We followed the moat northward. The water was shallow, grass turning yellow and willow trees shedding their leaves. The foot of the wall stank. A couple of stray dogs barked at us from the opposite bank. Dian Wen bent to pick up a small stone. The dogs turned and ran. He threw the rock so it skipped six or seven times across the surface of the green water before it sank.

"Some day we'll come here to fish," Dian Wen said. "I caught quite a few last Sunday and my mother made a soup of them. Too bad you can't come. It may take half a day to catch anything at all. You can't deceive your mother for so long, can you?"

"Of course I can," I put strength and firmness in my voice, my mind struggling for a workable lie. I might tell Mother the teacher was calling a Young Pioneers meeting. There were no other Young Pioneers in our alley to blow my cover. I didn't tell Dian Wen about the lies to Mother. I wanted to give him the impression I was honest and decent and different from him and his pals because my family was different from theirs.

We reached the West Gate. All the wild jujubes had been picked clean, except for those at the very top where few boys dared to climb. Big red dates hung on bare twigs. Dian Wen asked me to wait as he climbed the ancient wall, his feet and hands clinging to the narrow ledges of each layer of brick. When he was halfway up, I tried. The ledges were only an inch and a half wide. I imitated him by squeezing the outside edge of my foot onto the ledge and grabbing the seams with my fingers. I thought I could make it. Dian Wen looked down, turned his head back and continued to climb steadily.

He reached a cluster of sturdy bushes, picked several juicy dates and stuffed them into his mouth. My mouth began to water. Behind him the sky was blue with wisps of white clouds. I felt a sudden dizziness and hastily lowered my head. My fingers ached and I was afraid I could not hold onto the raw ledge any longer. Something crept out of a hole. I decided to back down and wait below to pick up the jujubes Dian Wen threw down.

I was not made for wild action, I comforted myself. I should use my brains instead of my limbs. Our ancestors taught that those who work with their brains rule and those who work with their brawn are ruled.

The formidable gate tower with its defense work needed repair. But there was talk of tearing down all the gates as well as the wall to make room for the sprawling city.

Dian Wen had a couple of more tears in his jacket from climbing the wall. The sun had descended to the top of the Western Hills when we crossed the White Stone Bridge. While we walked on a dirt path along a creek, Dian Wen briefed me about the rules of a gang fight, which made me more eager to see the action.

There were eight roughnecks to each side. To my disappointment, this fight was done with boxing gloves. There were only a few bruises. It was not nearly as exciting as the scenes described in *Outlaws of the Marsh*. I had expected to see blood and battered heads.

At the end of August we began to go out of the city to catch crickets. Dian Wen had caught a Tiger Head and tamed it. He came over to try it on my inferior crickets. He always did that because he didn't want to hurt his own. I didn't mind at all. My best ones were those he discarded. The new cricket had a big head and strong jaws. With one toss it threw mine out of the jar.

"Hooray!"

I was startled. Mr. Bai was bending over us. "That's a superb creature," he said with excitement. "Look at his hind legs, the wide jaws. Whose is it?"

I nodded my head toward Dian Wen. "Where did you catch

it?" You are a good catcher. Look, its tails and feelers are intact. Excellent work!"

Dian Wen put the lid carefully on the jar and didn't speak. More to please him than Mr. Bai, I offered, "Dian Wen is an expert at catching crickets. He never breaks the tails or feelers when he finds a good one."

"Come, you two little brothers," Mr. Bai smiled at us politely. "Come to my room. I'll show you some good crickets."

Curiosity prevailed over our feeling of contempt for the Bai family. We followed him into his middle room. There in the center was a square table of rosewood. On it were at least three dozen earthenware jars arranged in four layers like a pyramid. "They were made by Master Zhao Ziyu," Mr. Bai said with restrained pride. We had heard of Zhao Ziyu who lived in the late Qing Dynasty and was famous for his earthenware cricket jars. We had never set eyes on a genuine one. Ours were discarded enamel tea mugs we scavenged at the garbage dump. We had to tamp in a layer of earth to block the rusted holes. His collection must be worth a fortune.

Mr. Bai picked up an empty jar and turned it over to let us examine the master's seal stamped in the bottom. "There are fakes," he lectured us. "You have to have experience to tell." He held the jar close to Dian Wen's ear and tapped at it with his long nail. "Hear? The sound tells this is genuine." He held it out to my ear. The ringing sound was musical. But the bowl in which Mother mixed dough sounded much the same.

"Master Zhao Ziyu's jars are cool in summer and warm in winter," Mr. Bai continued. "Some of my crickets can live through the winter. You know they wouldn't be able to in other jars."

He was eager to tell us more about his cricket-raising skill. "Good ones can be found only in wild places. That's why you have to go to deep ditches and graveyards to find them. The best come from gullies in the Western Hills. I have some from the mountains in Shaanxi Province." We both sucked in our breath and exclaimed in admiration.

In Mr. Bai's jars were porcelain dishes for water and food and short pieces of tube and other gadgets for the crickets to play among. His two pokers were made of mouse whiskers with ivory handles. We made ours of a strong stem of grass.

Mr. Bai's long, slim fingers were paler than his face. I could almost see the liquid flowing in the blue veins of his hand as he carefully lifted the lid of a jar to admire his pets. He smiled when we involuntarily gasped. He caressed the feelers with the poker until it opened its brown jaws wide and lunged forward. Mr. Bai then tickled its head. It lunged again and spread its wings to chirp angrily at the provocation.

In one corner of the room were two dozen smaller porcelain jars. They were for taking crickets out to fight with others. Some people still bet on cricket fights even though the government had outlawed all forms of gambling.

Mr. Bai's crickets were superb. Dian Wen and I watched each one in fascination.

"I can't go out to catch crickets any more," Mr. Bai said. "Getting on in years. I buy them at the temple fair."

Dian Wen's eyes brightened. I knew why and said to Mr. Bai, "Dian Wen has several good crickets. Do you want to have a look?"

"Of course, of course," he said kindly.

We ran over to Dian Wen's room and brought five. Mr. Bai examined them expertly. "Would you mind letting me have these two?"

One of them was the Tiger Head. Dian Wen hesitated. "I'll give you fifty fen for them," Mr. Bai said.

Fifty fen! I wanted to shout for the luck Dian Wen had fallen into. That would buy eight pounds of corn flour.

Mr. Bai asked Dian Wen to let him know whenever he caught good crickets.

4 · I Suspect Dian Wen
Is Chasing Shalin

Before 1965 Beijing had few high buildings. One could see dark green mountains silhouetted against the horizon to the west and north. At the foot of them was Fragrance Hill, where the Foreign Trade Bureau had set up its language training school.

On March first I left home to begin my career. At Jade Spring Hill the old bus began to labor up an incline. On one side of the cobblestone road was a dry gully; on the other were orchards of apples, peaches and pears. I noticed tiny dark green buds on the softening branches.

In another ten minutes the bus heaved itself over a hump and the road leveled. We stopped in front of a row of one-story buildings which housed a general store, restaurant and police station. Four young men in winter army uniforms who had been sitting on the raised flagstone steps came over to the bus and greeted me with the warmth of old comrades. "Hello, come to register at the school?" one asked. Not waiting for confirmation, he took my suitcase. We exchanged names and began up the path flanked by stone houses with slate roofs. Open fields could be seen behind them.

My family had lived in Beijing for thirteen years, but this was my first trip to the Western Hills, famous for their autumn scenery, because the one yuan fare was always considered extravagant.

Fragrance Hill was very quiet, tranquil and rustic. For the school, the Bureau had converted one of the villas built on the slopes by wealthy families. The low buildings with fruit trees in their courtyards and the fields with last year's corn stalks reminded me of my home village.

It was an ideal setting for learning. Foreign language experts and senior translators were assigned as teachers. Our progress was excellent, and the prospect of becoming foreign trade experts stationed abroad boosted our enthusiasm.

I had been learning the rudiments of English and typing at the training school for a year and making satisfactory progress. Mother was proud of me, bragging around the neighborhood that I was learning a foreign tongue and would have a big job sitting in an office. Mr. and Mrs. Bai had me read to them a paragraph from the textbook. "Good, very good," Mrs. Bai commented, telling Mother that my pronunciation was beautiful. Mother was very pleased. The Bais had been abroad and had tasted milk and bread. That gave them authority in this matter.

I was not so sure. I knew I had problems. Six years in the air force standing close to roaring jet fighters had reduced my hearing sensitivity. A tooth protruding inward bothered my tongue when I tried to twist it to fit the foreign sounds.

The trainees were given a tour of the offices of Beijing Foreign Trade Bureau. The rooms were carpeted, the ceiling high, the desks big. There were sofas. And think of that, each room had a telephone, some even two! All the people in the five-story building were dressed smartly.

The building stood on the site of the graveyard. The area was totally unrecognizable. An asphalt road passed through the gap in the ancient city wall. Four-story apartment blocks stretched north and south on both sides of the road, taking up the vegetable gardens and wasteland. The railroad tracks were to be removed soon—too close to the new urban area. The houses inside the wall and their inhabitants looked even shabbier now.

I met Dian Wen on a Sunday morning by the tap when I was practicing,

> Spring is gay flower and song;
> Summer's hot days are long;
> Autumn is rich with fruit and grain;
> Winter brings snow and New Year's again.

A tall black American had taught us this poem. He had been taken a prisoner during the Korean War. He had been agitated when he read it. Perhaps he was thinking of his home in Georgia.

"Hi," Dian Wen came over, stretching out his hand and clamping it on mine. "I heard you're studying for a big job. How is it going?"

"Where have you been all these years?" I asked, feeling a rush of guilt. After I joined the air force I brushed off all my memories of the neighbors, including my best friend. At least I should have asked Mother about him after I returned home. After seven years he was still half a head taller than I, and handsome. He dressed in an army uniform with no insignia.

"One year after you left I was taken on the August First soccer team. Then I was demobilized. You know, too old to kick."

That team belonged to the army, which explained the uniform.

"What are you going to do?" I asked.

"I'm too stupid to learn big things, you know. As they say about us soccer players: well developed in limbs and simple in brains. The Veteran Placement Office got me a job with Beijing Foreign Trade Bureau. You are going to work there, too, aren't you? Shalin works there, you know. Isn't that great? Though we won't all be on the same floor. Shalin is in the reference room and I'm a messenger, with a car to drive. You'll be upstairs, of course."

He didn't sound jealous, but I felt a twinge of uneasiness.

Shalin and Dian Wen lived in the same courtyard and now were going to be close at work as well.

"That's good," I said. "Very good."

We talked about the old days for awhile and then I excused myself. "When you have time, drop in for a chat," I said.

I began coming home on Saturday.

"Does Shalin come home often?" I queried Mother.

Mother peered at me above her glasses, a little puzzled. Mother had stopped talking to me about girls since I'd gone off to school. She didn't want to disturb my studies when I was home. A good job would guarantee me a good wife, she believed.

"She lives in the Bureau's dormitory and comes home only for a couple of hours on Sunday afternoon," she said, taking off the glasses and rubbing her eyes. "Her stepmother treats her better now. But old wounds are not easy to heal. Stepmothers and stepchildren are not of the same flesh after all. Their feelings can never be genuine toward each other. Shalin sometimes drops in to see me. She comes after you leave for the Hills."

The following Sunday I didn't go back. I read a book near the tap for awhile, then helping Mother with supper, went to fetch water or wash vegetables at the tap two or three times. Shalin came home around four o'clock. Her hair was still short, though longer than when she'd just returned from the army. The red wool yarn was gone. She had the look of a college girl. Her face was not so round, her eyes seemed larger, her body slimmer. The purple sweater over a white blouse rose nicely on her full bosoms. She was prettier and fresher than in her uniform, and carried a new dignity incompatible with the surroundings. I ventured a smile and a nod. She put on a reserved smile in return. "You came home," I said, feeling stupid.

"Yes, so did you."

I couldn't find a thing to say. She entered her courtyard.

I hoped she would come to talk with Mother. She didn't. So I went out to fetch water for the fourth time.

I went over to the next courtyard and looked in through the broken gate. Shalin was talking animatedly with Dian Wen. She laughed and gesticulated. I wished she would be that free with me.

I walked in and greeted Dian Wen.

He turned to me. "Hello! Are you looking for me? Come. This is Shalin. Have you met?"

I confirmed by way of a smile toward Shalin, who smiled back. My face tingled.

"You know," he said, "though I haven't reported for work yet, they already have a car waiting for me to drive. Shalin told me that. I'll go see tomorrow morning. Can't wait to feel the steering wheel. It's a brand new Washa. Isn't it, Shalin?"

"I saw it in front of the garage and asked Driver Wong. He said it was for you to drive."

"You know, Longsen," Dian Wen said happily, "Erhu got a job with our Bureau, too." I felt uncomfortable with the words "our Bureau." The Bureau was the government's. And he had not even begun working yet.

Shalin examined my face. "You don't remember Erhu, do you?"

I paused and then it came to me. Erhu was the son of that widow who owned the butcher shop at the west end of the alley.

"He stole stewed pig skin for you. Have you forgotten?"

"You had your first fight with him, after your family moved to Beijing. Your only fight, as I remember," Dian Wen added good-naturedly. I was irritated.

"He's still big and strong and fat," Shalin said, laughing broadly. Her sturdy breasts, as round as steamed buns, quavered. "He's a plumber. The job suits him. Longsen wouldn't be able to lift the manhole covers." She looked at me. I couldn't tell if she was serious or mocking.

Dian Wen laughed with Shalin.

"It seems everybody in our alley is going to work in the Bureau," he observed.

"The Bureau is new and needs people," I replied coolly.

"Well," he said, responding to the chill, "any time you need a car, Longsen, let me know. We have our people downstairs and upstairs. We'll look after each other."

"Longsen is the only one upstairs," Shalin said sharply.

I liked the way she closed and opened her eyes to accent her sarcasm.

"Oh, Dian Wen, I came to borrow a pair of pliers," I said. I didn't want Shalin's implication to go deeper in his mind. "Do you have one? The front axle of my bicycle is loose." I admired my quickness in finding an excuse. "That's why I haven't left for the Hills yet." Immediately I realized the addition was stupid. I hoped the blush hadn't shown on my face.

"I'll come with you to have a look," Dian Wen offered warmly and went into his room to fetch the pliers. "Come on in, Longsen. You haven't been in my room yet."

The Dians had obtained another room in the west wing. Dian Wen's mother and sister slept there. He and his brother slept in the small room. The hand pump had been removed, the ceiling patched and the walls papered. It was brighter. The room had a cast iron stove with venting pipe. In the old days the family used a tinplate stove, and could only afford to build a fire for cooking meals. It would be extinguished after supper was cooked and relit the next morning. In winter it had been colder inside than out.

"I will begin work in June," I told Shalin. "We will see each other everyday."

"Yes, we shall." Her smile was reserved.

"Do you like your job?"

"It's all right. Sometimes it's boring, filling in cards and sorting books. But it's all right." Her skin was fair and smooth. Her fingers tapered delicately. I liked her plump wrists. Her lips were full and sensitive.

"You can read books," I said. "There must be many books in your reference room. I like books." Another stupid statement!

"Oh, you do. You can come to me to get new books."

"I will."

Dian Wen and I fixed my bicycle in no time. I had figured out that it only took fifty minutes to make the ride, enough time to catch my first class if I woke up early. I decided to go back on Monday morning instead of Sunday afternoon.

Mother sensed I was warming quickly toward Shalin. With a purpose she asked Shalin to come over for Sunday supper and volunteered to teach her how to use the sewing machine and to cut patterns. When Shalin was in our rooms she was cool and seldom took the initiative in talking to me.

On the other hand, I saw that she was getting closer and closer to Dian Wen. He bought a pair of badminton bats. They would play together in the park when the wind was not strong. That felt better than when they stayed home. I could at least watch her play through a hole the children had made in the park wall so they wouldn't have to go around to the gate. When they were not playing, I would find an excuse to look for Dian Wen. To my great relief, every time I went over he was in his room, building a transistor radio. Parts, wire and tools were spread all over the plank bed he shared with his brother.

In desperation I asked Mother to make a formal proposal for Shalin to be my girlfriend.

"Her parents are willing, but Shalin said she wanted to wait awhile."

I begged Mother to talk with Shalin directly. She did. Shalin agreed we could begin to seek "mutual understanding." She promised nothing.

My self-esteem sagged greatly. I had expected she would rush to accept the proposal since I would be working upstairs above her.

The grass was turning a tender yellow-green where the sun could reach but not the wind. Young trees and bushes were putting out tiny buds that would open into leaves and flowers. In 1959, Chairman Mao had instituted the Great Leap Forward to boost China's economic production. Young mothers in our alley had gone to work in small workshops in the neighborhood. So now only old people and their grandchildren could be seen in the park. Near a crudely built pavilion, a dozen elderly women and men had gathered to chat, oblivious to the passing of time as long as the sun was in the sky.

One Sunday, Shalin and I met formally in the park. She had a wicker basket with several turnips and a head of cabbage. "Why pretend to be out shopping?" I asked under my breath.

We stood on the path beside a bench. "Would you like to sit down?" I ventured.

"No. It's better this way."

I glanced northward. The group of elders were chatting, their young charges playing nearby. No one bothered to look our way.

"Fragrance Hill is very beautiful," I said.

"Well?" Shalin looked me directly in the eye. I looked down at the cabbage in her basket.

"I wonder if you have ever been there. You should go there. Right now the plums are budding. The color is more beautiful than when they are in full bloom. And you should be there in late October. The maple leaves are truly ruby red. The whole south hillside is a cloud of color in the setting sun . . ."

She did not seem interested.

"I think I should go home to cook supper," she said.

She continued to play badminton with Dian Wen on Sunday afternoons. I came to resent him. He was my best friend, he claimed. He must have realized by now that Mother had made the proposal.

"Dian Wen is too simple-minded," I said to Shalin after we had talked about her work and my studies for awhile. We were more at ease with each other now when we were alone in the park.

She looked up, her solemn face a shade darkened.

"He says himself that he's well developed only in limb," I explained hastily.

"Don't say unkind things about others behind their back, Longsen."

I regretted what I had blurted out and became even more resentful toward him.

Shalin and I began to go to the movies together and she had Sunday dinner with us more often. Our courting period remained cool throughout.

5 · I Get Shalin When She Is Ill

An uneasiness stirred and spread through Beijing in 1966. In March all the Central Party leaders disappeared from the news media. The authorities issued an order to all office employees and college students to watch some thirty films they had selected. We were required to pay close attention and distinguish poisonous elements in them. It was fun to watch the first several for free. Then they became boring. My head would swim and ache after two or three in succession. I could not detect any poisonous elements, but had a premonition that something very grave was going on at the very top—possibly a power struggle.

In July all the schools in Beijing were closed down by zealous students who wanted to devote all their energy and time to making revolution and defending the proletarian dictatorship which Chairman Mao commanded. Our job training program lingered on for three more months, was closed and disbanded. Nominally we had been assigned jobs in the various departments of the Bureau. The offices were already overstaffed and did not need us—a batch of Hill wolves who had not developed enough skill to carry on the routine work; potential trouble makers at this disturbing time when young people thought of themselves as born revolutionaries and of others as targets of revolution.

"We are organizing a veterans' Red Guard group," Dian Wen came to my home to inform me. "All the veterans in the Bureau have joined. Erhu and Shalin, too. How about you?"

"I'm not joining any Red Guard group," I said coolly. No matter how much I tried, I could not suppress my resentment of his closeness with Shalin. "We are not students. They have

30

nothing to do so they make revolution in the streets. We are nearly thirty and have jobs."

"But every office and factory has organized Red Guard groups," he answered defensively. "Those pen pushers in the Bureau will look down on us and bully us. The Party says workers, peasants and soldiers should take the lead in the Cultural Revolution. Chairman Mao himself called on us to wipe out feudal and bourgeois vestiges in our socialist China. We can't let pen pushers dominate us. Come on, Longsen. Let's do something big together."

I looked at Dian Wen, his face flushed with enthusiasm. His army uniform was neat and clean, complete with cap and officer's leather shoes. I resented any uniform. It reminded me of that unreasonable political director in my battalion who picked on my faults all the time. When I came home I gave all the uniforms to my brothers.

Dian Wen wore his uniform smartly, which enhanced his physical grace. Shalin must love it.

"No, I won't join your group," I said firmly.

He left, dissatisfied.

"Why are you so cold to Dian Wen?" Mother asked reproachfully. He's always nice to you. Whenever I need to move heavy things, he comes to help. He takes you as his best friend."

"His being nice to us is one thing," I retorted. "Involving me in politics is another. You don't understand politics, Mother."

"But at least you shouldn't be rude to him."

Mother was right. I just couldn't help it.

One night after supper Shalin came to our rooms carrying an armful of red cloth pieces. "Aunt Huang," she greeted Mother, "may I use your sewing machine to make some armbands?"

"Of course, come on in," Mother said enthusiastically and held the door open for her. Mother moved the thermos bottles and tea pot and cups away from the top of the machine.

"Let me prop it up, Aunt Huang." Shalin set the cloth on the table and came over. She lifted the lid and fished the machine out of its cradle. She aligned the leather driving belt to the wheel and pedaled it to see if there was any obstruction.

"You joined the veteran Red Guard group?" I asked, feeling anger well up in my stomach.

"Yes, well?" she looked at me inquiringly.

"You shouldn't."

"Why shouldn't I?"

"You know," I faltered. Who was I to be giving advice that sounded like orders? "You know, the situation is very confusing right now. The Cultural Revolution is a mystery to me. Who can figure out what's going on in the high places. Perhaps a power struggle. But which direction is the wind blowing, do you know?"

"I don't know." She sat down on a stool and threaded the needle. "I only know that young people should not shun their revolutionary responsibilities. We should follow Chairman Mao's commands to cleanse China of all bad old things."

"So we beat and kill old people in the street?"

"That's not the fault of the Cultural Revolution. Every revolutionary movement may go a bit beyond its goal," Shalin said without raising her eyes from the machine. "You don't have to look for bones inside an egg."

"I'm not old enough to have experienced the political campaigns of the past." I swallowed to mellow my tone. "From what I've read, however, I know that in every campaign there have been wronged ghosts. It would be safer if we wait awhile to see what happens."

"Pumph!" Shalin sneered. She might have said "coward" aloud.

"Please think it over carefully." I was genuinely concerned and felt unrewarded for my caring.

"Thanks for the advice."

I sat by the window to read. Not much light could reach my seat from the 25-watt bulb dangling from the ceiling. My mind

32

registered nothing. I had to find a way to keep Shalin from being involved. Young Red Guards were running wild, parading people and beating them with brass-buckled belts. To the common people, Red Guards did not seem as lovable as Chairman Mao's wife, Jiang Qing, eulogized. Sooner or later they would fall into disgrace once the people recovered from the shock of this Red Terror.

"Yesterday a group of middle school Red Guards came to search the Bais' home," I told Shalin. It was nice to watch her so concentrated on the work—her brows arched, lips pursed and her lovely fingers busy feeding the machine. The dim light fell softly on her round shoulders. I wanted to touch her.

"Did they?" she responded absent-mindedly.

"They took away their piano, many books and the Seven Star sword which had been passed down from Mr. Bai's great-grandfather. A boy slapped him on the face because he protested that the sword had not been sharpened and was harmless."

"That can't prove the Red Guards are wrong," Shalin said coldly. "Why don't you mention how many antiques, and gold, silver and precious stones they have confiscated and turned over to the state? These rich families hoarded them for many years despite the government's appeal to turn them over to help the country. Why did they hide them? They hid them against the day when the Communist Party loses power. Do you sympathize with them?"

Yes, they had my sympathy. I wanted to kick those young radicals who beat old people up.

"Well," I said, "it is not middle school or college students' right to search people's houses. Police could be sent to demand those things."

"But don't forget that this is a dictatorship of all the people."

I lowered my eyes to the book in my hand and kept silent.

"You go to sleep," Shalin said. "I'll try to make as little noise as I can."

I didn't go to sleep. I liked being with Shalin at this late hour.

My family and the courtyard had gone to sleep. I wished the clock would stop or her work would not end.

It was well past midnight when she finished her two hundred armbands. I saw her to her courtyard, trying to say something to please her. I failed.

Dian Wen moved to the Bureau's dormitory. I suspected he wanted to be close to Shalin more often. I decided to move there too. I told Mother that my little brothers were growing up and needed more space in bed. Three of us in one double bed was overcrowding.

The veteran Red Guards set up their headquarters in a room on the first floor of the dormitory, in the Bureau's backcourt. The girls' rooms were on the second floor and the boys had the third and fourth. Members would get together every day in the headquarters to discuss "ferreting out the class enemies" in the Bureau and play cards and joke about the silly behavior of those they had paraded and denounced at public meetings. I went there frequently but did not see Shalin. She stayed in her dormitory room or the reference room to make large posters on colored paper criticizing identified detractors of socialist China.

The group was very busy. Dian Wen attended meetings, went searching people's houses, and played. He and Shalin didn't see each other at all. Soon I found out that he was not interested in Shalin in any special way. He treated other girls in much the same carefree manner.

One evening around ten o'clock Dian Wen rushed into my room to tell me that Shalin was very ill. "She's running a high fever. Her head is burning," he said anxiously. "I'll drive her to the hospital. Would you come to help?"

The diagnosis was meningitis. Shalin didn't utter a sound as the nurse inserted a long needle into her spinal cord.

Her father was in Guizhou Province. Her stepmother assured me she would visit the hospital the next day. But I needed one hundred yuan deposit for the hospital and it was too late to get any money from the Bureau's accounting office. I asked Mother for the money, assuring her that the Bureau would refund it. "Shalin will need some clothes to wear in the hospital," Mother said. "I have some cloth here and can sew up a shirt and pair of trousers right away."

Shalin's stepmother went to see her the next afternoon and left before I arrived. Shalin was in bed with intravenous bottles hanging above her.

"That was her mother?" the nurse asked me.

"Her stepmother."

"No wonder she didn't seem worried when the doctor told her the situation is dangerous. She took the watch from Shalin's wrist. That was the only time she touched her. Perhaps she was afraid of being infected." The nurse, about Shalin's age, wrinkled her nose in disgust. "Ah, stepmother!"

I went to the hospital every afternoon. There was no work in the office anyway. It took forty minutes to cycle from home to the hospital in the northern suburbs. Every day Mother would cook something for me to take along in a lunchbox. "The hospital food is no good," Mother would say. "Take this pot of noodles and chicken broth to Shalin. She needs nourishment."

I would sit by her bed for half an hour and begin feeling uncomfortable. There were three other patients in the room. They had no difficulty figuring out why I was there. They would giggle if I made a foolish remark out of embarrassment. I would find an excuse to go out for awhile and return. I knew Shalin wanted me to be there, though she didn't have much to say. I felt stupid sitting there and asking, "Want some tea?"

When Shalin was better we would sit outside, still having little to talk about. Mother came several times. It seemed she and Shalin had a lot to say to each other. They talked about small things that seemed a waste of time to me. When I got the hundred yuan back from the accounting office, Mother told me to buy some wool, so Shalin could knit. "Her sweater is at least ten years old. Her stepmother didn't want it and gave it to her. She re-knitted it."

I didn't go to the hospital on the first Wednesday after she was out of intensive care. On Thursday, I found Shalin lying in bed with her back toward the door. She didn't turn over. I said sheepishly, "I'm here."

She didn't respond. I heard the whispered giggling from the other beds and felt hot along my spine. Sweat oozed slowly from my hair line. "Hi, I'm here," I said cheerfully.

"You don't have to come at all," Shalin said, dabbing her eyes.

I was terrified, searching my mind for what I might have said or done the last time I was there.

The nurse came in and asked, "Why didn't you come yesterday?"

"Your hospital doesn't allow visits on Wednesdays except for intensive care patients."

"You idiot," the nurse scolded playfully. "The rule is for idiots. You should know I would let you in if you came."

I expressed my thanks profusely. Now I was sure I had got Shalin.

6 · We Court
without Romance

Emperor Qian Long, who brought "culture" to the Manchu court, was wise, romantic and adventurous, and enjoyed many hobbies in his long life. One was fishing. He built a Fishing Terrace beyond Fuxingmen Gate. His successors were not outdoor men. They preferred concubines, dancing girls and food. The Fishing Terrace was neglected and the river shrank. By the early 1950s, the river had become a trickle meandering among marshes thick with grass and reed. Silt was more than a foot deep at the base of the Fishing Terrace. The marble balustrade was long gone. Many bricks were missing.

On a Saturday in summer our primary school class had gone there for a picnic. Armed with pots, spades, noodles, salt, peanut oil, scallions, ginger and a bundle of chopsticks, in mid-afternoon we marched off through the gap. The red flag with its yellow Young Pioneers emblem flew proudly in the lead. Beyond the wooden bridge over the moat, we trudged along a dirt road worn a foot lower than the flanking fields by wooden cart wheels and the hooves of oxen and mules. We bought tomatoes and eggs at a farmhouse.

We dug out fire pits and propped up the pots. Our teacher showed how alum added to the pot would settle out the mud so the river water could be used for cooking. The green wood we collected from trees and shrubs refused to jump into flames. The noodles melted in the lukewarm soup and our picnic was a pot of wheat flour paste. The shallow river was not teeming with the fish we had expected, though Dian Wen and some others caught a few one-inch fry.

Daylight lasted longer outside the city. At half-past seven we were still roaming the mounds and marshes searching for butterflies, grasshoppers, beetles, frogs and other insects for our specimen case.

The teacher gave the order to return. Dian Wen came to me and asked, "Do you dare to stay here tonight?"

"Of course I do," I replied without giving it a second thought. I always wanted to show the tough guys my bravery.

"Okay," Dian Wen said, satisfied. "Now we have five."

I asked Mrs. Chang to tell Mother the Young Pioneer squadron was holding a bonfire party after the picnic which would last very late. I would stay at the school that night. "Don't tell her I am here," I warned Mrs. Chang, who was only too glad to lie for me.

The others left. Erhu led us in singing wild songs, mimicking a young woman's voice:

> As soon as I went out the back gate,
> I saw a soldier with his gun in hand.
> I wanted to shout, but my voice was weak;
> I wanted to run, but the sorghum grew thick.

Then we fought using branches for swords and spears.

Erhu caught a snake. He slit the skin around the head, carefully slipping it back, revealing the white flesh. He filled the tube of skin with sand. "Watch! I'll make a fiddle. Snake skin is the best material for a sound box."

The wet twigs from our picnic had been baked dry by the embers. They now burned lively. It was a pity the pots had been taken back to school. If we had one we could make tomato-egg soup. Erhu roasted the snake over the fire. Fat dripped into the flames and sizzled. He and Dian Wen ate it, pretending relish. The rest of us said we were too full from the noodles.

Dusk fell. Mosquitoes swarmed and buzzed around us, attacking any exposed skin. The hushed rustling of grass and reeds which had been so pleasant during the day now was a weird whistling of terror and mystery. A grown-up passed by and glanced at us. We thrust our chests out.

The real darkness came. I remembered the white circles on farmhouse walls, drawn to fend off wolves. I had never guessed a July night could be so cold.

I knew the others were scared too. So I waited. I chatted casually about *Outlaws of the Marsh*. We all knew the nicknames of the hundred and eight outlaws. I wished someday I would become such a hero, who could get away free after killing a street bully. The others pretended to listen nonchalantly, but glanced sideways frequently.

"Damn it!" Erhu said angrily. "These motherfucking mosquitoes! I wish they were a pack of wolves so I could strangle them. But you can't grab a mosquito! Disgusting."

We agreed with angry grunts. "Fuck the mosquitoes' mother!" Erhu roared too loudly.

"Let's get out of here!" Dian Wen gave the order.

I restrained myself from running.

That night my reputation rose among my schoolmates because even Erhu and Dian Wen, the famous toughs who had friends among the street gangs, gave me respect as a man of wits and guts.

Twelve years later, the area around the Fishing Terrace had changed beyond recognition. In 1958, thousands of volunteers in Beijing were mobilized to dig August First Lake out of the marshes. The silt was piled into mounds on which trees were planted. The trail that led from Erligou to the Fishing Terrace was now a thoroughfare flanked by apartment and office buildings. The State Guest House for foreign heads of state sprawled majestically along the eastern bank of the lake. The Fishing Terrace had been retained, its front embedded in the gray brick wall of the mansion. The three beautifully carved characters in Emperor Qian Long's calligraphic style could still be seen.

Shalin and I were walking along the bank of the lake. The golden spire of the Military Museum rose into the sky to the south. Traffic noise from the boulevard droned vaguely. The trees were shedding their leaves. The grass was yellowing in the dry, brisk autumn breeze. The water was calmer and bluer than in summer. Shalin had lost her plumpness but gained a graceful delicacy. I had never cared for the beauty of the ailing women described in ancient poems. Now I believed in it. Shalin was prettier, without her former sharpness in talk and manner.

"Do you remember the picnic we had here?" I asked.

"You made your name that day," she said in a weak voice. "But you paid for it with a spanking from your father."

"When you girls went behind the bushes to pee, some naughty boys followed to watch." I laughed silently, remembering the tousled heads popping up and down in the dense branches.

"You were among them too. But you were a little farther away. Perhaps even Dian Wen hadn't noticed you. You know what? Sometimes I think you are hypocritical. Erhu and Dian Wen were straightforward. They would run up to us and tug our braids. You never dared. You would stand aside to watch and imagine."

My face tingled. Shalin took my flirting remarks so rigidly that I lost my humor.

"Dian Wen and others have gone off to travel in the south." I changed subject as well as tone. "Red Guards are making expeditions to exchange revolutionary ideas. The central authorities have ordered the whole country to provide them with free transportation, lodging and meals. Dian Wen urged me to join their trip.

"Oh?" she sounded unconcerned. "Why didn't you go? It would be a good chance to see the country."

She ought to know why I hadn't gone. I felt I was being wronged.

"Let's sit down and take a rest." Shalin pointed to a sunny spot in a hollow between two gentle mounds. The grass was soft and inviting.

"This may be the only place in Beijing that is quiet," she said. "Everywhere are crowds of Red Guards. Those who have to take the bus to work must really suffer."

40

It seemed the meningitis had sapped a great deal of her revolutionary zeal. She had forgotten she was a member of the veteran Red Guards, which was now called the Red Flag Detachment.

We sat side by side, a couple of feet between us. I moved closer, deliberately touching my knee against hers. She retrieved her knee a bit, but did not move away.

"Mother wants us to have supper at home," I said. That was true. Food at the office canteen was not good. Mother worried about Shalin's recovery. "Sooner or later she will join our family," Mother had said to me. "You'd better take good care of her." After she was released from the hospital she should have stayed home for recuperation, but she went directly back to the dormitory.

"No. It's all right to eat at the canteen."

I had not expected she would come. We had not talked about marriage yet. And she had to think how her stepmother would feel if she ate with us.

I shifted my position again so that my knee was so close to hers that they would touch unless she moved away. She didn't. That was encouraging. I stretched my arm out to wrap around her waist. She pushed it down a little. I kept it at her hip. I leaned over and kissed her. She was startled and jumped up. "What are you doing?" she demanded angrily.

"Take it easy," I said placatingly. "Take it easy. We both know that we are going to get married. Why don't we put it in the open? I'm twenty-six, not too young for marriage. Shalin, I care for you. Mother thinks a lot of you. Let's get married."

Shalin stood there, her face flushing. I was afraid I had gone too far. She might think I was frivolous and say "no" to me.

"All right. Let's go back, we've been out too long," Shalin said. "I am beginning to feel cold."

I released the deep breath I was holding. Hastily I pulled off my jacket and handed it to her. She took it and tugged it over her shoulders, the color in her face fading.

She continued to eat at the canteen. However, she came home with me on Saturday afternoons. After supper she would chat with Mother or help her with some sewing or mending.

I became more cautious in dealing with Shalin. The boldest thing I did was to hold her hand in the movies, where we went four or five times in the three months before we took out our marriage certificate. After that she allowed me to kiss her, but not every time we were together.

7 · The Great White Pagoda

The trees in the park were maturing. The Great White Pagoda was invisible from the alley now, except for the crown when the trees were leafless. The temple fair had been abolished in 1956 when merchants were incorporated into government stores in the move toward socialization. The compound inside the White Pagoda Monastery was crowded with low houses built by squatters from the exploding alleys nearby.

Prior to 1965 Beijing had few high buildings. The Beijing Hotel west of Tiananmen Square was the tallest with twelve stories. The highest place in the city was the pavilion on Jingshan Hill behind the old Imperial Palace. Alley boys rarely had a chance to go into that affluent district. The Great White Pagoda was the tallest place we knew, except for the Western Hills which the grown-ups said were higher.

There are two white pagodas in Beijing—the Small White Pagoda in Beihai Park, a former imperial garden in the central area of the city, and the Great White Pagoda in the White Pagoda Monastery to the west. Old people said that under each there is a tunnel connected to the eastern sea.

Legend has it that when Emperor Cheng Zu ascended to the throne in 1406, he decided to move his capital from Jinling (now called Nanjing, meaning Southern Capital) to the north. He sent his trusted councillor Liu Bowen to survey the site. Liu found the area troubled by four evil dragons. Everywhere there was water. After fierce battles the evil water gods were captured and the flood subsided to the Eastern Sea. Outside the West Gate today is the Gao Liang Bridge in memory of a brave general who drowned in battle there.

Liu Bowen dug four wells in the new capital (called Beijing, or Northern Capital) and confined the dragons in them, tying them to long iron chains. On top of two of the wells Buddhist monks built the pagodas.

Historical record contends that Liu Bowen was a court minister of Emperor Tai Zu, father of Emperor Cheng Zu. But Beijing residents loved the wise minister so much that they attributed to him the grand deeds of founding their city. Records show that the Great White Pagoda was built by a young Nepalese architect with one hundred and eighty Nepalese artisans in the Yuan Dynasty, some hundred and sixty years before Liu Bowen was active in the Ming court. The Buddhist sanctuary was named Eternal Peace Monastery, but local residents called it White Pagoda.

As the national capital for six hundred years, Beijing had seen an easy life-style cultivated by hordes of bureaucrats. Many people spent their days at teahouses. Here was the source of the Great White Pagoda in folklore.

The most ancient story tells of Lu Pan, the God of Carpentry. One summer night during the reign of Emperor Qian Long, the wind was howling, the thunder deafening and rain falling in torrents. Children cowered deep in the arms of shivering mothers; fathers were busy trying to find a place to keep the family possessions from being soaked. A thunderclap exploded, lighting the sky. The world was suspended for an eternal moment. There was a roaring sound which seemed to come from both heaven and deep within the earth. Perhaps it was the end of the world.

The next morning there were several vertical cracks in the huge body of the Great White Pagoda. If it fell, the people said, the evil dragon in the well beneath would come out and bring water from the Eastern Sea to flood Beijing once more. People cried and prayed, but there was nothing they could do. Some fled to the Western Hills.

Three days later, an old man came to the neighborhood, his long white beard glistening in the sunshine. He had a wooden box slung over his shoulder with a cowhide strap. He sat down at a door and asked for a bowl of water to drink, telling the neighbors he was a tinker. A young man responded, "Who has the heart to mend bowls and plates when we are going to die soon?"

The old man said he did not mend bowls and plates; he mended only big things. The man pointed to a large earthenware jar, the kind used for pickling, and asked him to clamp it. The old man said it was too small for him.

Then the young man said, "We indeed have something big here. But I am afraid you cannot do it."

"What is it?" the old man asked.

"Look over there," the young man pointed to the pagoda. "There are seven cracks in its body. I hope that is big enough for you."

The old man smiled, thanked the woman of the house where he had sat and walked away.

The next morning the neighbors saw seven iron bands around the body of the White Pagoda. The cracks sealed up. That was Lu Pan.

A modern story tells of Japan's occupation of Beijing during the Second World War. The Japanese wanted to end the superstition about the Great White Pagoda. They sent a platoon of soldiers to the monastery in three trucks and summoned the local people to watch how their emperor's power could overwhelm the Chinese divinities.

They pried away the great stone cover of the well beneath the pagoda, which had not been moved since it was first laid there by Liu Bowen. A chilly jet of air gushed out. The four soldiers nearby were pushed back several steps. Four more came to help. The iron chains in the well were attached to a winch. The clanking sound seemed sad as the chains were drawn up. They seemed endless and the wind from the well became chillier and the noise louder. Despite their Samurai heritage, the soldiers hesitated. The weeping sound became a howling. The noise was like an angry sea. The captain decided to compromise his emperor's prestige and ordered the chains pushed back into the well and the cover replaced.

With the flow of people coming to worship on major holidays, every temple in China eventually would become a market place. Soon after its completion, the imperially patronized White Pagoda Monastery was flourishing as one of Beijing's four largest temple fairs. Hundred of vendors moved among the four fairs, staying three days at each. Things of every description could be found: secondhand clothes, household tools, axles for horse-drawn carts, wooden trunks, snacks of a thousand varieties, birds in cages and, in autumn, crickets in delicate earthenware or porcelain jars. Wrestlers, singers, acrobats, jugglers, magicians, fortunetellers and storytellers each had a spot, some sheltered with canopies or bordered with patchwork cloth.

Some peddlers cleared debris outside the crimson walls of the monastery and put up frames of wooden poles and covered them with oilcloth and tar paper, providing a protected place to sleep. Then simple shacks of broken bricks appeared. Families moved in, children grew up, and narrow alleys took shape.

Old folks said that the lions carved in the marble balustrade of the Marco Polo Bridge were uncountable; so were the alleys of Beijing. They came to bear colorful names, indicating that the place had once been a noble house, such as Alley of Marquis Duan's Mansion, or what other kind of place had been there. There was an alley called Eighteen Turns. Before running water was installed, local wells were the only source of water. Some sixty alleys were named for their former wells.

There were also Silk Washer Alley, Bean Curd Chen Alley, Paper Horse Wang Alley, Apricot Blossom Sky Alley, Depth of a Hundred Flowers Alley and other beautiful names.

The major streets of Beijing were laid out at right angles. Any stranger should not be afraid of losing his bearings among them. But even an old Beijinger could get lost in the labyrinth of alleys in a distant part of town. He knew, however, that the way to get out was to keep walking in one direction. Sooner or later he would reach a major street that connected to the rest of the city.

The several hundred alleys and side streets around the Great White Pagoda were inhabited by people at the bottom of society. Those did not have beautiful names. One of them was Tanyin Alley. Its name had no apparent meaning. Neither did the lives of some two hundred families who inhabited its fifty-seven courtyards.

8 · Marriage Depends on a Room

It was already a month since we had obtained our marriage certificates and I had been looking for a room for us to live in. Shalin insisted that unless we had a formal wedding we couldn't sleep together. Pure nonsense! College boys and girls were sleeping together, since they had no classes to attend. Hu Bon and Wang Shen, Dian Wen's new buddies from the Red Flag Detachment, did not bother to keep secret that they spent nights with their girlfriends. And they had not yet gotten marriage certificates. It seemed they didn't want to waste time going through the legal formality.

I went to the Bureau Housing Office almost every day and got the same indifferent answer: "We don't have a room."

The population of Beijing had exploded in the late fifties. Government establishments moved from old courtyards to sprawling new multi-story complexes and hundreds of factories were built to show that the ancient capital of dynasties was no longer a parasite feeding on tributes. Bureaucrats, office staff and factory workers moved into the capital of the new China in tens of thousands, bringing along hundreds of thousands of family dependents.

In 1956, in a drive to put private business under socialist control, most of the buildings were claimed by the Housing Administration of the city. Government organizations and large state factories each had an allotment of living quarters for their employees.

Once I was told, "We have no control over housing now. If you can find a place for yourself, grab it and it's yours."

At last a middle-aged woman working there became sympathetic and told Shalin in private that there was a room at 6 Tanyin Alley, a courtyard the Bureau owned to house its low-ranking workers.

With Dian Wen's sister and brother both married and with children, their old place was too crowded. Six months earlier Dian Wen had secured a room at 6 Tanyin Alley and moved there with his mother. He offered to take us there to have a look.

"There are already three veterans living in the courtyard," he told me with great enthusiasm. "All ten families except one belong to the Revolutionary Rebels. We will make our courtyard a bastion against the Red Alliance."

These two groups were rival Red Guard factions in the Bureau. Hu Bon's Red Flag Detachment was the backbone of the Revolutionary Rebels. I felt disgust whenever there was talk of faction affiliation, as if people were bound by it. They imbued it with comradeship or brotherhood. I had not joined any Red Guard group, and had no intention of doing so. I was not interested in which side was strong at 6 Tanyin Alley. I only needed a room for my marriage.

Next morning, Dian Wen took Shalin and me to see the room. We rode bicycles along neat roads in a new suburban area. After ten minutes we reached the edge of the old city. The wall had been torn down and the moat drained in preparation for construction of China's first subway. The wooden bridge over the moat had been dismantled. We had to make a detour over a temporary crossing of thick steel plates.

West Gate, stripped of the magnificent walls, was visible to the north. Once so proud, it was a scene of desolation. Liang Sicheng, the famous professor of ancient architecture at Qinghua University, was said to have wept over the decision to demolish the wall. West Gate was like an ox who knew it was to be slaughtered soon.

We meandered through a maze of side streets and narrow alleys. Twenty minutes later we were in the shadow of the Great White Pagoda which loomed in the hazy morning glow. It appeared a dirty gray at its base through the smoke from a quarter million stoves burning coal. And its crown seemed a burnished gold from the fine dust blown in on the spring winds. Shalin had just learned to ride a bicycle. Several times she nearly bumped into a street light pole or kids playing.

Tanyin Alley went zigzagging through five or six sharp turns. Five feet at its widest, the alley was squeezed in by adobe-like one-story houses. Broken bricks were falling out of the walls.

For hundreds of years Beijing residents had been dumping coal ash and garbage into the streets. The accumulation was thicker in poor neighborhoods where the crowded houses were built of brick or rammed earth. They collapsed easily in a rainy summer and were rebuilt as easily on top of the debris in the fall. The alleys immediately outside the crimson walls of the monastery were six feet higher than the ground level inside. Tanyin Alley appeared worse than our old alley.

Number 6 courtyard was in the middle of the alley.

"This used to be the stable of a court official in the Qing Dynasty," Dian Wen spoke like a tour guide. "The courtyard was an open lot for walking horses. Later the place changed masters and our courtyard became a hothouse for raising flowers. There's the room."

The empty room was in the middle of the south row, the smallest of four rooms. Shalin was greatly disappointed at its poor state. It could hardly be called a room fit for human habitation. The window panes were warped and tilted. There were cracks an inch wide between the window frame and wall. The upper part of the window was covered with paper. The lower panes were glass; age and scratches obscured any view. It would be cold in winter when the prevailing northwesterlies blew directly into the room, and stiflingly hot in summer because the taller house behind the room would block the southeasterlies. One panel was missing from the door.

Dian Wen unlocked it—it was unnecessary to lock it in the first place. Stepping inside I was assailed by the usual smell of damp, unused rooms, and the presence of mice.

"A young couple moved out two months ago," he continued apologetically, as if he were the landlord renting out an unwanted basement room. "They were lazy people, never swept the area in front of their door. Nobody in the courtyard liked them. Ah, they were college graduates. You know those bigwig intellectuals!"

The room was almost square, about eleven feet on each side. The walls were sooted to dirty gray. A hole in the ceiling revealed blackened rafters and beams. Along the edge of the floor were a continuous chain of holes and piles of dirt dug out by mice, like a range of miniature mountains. The floor was paved with those small square cement tiles commonly used for sidewalks. Shalin remained outside while Dian Wen and I surveyed the dark room.

Dian Wen kept chattering about the merits of this particular courtyard. "The Bureau has four residential places. The other three are for officials and higher office workers. Only this courtyard is for us common people. You don't want to mix with those arrogant prudes, do you?"

I said nothing.

He brought us to his room, which was next door, and offered a lunch of noodles. Everything was impeccable. There were two single beds, one for his bed-ridden mother and one for himself. His mother mumbled an unintelligible welcome. The stove was lit, even though it was already May.

"When I first moved in," he said, shoveling some cucumber slices into his mother's bowl, "this room was in the same shape as the one next door. I took it because it is convenient for my mother. Here the neighbors can come help her and chat. They are very nice, unlike those bookworms who care only about themselves. Hu Bon, Wang Shen and Erhu helped me whitewash the room three times, fill in the mice holes and repaint the window frames. See, it is not so bad, is it?"

It was not so bad. The window paper was snow white, very transparent. The glass in the lower part had been replaced. The windowsill was covered with durable paper. The table, two chairs, cupboard, every piece of furniture were all spotless. It must have taken a lot of effort to keep the room so clean in dusty Beijing.

The city was becoming even dustier, with the digging of air raid shelters against Soviet attack. Also, in recent years herdsmen from Inner Mongolia had reclaimed large stretches of pasture land to grow grain, while peasants in the mountains cut trees to make new fields, under the central authorities' decree that the rural population be self-sufficient in food production. The wind brought more and more dust into Beijing, which penetrated the smallest crack. It was a marvel that Dian Wen could maintain his room so well.

After lunch we declined Dian Wen's persistent exhortation to stay longer and went to my mother's, ten minutes away by bike.

"Well," Mother said, "I wouldn't suggest you live in a room that can't get sunlight. In all my years only once did I have a sunny room. That was when I was in the hospital. Back in our native village, your grandparents had the main rooms facing south. Your uncles and father had the wings facing east and west. My room was low and small. A room that has no sunlight can be harmful to a woman during her confinement. You'd better think it over carefully before you move in."

Although I was anxious to get a family started, I hated the idea of living in a dark hole in that courtyard amid run-down houses. And I did not want to raise children in a place where they had to mix with children of uneducated laborers. My enthusiasm for a happy married life was sapped.

9 · A Sweet and Horrible Night

Living in the dormitory and having nothing to do at the office, I was overwhelmed by boredom. Two years had passed since the two hundred demobilized soldiers were assigned to various departments of the Bureau to do supplementary work. I was going on thirty. According to Confucius, at thirty one should have established himself in a career and family life. I was not content with being a mere proofreader for the rest of my life. I was confident that, given a chance, I would be able to make it big. I might climb up to department chief or even Bureau chief someday. But the Cultural Revolution seemed to go on forever. In such a chaotic situation there was no telling which direction the political wind was blowing. How could I advance?

Hu Bon and his lieutenants of the Red Flag Detachment, however, were having the time of their lives. They were merry and gay even when they were criticizing "bad elements" or "Capitalist Roaders." They played cards and mahjong in their headquarters in the dormitory building. They had confiscated a very expensive mahjong set with ivory tiles, and piles of forbidden books. I had become indifferent toward their radical ideas and actions. I liked to drop in at their place to play and wile away my boredom.

Shalin did not like me spending too much time with them. Since her illness her attitude toward Red Guard politics had changed and she talked as if she had never had the zeal to support it. "You and they," she would say seriously, "are not birds of the same feather. Hu Bon wants to become a big shot through a short cut. Red Guard politics suits him. You should stay with your books and advance in your profession step by step on solid ground."

I wanted to retort by saying, "If you allowed me to spend more time with you, I wouldn't bother with them." But I dared not. I was a grown man after all. I wouldn't let her get the notion that I yearned for her.

The unrewarding search for a room plunged me into a depression. I was annoyed with Shalin. If she went to the Housing Office, they might be more helpful. In defiance of her warning, I spent more time with Hu Bon's group.

I played mahjong at the Red Flag Detachment headquarters for five hours after supper, pretending to enjoy myself. Around eleven o'clock I returned to my room, knowing how mad Shalin would be for not having my daily report to her. I dropped onto the bed, propped against the wall with the quilt rolled under my back, and took up the tabloid Hu Bon had given me. It was one of thousands of papers put out by Red Guards. Mostly they were filled with political rumors and bragging. I threw it on the floor.

Damn the Red Guards! They talked in high sounding words. "We must not be afraid of losing our lives to protect the proletarian cause and Chairman Mao's revolutionary line!" But I knew the leaders of both Red Guard groups in the Bureau. Everyone was trying to profit from the chaotic situation. They were climbing on top of each other to grab leadership in the Bureau, and from there, the higher rungs of the ladders of officialdom. No matter how stupid a man might be, as soon as he had power, he would have everything. And whoever fell for it was like an opium addict. The Cultural Revolution was providing a good chance for hypocrites and speculators. The pity was, there were always fools willing to follow them.

Outside the window, the compound was deserted. The May night would have felt pleasant in peaceful times, filled with chattering and laughter at this hour, with the air fragrant from the strings of white blossoms on the scholar trees. The singles in the dormitory buildings would prefer to spend half the night in the open. Many rooms in the office building would still be lit with late workers and ambitious young staffers. But now, with all the political study sessions and arguments, plus confrontations between the Red Alliance and Revolutionary Rebels, very few people wanted to venture out after dark. Only two days earlier the two factions had had a real fight. There had been a few cuts on faces and arms for both sides. The Revolutionary Rebels had abducted a leader from their rivals and hidden him for "investigation." In retaliation, the Red Alliance had ordered the Kitchen and Water Supply Office, which they controlled, to stage a boycott. The atmosphere was highly charged.

Instinctively, I looked at the corner behind the door. The thick wooden stick was still there. Although I was not affiliated with any faction and had made no enemies, one just couldn't be too sure what would happen these days.

It was too late to see Shalin. She would cut me dead tomorrow, for sure. I·had better not offend her further. But I rose from the bed and walked down from the third floor to the second. Shalin's room was still lit, so I knocked on the door.

"You may as well not come at all," she said, her tone lashing me like a whip.

I knew at the same time, to my delight, her roommate was not in. Otherwise she would not have spoken that way. I pushed the door open and saw her sitting on the bed, properly dressed, knitting a sweater. I explained my difficult situation with Hu Bon and his group."You know," I pleaded, "if I didn't join them they would laugh at me for being afraid of my wife."

"You don't have a wife yet," she said, not joking.

"Hasn't Li Sunro come back?" I asked to distract her anger.

"No. She's come in late the last several nights."

"She's not been courting, has she?"

"Courting, at her age? Don't talk nonsense."

I was pleased with my little joke.

"Well, who knows," I said. "They say that women in their thirties are like wolves in heat and in their forties like tigresses."

Shalin glared at me. "I warn you. You'd better not tell me what you learn from Hu Bon and his lot. They have mouths that spit dung."

I had to change the subject again. "You know . . . Lu Fusang is away for a family visit. Why don't you come to my room for the night. I'm worried about you alone in this room."

I was serious, not merely thinking of an excuse to induce her to bed. Under the circumstances, a young woman staying alone in a dormitory room was not a good idea.

"No," she sounded firm and final. She refused to be together with me until we had our public wedding. "Li Sunro may be back tonight and I don't want her to imagine things between us."

I lingered a little longer and returned to my room. I did not understand why there was not much for us to talk about, as I saw there was with other young people in love. Tossing in bed, I was frustrated by her stubborn adherence to propriety. Hu Bon and Fanhua must be enjoying their wonderful night after a driving excursion to the West Hills.

Oh, Hu Bon and Fanhua were a pair of queer birds. He was like Erhu in his carefree and sometimes reckless life. But he was not Erhu; he had wits. That was why Hu Bon was leader of the Red Flag Detachment gang. Fanhua was 5'10", a full three inches taller than Hu Bon. He was solidly built, though he looked small under the huge young lady whom we called Big Beauty.

Had they read the picture book about love making? I had seen it under his pillow. It must be one of the forbidden books they had confiscated from a disgraced family. Perhaps they were trying all the ways described in it right now.

There was a light tap on the door. I held my breath. There was another. I turned on the light and having made sure the stick was still leaning against the wall, I asked who it was. I jumped out of bed with joy. It was Shalin's voice.

"Li Sunro has not come back yet," she glanced around. "I didn't tell you that someone turned Lin Fen's door knob last

---

56

night. I suspect the lock on my door was tampered with. I don't know why Li Sunro is so late tonight. It's nearly midnight."

"Why bother with her," I said. "She must be sleeping somewhere." I refrained from saying, ". . . safely in someone's arms."

"I'll stay here tonight."

"Of course, of course," I began fussing with the sheets on my bed.

"I'll sleep in your bed and you sleep in Lu Fusang's."

My heart sank, but I had to comply.

I nestled down in Lu Fusang's bed, unable to sleep, and hating Shalin.

"Haven't you fallen asleep?" she asked.

"Of course I haven't!" I said irritably.

"Then come over."

I jumped over in one leap.

My sleep was sweet.

But good dreams don't last long. I was shaken awake and heard Shalin saying, "Listen!" I lingered several seconds, savoring the sweetness before I became alert to the tension in her voice. I listened. There was nothing. Sleep carried me away again. "Listen!" I shook off the black clouds. There was a moan, more like a sigh. The sound was low but clear, conveying such horror that my hair stood up. Another moan distinctly carried tremendous agony. I felt Shalin's body tense against mine.

"We should go and have a look."

I was not sure that it was a good idea to go out under such circumstances. If we had heard the groan, several dozen others in the dormitory must have heard it too. There were no footsteps in the corridor. Should we face the risk of an unknown danger?

"Someone must be badly hurt. He needs help," Shalin urged.

At the moment, the last thing in the world I would do was displease her. I started dressing, slowly, purposefully. I was greatly relieved to hear someone walking cautiously down the corridor. I jumped out the door gallantly, armed with the stick.

I was shocked to find Li Sunro on the entrance steps. A square scarf was under her head. Blood dripped from her nose and mouth. Ren Rong, the accountant of the office kitchen, bent over to check her injuries. Three more men came. Li Sunro murmured, "Kill me, please kill me."

Someone ran over to the night duty room of the garage. The driver there brought a car around. I helped carry her and put her in the back seat, lingering behind so that two others got in the car before me. I put an expression of grave concern on my face for Shalin to see.

In those days I would rather keep a distance from such incidents. On the street I would not come close to see a traffic accident or a brawl. Beijingers were eager spectators for any kind of curiosity. But with the Red Guards beating and killing people in the street, curiosity or eagerness to give help to strangers only invited trouble.

We returned to my room. "What shall I say to the police?" Shalin asked me, worried. "They will surely come to investigate. Shall I tell them I was with you? Then everybody will know we are together."

It was no time to care about a sense of propriety and I said, "You'd better tell them the truth." My mind had begun working fast as soon as it occurred to me that Li Sunro was Shalin's only roommate. "You might say you were afraid to be alone in the room, that you needed company. Tell them that Lin Fen's door knob had been jiggled that night."

I looked at her face flushed in agitation and tried to be funny to lighten the tension. "Of course, it's totally unnecessary to inform the police that when you heard the moaning you were in my bed."

She was too anxious to notice my untimely humor.

"Tell them the truth," I repeated. "That you'd waited until late and were afraid. So you came to stay the night with me."

"I'm afraid of going back to my room," she said, dejected.

"You are not going back to your room. Tomorrow, I mean

after daybreak, I'll take your things out of that room. You can stay with Lin Fen for the time being. She's alone and needs company."

It was much simpler than we had anticipated. All the police officer asked Shalin was when she had last seen Li Sunro. He didn't even ask if she were in the room that night. Like many other unnatural deaths since late 1966, the coroner announced that the case was suicide by jumping out of her window. She did not die instantly, but of internal injuries. She had jumped and hurt herself, crawled to the entranceway for help, but could not move further. That was the official report.

"Poor Li Sunro," Shalin said sadly. "When she was twenty-two her parents sent her back from Japan, to help build the new China. Being fluent in Japanese, it was easy for her to find work as a translator. In 1957 her young man was branded a Rightist and sent to the northeastern wilderness to do manual labor. She received a severe dressing down from the Party secretary for her lack of vigilance against reactionary ideas.

"She became a loner. At first, her older colleagues tried to persuade her to get married. They even suggested a few young men. She thanked them politely but wouldn't meet them. Now she's gone."

"Jumping to her death from a second floor window?" Hu Bon talked at the Red Flag Detachment headquarters. "Totally impossible. There must be something going on. Li Sunro was a member of the Red Alliance and had been threatening to withdraw from it because she believed they were doing things which were not above board."

I caught the implication but did not think that was the likely cause. Red Guards had been killing people in the street, that was true. But only young people did that kind of foolish thing. Red Alliance members were adults with families. Killing people of a different viewpoint was a grave accusation. The Revolutionary Rebels were trying to use the incident to punch a hole in the bucket of their rivals, which was already leaking, for its members were mostly from families who had been rich in the old days.

Shalin was scared to live in the dormitory after Li Sunro's death and urged me to get formally married. "All right, you go clean up that room at 6 Tanyin Alley," she ordered me. "If others can live in that courtyard, so can we."

10 · We Build a Love Nest on a Mouse Hole

"You are sure to like our place," Dian Wen said, anxious to convince me I had made the right decision to move in. "The neighbors are very nice. We are like a big family."

He offered to help me clean up the room. First we shoveled out the miniature mountains of dirt excavated by the mice. Granny Yin next door came over. "I put the tea pot and cups outside," she said to Dian Wen and smiled at me. "It's too dusty inside. You'd better stop for a break and have some tea."

Dian Wen introduced Granny Yin. "She's the guardian of our courtyard. She knows everything."

She was about sixty, lean and in excellent health. Her eyes conveyed wisdom. Her cotton jacket was obviously hand sewn. The dark blue was faded. Her feet had not been bound, which surprised me in a run-down neighborhood like this. Walking around, she checked our work. "How are you to fill the mouse holes?"

"Granny Yin," Dian Wen answered cheerfully, "are you testing my memory?" Fill the holes with a mixture of human hair, sand, lime and cement. I remember that. You told me six months ago when I moved in."

She smiled with approval, flashing her neat full rows of teeth.

"Don't spare your effort," she advised. "Do a thing thoroughly in the beginning and you'll save a lot of trouble afterwards. First, sweep the wall with a stiff broom to scrape off the loose layer of whitewash, so the new layer will stay longer. I have a piece of cardboard large enough to patch the hole in the ceiling. Dian Wen, go over to my room and get it. It's under the bed."

He went out obediently. "This room is certainly unsatisfactory for you young people," the old lady said to me. "You want a nicer place. But housing is tight. You'll have to do with it for the time being. The rooms across the courtyard are new. When someone moves out, you can move there."

It was only a sympathetic consolation. No living quarters were being built in Beijing. Ever since we had been told that a war with Russia was imminent, all available cement and bricks were poured into the ground to make living tombs, as the air raid shelters were called.

Dian Wen returned with the cardboard. Granny Yin insisted we stop for tea.

Like all the houses in Tanyin Alley, Number 6 had three levels. The ground in the alley was eighteen inches higher than the courtyard, and the courtyard was five inches higher than our room. The courtyard was unusually large and the houses in better condition than others in the alley. A pole in each direction and one in the center were strung with clothesline. In front of the east wing were two gigantic jujube trees. There were two water taps; one near the entrance and one just outside the toilet in the southeast corner where a widespread locust tree shaded much of those two wings.

The northern row of five rooms had been rebuilt with new bricks and bright glass windows. Its foundation had been raised to the level of the alley and its roof was well above the gray wall that separated us from Number 4 courtyard. The east and west wings with two rooms each and the south with four were more than a hundred years old.

"At the end of August," Dian Wen continued to sing praises of the courtyard, "the jujubes bear a huge amount of dates. They're very sweet, I tell you."

The sun had come over the locust. Its reflection off the windows and red bricks of the north row was comforting and bright. I looked at the warped window and door frames of my room. From the black hole of the doorway, dank currents and the smell of dirt and lime dust sailed out.

Granny Yin went to a wooden box under the eaves which must serve as her family storehouse. She dug out some tufts of hair and passed them to Dian Wen. "I keep them in case someone needs them."

"With four women in your family you can save a lot of hair," Dian Wen said, with no trace of teasing. "You know, Longsen, Granny Yin saves anything and everything. One day the things which seemed garbage will turn out useful. If nobody here finds a use for them, she can still sell them to the junk collectors.

"You boys have lunch with me. Nothing special, only noodles," Granny Yin invited.

Before I had time to decline out of politeness, Dian Wen replied, "That's fine. It gives me more time to help with the room."

Around 11:30 I found an excuse to go to the store at the west end of the alley, where I bought a pound of cooked pig head.

"You shouldn't have done that," Granny Yin protested. "You're moving into this courtyard. We'll be neighbors. As the saying goes, close neighbors are better than faraway relatives."

"Right, Longsen, you shouldn't be so polite," Dian Wen advised. He ate with relish, consuming more than half the meat. After he finished, he checked to see if his mother was satisfied with the rice porridge he had made for her.

We patched up the hole in the ceiling with the cardboard, filled in the cracks in the walls with mortar and stuffed the mouse holes with Granny Yin's formula. She said that mice could chew through brick, but not hair. Then we splashed the walls with water and scraped off the lose layer. We put a thick layer of crimson paint on the window frames. I lit a borrowed stove and asked Dian Wen to keep it going to dry the room in preparation for whitewashing.

Two days later, I came back and pasted thin paper sheets on the upper panels of the window, replaced the broken glass in the lower panels, and whitewashed the walls. Shalin came to inspect and found that this former garbage dump was not so bad after all.

Hu Bon's group came to help me transport our belongings.

All that Shalin and I owned was put in a pickup truck which Dian Wen borrowed from the Bureau. A double bed, a desk, two stools and cupboard were office property which we rented for a monthly fee. As wedding presents my parents gave us a pair of wooden trunks, as did Shalin's. We piled two in the corner of the room and shoved the other two under the bed. I bought a stove and several sections of pipe. Knowing that we were practical people without much money, friends and relatives bought pots and pans, bowls and plates, instead of fashionable presents like copies of Chairman Mao's calligraphy embroidered on silk and expensively framed.

The pickup had to stop at the eastern end of the alley, which was not wide enough to accommodate it. The neighbors in the courtyard showed their welcome by helping move our things the five hundred yards to the room. Under the guidance of Dian Wen all ten children, ranging from seven to twelve, carried the smaller objects, cheering and yelling.

"We are having our wedding ceremony right now," I said to Shalin who was obviously moved by the warmth the neighbors were showing us.

"We should have thought to buy some candies to distribute," she said with an uneasiness. I had thought of that but was afraid that she might not agree, since she had wanted a formal wedding ceremony. Now hearing her say this I ventured, "Should I go get some on my bicycle?"

"My dear neighbors," Dian Wen announced to the gathering after the major pieces of furniture had been neatly arranged in the room. "Now we have new neighbors—my best friends, Longsen and Shalin. They are good people, I tell you, and you'll find out for yourself very soon. We'll help them set up their new household. So, Longsen and Shalin, whenever you need anything, don't hesitate to ask."

Our new neighbors, grown-ups and children alike, listened attentively, smiling at him. Then he began to distribute candy to all present. He didn't leave any for himself.

"You should entertain us with a dinner," he said to me. "But today is too late and your room needs a lot of work. So you will eat at my home. Oh, Hu Bon, you guys stay too."

I had seen the strength of brotherhood among Hu Bon's people, so didn't protest. Shalin felt uneasy but said nothing. Seven of us had a noodle dinner.

On a Sunday soon after we moved, I bought a raw pig head, some sausage, five pounds of pork, several bottles of liquor and some vegetables. I cleaned the pig head, cooked it and cut the meat into cold dishes. Dian Wen, making himself half the host, stir-fried the vegetable dishes.

My thank-you dinner was successful, except for the remark Driver Wong made after two cups of liquor. "Longsen is a clever host and an excellent cook. A pig head costs only three yuan at the most but it makes up three main dishes of a dinner. And all are delicious."

My face flushed. Had I been too stingy for such an important occasion? The whole dinner was worth only twenty yuan. Fifty was the rule for other veterans making a wedding feast. Well, this was not a wedding, I comforted myself; and decided when my financial situation improved I would give the same people a good dinner.

11 · Mr. Yin Is Not Content with Life

Shalin and I had not done much courting. The austere atmosphere in the streets and public places discouraged any form of romance, and Shalin was no romantic type. Nor were we having a honeymoon. "We'll do it at most once a week," she declared the second night as we were preparing for bed. "It's harmful to your health to do it more than that. I read that in a book."

I had not read any books on married life, so I believed her. Later I would often be frustrated by her sticking to book discipline.

So we began a "normal family life" right from the day we moved in. For the first two days, Shalin stayed home cleaning and tidying things up. The third was a Sunday and we made the rounds to pay get-acquainted visits to our neighbors. Monday Shalin roused me at six and cooked a pot of rice porridge on the stove which I had set up under the eaves in front of our window, as the other families had. We ate the porridge with a little tangy pickled vegetable then rode our bicycles out of the city through the alleys to the office. For more than a year in the dormitory I had not been up that early. No one went to the office on time. I still felt groggy at ten o'clock. Shalin wanted to wait for the bell to ring to go home. I told her I was going back earlier to start the fire so we wouldn't be late making supper.

"Hi," Mr. Yin greeted me. He sat on a stool by a low table. "Come and have a sip of this stuff." He raised his cup toward me.

I propped up my bicycle and went over. There was a saucer on the cracked table with several pickled hot peppers on it. The liquor bottle was one-third full. "Thank you," I said. "I haven't learned to take that strong stuff."

"You will," he said, waving me to sit down on a stool. "Living in this courtyard, you will learn to drink very soon. Almost all the men drink. Dian Wen is the exception. He was born against alcohol. Now you have a family, eh? Whenever you are in need of something," he swept his right hand and pointed the chopsticks toward the coal cakes, stools, fire pokers and dust pan under his window, "come over and take it yourself."

"Thanks," I said politely.

"You are like a book reading type." He looked me in the eye.

"No," I denied. "I had not even finished middle school when I joined the air force." Inside I was pleased with his remark. I had been trying to be a man of book learning, at least to look like one.

"But you are one who uses brains." He bit off half a pepper, munched on it and drew a long, careful sip from the cup with whistling inhalation. My mouth watered and tingled. Imagine, caustic liquor plus caustic pepper!

I stood up and went over to my stove. The Japanese invented honey-comb briquets to replace the small clay-mixed coal balls when they occupied Beijing in the early 1940s. They were made of coal dust mixed with lime and rammed into rounds seven inches in diameter and three thick. A dozen holes were bored vertically through the cakes. When used, a piece was placed on top of a burning one with the holes aligned so that air could pass from the bottom of the stove without obstruction. They lasted longer than coal balls, but gave less heat. People liked the new invention because the briquets produced less dust. If banked properly, they could last from early morning until supper time.

I took the cover from the top, opened the door at the bottom and put in a short cast iron chimney to help the fire flare up. Then I fetched some water at the tap to wash the spinach I had bought on my way home.

"Not very convenient to live in a courtyard, is it?" Mr. Yin watched me. "Nasty, I tell you. Our rooms are near the toilets. When the weather gets warm, they smell. In the morning, everybody is in a hurry to use the toilets. The children shout and bang the door, 'Please be quick. I can't hold it any longer!' Ha, ha, you come out half finished. I never use them. I go to the public lavatory at the east end of the alley."

I decided I would too. The toilet in the courtyard had only two stalls separated by a brick wall and illuminated by a single bulb above the partition. There were thirty-five people in the courtyard.

"Wait until winter comes." Mr. Yin was in high spirits. His lower jaw protruded outward. Someone had told me that was a sign of being smart. I tried it. My teeth wouldn't mesh. "We have to shut off the tap near the entrance and move this one inside the toilets and keep a stove in there to prevent the pipes from freezing. Ah, you drink the water right from where you piss it out. By the way, it's better to fetch water from the tap near the entrance. The one here is used for everything—diapers, night pots, anything gross."

I sprinkled the spinach water on the ground to keep down the dust. The weather was getting warm and the air getting dustier. I went to the entrance tap to fetch another bucket of water for a second wash.

"What is your job?" Mr. Yin asked.

"Proofreading. In English," I added to make an impression.

"Oh? Proofreading in English. That's great," Mr. Yin said, sipping at his spirits. I couldn't tell from his tone if it was a compliment or a gibe. "That's great," he repeated.

I rinsed a bowl of rice and put it in a pot to cook. The flames were metallic blue. That was all right for cooking rice. Stir-frying needed stronger flames. By the time the rice was cooked, the fire would be high. People kept coming in, bicycles clicking and creaking. A bicycle bell rang merrily.

"You can always tell who's back by listening to the sound each bicycle makes," Mr. Yin smiled at me. He looked toward the entrance and shouted, "Hey, Dian Wen."

"Hi, Mr. Yin," he responded with equal enthusiasm. "How about a card game tonight?"

"That's fine with me if we have enough hands," Mr. Yin said

cheerfully. "You didn't come back Saturday and yesterday. We missed the weekend game without you."

"I stayed at the Bureau. We are busy. Hi, Longsen." He put his bicycle under the eaves, went into his room and brought back a duster and a piece of rag, and began to wipe his new bicycle. It was his baby. "You don't come to our headquarters these days. Drop in tomorrow. We are working on something big."

"What's that?" I asked.

"Li Sunro's death."

"Stop talking death," Mr. Yin interrupted. "There have been too many deaths these days. A man in my factory drowned himself this morning in Houhai Lake. When I think of it, I lose my appetite. Dian Wen, come and have a sip. I have a bottle of Erguotou. Real good stuff."

"No thanks. Not for the life of me. I don't think I'll ever learn to handle it. A swallow of beer makes my face burn. Longsen," he turned to me, "we have a card game club in this courtyard. Join us. We'll play tonight. Oh, by the way, my Big Brother can buy pressure cookers at a good bargain. Through contacts, of course. Do you want one?"

"No. Shalin is afraid it will explode."

"Don't use the damn things," Mr. Yin advised. "They do explode. Someone burned his face when a pot of porridge burst open."

The Yins' room, to our right, was one-fourth larger than ours. A single bed sat near the door and a double bed was pushed in one corner. The rest of the space was taken up by a cupboard, a low wardrobe and a pair of wooden trunks. Every evening before bed, Mr. Yin would prop up a plank hinged to the single bed so that Granny Yin and the two girls could sleep on it crosswise.

Shalin hit it off well with Mrs. Yin, both being unsophisticated. Half a head taller than her husband, Mrs. Yin was barely able to read children's picture books. In 1958 China had entered the Great Leap Forward and housewives were urged to "take up the other half of the sky" by going out of the home to work.

Mrs. Yin joined a dozen semi-literate women to work for a neighborhood zipper factory. She came from a much better off family than her husband and had brought with her a fairly large dowry. In their quarrels, which were not frequent, she would point to items of furniture in the room and tell Shalin, who would come over to mediate, "I brought this and this and that. Without them we would have been sleeping on the bare floor all these years."

Now working with a regular monthly salary of thirty-eight yuan, only eighteen less than her husband's, she was more dominating than ever. But she was very humble in front of her two daughters who were seven and nine. "You're spoiling them," Mr. Yin would say after supper was over. "They are old enough to do the dishes." Mrs. Yin would command, "Leave the dishes there. I'll wash them after I have caught my breath." She would never be able to catch her breath. So Granny Yin would do the dishes.

Mr. Yin was pretentiously obedient to his wife. "Yes, Madame," he would sing out, mimicking a Beijing Opera singer, "whatever you say." But he said to me, "Women are most difficult to deal with. The best way is to go along with them over trifling matters. But remember, don't budge on the big ones. That will be the ruin of you." Mr. Yin started working at the Bureau as an office messenger. That was why he got a room in Tanyin Alley. In 1958 he was forcibly transferred to the Chemical Machinery Plant in the eastern suburbs beyond Jianguo Gate. A job in a factory was far from as easy as an office job. One had to be at work on time. And every day. Mr. Yin would get up around five when all others were still in bed and take his bicycle out of his room. Half way to the factory he would stop at a breakfast shop near Beihai Park to have a bowl of soy bean milk and two fried rolls.

"Some life, isn't it?" Mr. Yin chuckled bitterly. His cynical chuckles blended with the courtyard sounds.

Many factory workers didn't bother to change clothes at the end of the day. Mr. Yin would always take a shower at the factory and change into clean clothes before he returned home. I suspected he was afraid of being looked down upon for being a plumber. Back home around five, he would make a large mug of strong tea from one of the three thermos bottles his mother had filled with boiling water. He would light a cigarette, drink tea, and read the newspaper he had brought back from his workshop. "No one there reads," he explained to me.

While Granny Yin was preparing supper, Mr. Yin would bring out the bottle of Erguotou from the food cupboard and sip it out of a small porcelain cup. He would have a cucumber or turnip to go with it when they were not expensive. Mostly he would have a dish of chopped brine pickles. Occasionally he would bring home a package of cooked meat. He would leave the greater part of it for others. I soon learned to handle the marinated hot peppers, though not the fiery liquor. The slender pepper burned my throat as I swallowed it. "You eat that hot stuff regularly and the pungency will build your will power," he expounded his theory. "If something happens to you, you won't panic easily. You'll remain cool even if the sea boils in front of you or a mountain quakes behind you."

I recognized this quotation from some ancient sage.

Shalin and I went over to the Yins' for a chat. "We were just talking about you," Mrs. Yin said pleasantly, moving to sit on the double bed, so Shalin and I could sit on the other one. "Mr. Yin thinks Longsen can make it big in his profession some day."

"Impossible," Shalin said. "How can he make it big without a college degree?"

"Of course he can," Mr. Yin said. "He's very intelligent. He served in the air force and is a Communist Party member. That's a political guarantee. Nowadays, book learning is not enough. One has to have political guarantees. Learn your job well, Longsen. Get a foothold in the office. You won't be kicked around then."

I discerned a sadness in his tone. "I was born in the right time but the wrong place." He looked at me. I felt he was trying to convey some meaning. "Look at those big shots. How much do they know about running the country? They happened to join the side which won the war. I would be capable of commanding a million men, and better than any of those generals, I tell you."

Mrs. Yin cut him off. "Stop bragging. You think too much of yourself. You'd better be content with three full meals a day and a cup of that horsepiss of Erguotou. Longsen, don't listen to that shit. He's had a drop too much tonight. What he is capable of is crawling in the sewers like a rat."

"All right," he chuckled. "I'm a rat. Then what are you? Ha, ha . . ."

His chuckle tonight was bitter.

12 · Wise Granny Yin

I suffered from a cold three-quarters of every year we lived there. The doctor said it was my paranasal sinus that was sensitive to drafts and coal dust, which were unavoidable in that room. As long as I had the energy for the twenty minute ride, I would go to the office instead of staying in bed. It was all right to sleep at home during the night, but very uncomfortable to stay during the day. It was late June already, but the air in the room was still soggily chilly. Even when I wasn't suffering from a cold, the dank smell made my head split.

I was running a fever. The penicillin injection the day before hadn't helped much and I had no energy to go to the office clinic for another. The sun in the courtyard was warm. I sat in a chair, wrapped in a quilted jacket and watched Granny Yin chop leeks.

"Taken any medicine?" she asked as she looked over at me. "You look feverish."

"I hate medicine." My overheated system shivered in a spasm.

"Then have a bowl of ginger tea. It will cure you."

Mother used to give me a bowl of that when I had a cold. But right now I did not feel like doing anything. The sun was warming me up. Also, I had neither ginger nor brown sugar, and the stove was banked. It was not worth opening it to boil a cup of water. It would need another briquet.

As if reading my thought, Granny Yin said, "I'll make the broth for you when the fire is hot. I am about to boil some water anyway."

I watched her with fascination. She held a thick tuft of dark green leeks in the left hand, wrapping her thumb and fingers around them tightly, and cut them into fine bits with a quick rhythm. The knife rose and fell so close to her fingers that I expected blood at any moment. My eyes shied away from her fingers, only to be drawn back again. The skin on her hands was semitransparent, blue veins jumping slightly beneath it. The chopped leeks smelled fragrant.

"How do you make jiaozi that are so tasty?" I asked her. "You don't use much meat, do you?"

I was not intending to flatter her. Granny Yin's jiaozi and steamed baozi were famous in the courtyard, more succulent and tastier than anyone else's. She used all kinds of things in the stuffing: cabbage, turnip, eggplant, squash, tomato, cucumber—whatever sold cheap on the street. In summer she even used the inner side of watermelon rind. Sometimes she didn't use any meat, but would fry two eggs or buy an egg roll to chop up with some pork fat.

"There is no secret," she laughed. "Many people just don't know how to mix the filling. You have to dilute the ground meat with water, as you do sesame butter. Add the water a little at a time and whip the meat like eggs. Chicken broth is better, but for us common folks, water will do. When I worked at Mr. Ma Lianliang's house, I would put sesame oil in the meat. He was very rich. Even in those days people paid five yuan to see his show at the Changan Grand Theater. I cooked jiaozi for his family with fancy things—shrimp, mushroom and sea cucumber even. The meat must be very fresh and chopped fine. We didn't have a machine to grind meat in those days. We chopped it with a cleaver. Oh, those jiaozi tasted real good."

Granny Yin had been maid for the famous Beijing Opera singer for many years. Though generally not a talkative old lady, she liked to tell us about her years at Ma Lianliang's grand mansion on Changan Boulevard. She still remembered the names of the children who were studying with him; and of the other three maids who would save the used tea leaves after

74

serving his distinguished guests. "Rich people served tea only for show. Still, they used the best brands. We would drain the tea leaves and dry them for ourselves to drink later."

The kettle on her stove popped and steamed. She went over to fill the thermos bottles. "Shichi drinks a lot of tea when he comes home. He began to drink tea with us at Ma Lianliang's house. He was only five then."

She put an aluminum pot on the fire. The outside was blackened and bore the marks of many years' use. She dug a lump of ginger out of the sand in a flower pot, washed it at the tap and chopped it into fine bits. "It stays fresh in there."

She continued to explain the details as she kneaded the dough. She must have been a very capable maid in her young days. She did everything expertly and quickly.

Granny Yin was widowed at twenty-three and never thought of remarrying, but devoted what time and energy she had left after her ·strenuous day to her only son. She had little, but enough to eke out a living at a time when beggars were starving in Beijing streets. She'd seen corpses by the old wall. The huge mansion protected her and her precious son. She became smarter and shrewder as she aged, and was known to her neighbors as a wise old lady. In recent years she had developed a feeling of remorse or guilt when she realized her son was far from content with life.

She set the dough aside to rest. "Shichi is intelligent. I should have sent him to school. Four years would have been enough to change his lot. He wouldn't be crawling in ditches today. If only I had known how good it would have been for him! But even if I had worked myself to death, I would not have saved enough to send him to school."

The pot on the stove was boiling. She scooped up the remaining chopped ginger and put it in the water.

"There are a few people he can talk to," she said, sitting down on a stool and picking flakes of wheat dough off her hand. "You're here now. That makes him feel better. But you mustn't let him go too far. Put on the brakes from time to time. He needs a guard for his mouth. He lost his job at the Bureau because of his big mouth. The only reason he escaped being labeled a Rightist was that he was merely an office boy—no one took him seriously. He has not changed since then; still complaining too much."

She went into her room and brought out a glass jar. The brown sugar in it must have been two years old. It took three minutes for the lump to dissolve in the boiling water.

"Drink it while it is scorching hot," she urged me as she poured it into a bowl. "And get in bed, cover yourself with the quilt. You'll have a good sweat. That's what you need. I will go over to see if Granny Dian wants something. Dian Wen said he's not coming home tonight. I don't understand how he is so busy when others have nothing to do at the office."

I drank the pungent tea and climbed into bed. Semiconscious, I heard the coal man come into the courtyard and greet Granny Yin who directed him to pile the briquets by the door of each family. She paid him with money each family had left with her that morning. I admired her sharp mind and good memory. She never mixed up the accounts of the ten families.

True to the title we gave her of Courtyard Guardian, Granny Yin took care of everything. When the Neighborhood Committee came to issue ration coupons, the old lady would receive them, give them tea, and sign all the receipts. We never worried about clothes drying in the courtyard when it began to rain. She would collect them and take them into her room.

"Granny Yin," I heard the loud, familiar voice at the gate. "I have a bundle of celery left for you. I got it this afternoon."

"Come on in and rest your feet for awhile," she responded warmly. I knew that Aunt Chin had sold out her goods and wanted to have a chat with Granny Yin before she returned to the store at the west end of the alley. This morning she had made a special delivery of leeks to Granny Yin and promised to have a cup of tea when she finished her rounds of the dozen alleys. Every day she would push her cart from door to door. Six wicker baskets would be loaded with eggplants, bundles of spinach, peppers, and greens in summer; turnips, potatoes and cabbage in winter. She would call out her goods in a husky but musical voice. The neighbors were never in a hurry to buy; they would chat with her about the weather, her health or any casual matter just to enjoy the pleasant old woman.

"Sit over here," Granny Yin said. "The tea is freshly made. Are you still fit to push that cart with a thousand pounds?"

"No problem. I eat three bowls of rice for lunch and supper; two cakes, two fried rolls and a bowl of soy milk for breakfast. My sons pester me to retire. What would I do at home? They just want me to look after their babies. Those clever rats! I want to make my own money and spend it the way I want."

"But you should ask to stay in the store to get out of the nasty weather. There are so many other people there—let them work the street."

"They are young and have a dozen years of schooling," Aunt Chin explained. "Yelling out in the street is embarrassing to them. I'm just an old sack. The skin on my face is as thick as the Old Wall. I'm not afraid of losing face. Besides my old neighbors would buy only from me. You don't laugh at me, do you?"

My mind went into oblivion. When Shalin woke me I was soaked and could breathe through my nose again. Granny Yin brought over a bowl of jiaozi with hot soup, which made me sweat more.

13 · Patriarch Tong and His Family

Of the five residential communities belonging to the Bureau, 6 Tanyin Alley was the most "unintellectual." Mr. Tong was the only one in our courtyard with a diploma. He had obtained a Master's Degree in Chinese literature from Yanching University, which was built early in the century with funds from the Rockefeller Foundation. With the revolution came its new name, Beijing University. On a rare occasion he revealed that he was once very active in the students' movement against terrorist intervention by the Kuomintang's secret service on campus. After the declaration of the People's Republic, he discovered that the students' leaders were underground Communists.

He felt proud of his share in the just struggle. So in 1957, when the Communist Party was encouraging people to criticize its members, he felt it was his obligation to point out some improper behavior of a Party leader in his department. Because he had been "led astray by vicious persons harboring evil motives," and because he was considered an honest and good man, he escaped the murderous label of Rightist for his attack against the Party. And he was even allowed to transcribe reports and proofread them.

He had, however, learned a lesson: never be too honest. He cut all social contact, stopped entertaining friends at home or visiting them, and constantly reminded himself to be careful about what he was going to say. "Think three times before you talk," a wise Chinese saying warns. When he had an urge to make a suggestion at the office, he would remember the immortal motto, "All trouble comes out of one's mouth."

Now fifty, Mr. Tong had been gaining weight and losing hair, both rapidly. He bent his back a little to show his humbleness; and walked in a measured gait as if afraid of stepping on any living thing. Returning home from the office, he would sit in a worn-out stuffed armchair in his room, spectacles sliding down his stubby nose, and read some book yellowed through the years. He congratulated himself that the Red Guards had not confiscated his precious library.

Mr. Tong had developed his own philosophy: to lead an exclusive life in a noisy world. "I hide myself in a small tower under my own dominion. Why should I care about the changing seasons outside?" He never mentioned to the neighbors that these two lines came from the great proletarian writer Lu Xun, whom the Communists eulogized. The rebellious giant of modern Chinese literature was jeering at the corrupt rule of Chiang Kaishek's Kuomintang.

"Lu Xun would have been branded a Rightist in 1957 if he had lived until then." Mr. Yin talked about the two lines after we had happened to find them in Mr. Tong's handwriting one day. "By nature, Lu Xun was a complainer." I fully agreed with him.

In the office Mr. Tong was a harmless old man, doing the work assigned to him. The younger people were making revolution—attending study sessions of Chairman Mao's works or meetings to criticize former capitalists, government employees, and those with overseas connections; later they added Communist officials labeled "Capitalist Roader." Mr. Tong went to these meetings when asked by his young colleagues; if not, he would pretend he did not know there was a meeting to be held. He did not take sides with the two rival factions. He did not commit himself to anything. "Old gentleman Tong," one of the Cultural Revolution activists would address him, "you cannot be a political loafer any longer. Write a criticism speech against Wong Sun. We'll have a meeting the day after tomorrow."

To his young colleague, he laughed innocently. "Don't make fun of me. I will faint in front of a crowd."

The young people in the office thought it was not worth their effort to persuade this bookworm and priggish pedant to join their revolutionary cause. On the other hand, they were glad there was a man in the their office to take care of the routine work, which was so boring.

Mr. Tong greeted everyone in the courtyard with a polite nod of his head and a courtesy question, "Have you had supper?" Every Beijing resident would greet an acquaintance this way after six o'clock. The difference lay in Mr. Tong's voice—cordial to grown-ups and benevolent to children. He performed this routine only when he was crossing the fifty feet from the courtyard gate to the door of his room. He reminded me of Mr. Bai in my parents' courtyard. Mr. Yin commented that Mr. Tong had a condescending manner.

In the courtyard we exchanged news we had heard during the day or talked about current political shifts, such as who had been criticized in the newspaper or who was becoming a political star. Mr. Tong never joined in the gossip. Of course, card or chess games were too far beneath his interest.

But I knew that this seemingly mild-tempered man was a tyrannical patriarch, lording it over his wife and the four children with absolute authority. His stern stare was enough to stop any member of his family from doing something he did not like. He displayed his power only behind the curtains, which were never drawn apart. Even in the hottest summer days their windows were shut. Other families had replaced the paper on the upper panes with thin gauze for better ventilation. The Tongs' were still papered, darkened through three seasons, and left tattered until the weather turned cold.

One Sunday I witnessed the formidable power of Mr. Tong over his family. A favorite meal for many Beijingers is noodles flavored with fried soy sauce or diluted sesame butter and garnished with cucumber, or scalded cabbage or bean sprouts when cucumber was expensive. When done, the noodles are plunged in cold water. Mrs. Tong was rinsing a potful of boiled noodles at the tap near the toilets. The slippery noodles ran over the edge of the colander and cascaded into the cement sink below. She shot a glance over her shoulder. Her husband was concentrating on a book just inside the open door. Tong Yi, the youngest son, who was sitting outside, saw the disaster. He hurried over and stood beside his mother to block the view, in case his father would look this way. Mrs. Tong scooped the noodles back into the pot and washed them several times more than was usually necessary. Granny Yin watched from behind the window of her room, holding her breath.

The Tongs had been permitted two rooms because they had four children. The eldest, Tong Hua, had graduated from high school last July and was preparing to go live in an undesignated village in Shaanxi Province. All middle school graduates were being sent to the countryside to receive re-education from the peasants, as Chairman Mao was calling on them to do. Tong Hua was eager to go. Mrs. Tong dared not complain. The instruction had come from the Chairman himself, and her daughter was a Red Guard. She wept while talking to Granny Yin in private. Granny Yin and her son agreed that it was a pity such a good girl should be sent to a backwater village. Tong Hua had been first in her class at the prestigious Number 5 Girls Middle School, and her teachers had been confident she would have no problem getting into Beijing University. Tong Cheng was graduating from middle school and would definitely go to live in a village too.

"Cheng is a boy," Mrs. Tong told the Yins. "I don't feel that worried about him. But my Hua . . ." she wiped away some tears.

"Don't worry too much," Mr. Yin comforted her. "She'll be with her schoolmates. There are many of them, and they will take care of each other."

I was thinking what it would be like when the time came for the Yin girls to go to the countryside. Perhaps they wouldn't talk so lightheartedly then.

14 · Driver Wong and
His Queer Wife

Driver Wong, who was my age, had finished his service with a tank squadron a year earlier than I did. Athletic and handsome, he liked to show his strength by letting boys hang on his arms and swing as they would on a horizontal bar. His jacket and trousers, the usual uniform required by the times, fit him better than they did others. His limbs and shoulders bulged to offer an appealing sight to feminine eyes. He was proud of his body.

I had met him by a peculiar chance on a fair day in November, 1966. The veteran trainees had not moved to the city yet. The Revolutionary Rebels' headquarters had sent two buses to Fragrance Hill to fetch sympathizers for a fight in the Bureau compound. The rival Red Alliance had called several dozen workers from a factory to help their side. The Revolutionary Rebels suffered a few bruises. Young and militant, they refused to swallow the humiliation. So they called for reinforcements for retaliation.

Two friends and I at the dormitory, bored and frustrated with playing cards and reading all day long, cheerfully got on the bus, which rushed back to the city. My spirits were heightened by the unison shouting of a popular song based on one of Chairman Mao's slogans: "Be resolute, fear no sacrifice, to overcome ten thousand difficulties, victory to win."

With four dozen young Hill men, the fighting atmosphere of the compound flared up. Women were cheering from windows and some ingenious ones had invented sand bags by filling office envelopes. They were throwing them out of the windows, hurting no one, but helping create a battle effect, as in a movie.

The Bureau people, after all, were more civilized than university students and factory workers. There were no cracked heads or broken limbs, only a few more cuts. The fight was mostly confined to shouting contests. I enjoyed the excitement tremendously. I hit no one and was not hit. Only once a young worker rushed at me. I stepped back and yelled at him, "Chairman Mao taught us not to fight with arms but debate with reasoning!" He looked at me, puzzled and stupefied. I kept my arms close at my sides. He walked away.

The fighting was over, with the factory workers finally being called back by their leaders. We all were thirsty and hungry, suddenly remembering that we had not had breakfast that morning. The only restaurants that were open at one o'clock were near the zoo. My chums and I went there, and gulped down two pounds of cold meat, a dozen steamed buns and six tankards of beer. We felt great as we swaggered back to the Bureau to see if we could hitch a ride to the Hill.

At the garage we met Driver Wong, washing a black 1945 Dodge. "Hey, man!" I called out at him, belligerence fostered during the fight and stimulated by alcohol. "Is there a bus or car or something we can hitch back to the Hill?"

Driver Wong raised his head and gave us an indifferent stare. I felt the sneer rather than heard it. He bent over his car, deliberately dropping the hose in our direction. Water gushed from the nozzle and splashed over my trousers. Before I knew it, I was at his collar, two buttons flying off his shirt. I had forgotten the motto I had adopted to suit my weak constitution: "A gentleman should use his wits instead of brawn in a fight." With a deft twitch, Driver Wong had my left arm pinched behind me and turned it the wrong way, making me clench my teeth and wince. He held me on my tiptoes for a long second during which I recalled my motto.

One of my companions, as sturdy and handsome as Driver Wong, knew his face as belonging to the Revolutionary Rebels and said to him. "Fellow, take it easy. Hu Bon brought us here to fight." The emphasis on the name worked and Driver Wong released his grip on my arm. Smiling, he said, "All right, you guys. The buses left half an hour ago. Hu Bon asked where you were. I'll drive you to the Hills. This old grandpa car was just overhauled and needs a warm-up exercise." He smiled at me to say "I apologize," which I found hard to accept.

We drove off, my face still burning with humiliation as the breeze blew in from the open car window.

Now we were neighbors.

I could not understand, as sturdy and handsome as he was, why Driver Wong had married a clumsy woman. Chunlun had a square face, thick waist and heavy thighs. In weight she matched her husband, but not the least in gracefulness. They both came from a Tong County village, the northern terminal of the Grand Canal, twelve miles east of Beijing. It might be that Driver Wong had had no chance to see city girls in his four years of army service, and Chunlun, robust as she was, was a beauty by country standards. It might also be that she had been pretty, but that her pregnancy had left her with a thick waist and fleshy chin.

She had given birth to a son three months before and was staying at her parents' home near the factory where she worked, so that she could nurse the baby during the day. We would only see her on the weekend. She would slip into the courtyard holding the baby, and go into her room in the northeast corner, as if the sound of her footsteps would scare her son. With her enormous build, I always expected something like the tempest of a buffalo herd.

"She's a queer bird," Granny Yin told us. "She doesn't talk to anyone in the courtyard, not often to her husband either. When he beats her, she only whimpers. You would think she was dumb. Don't mind if she doesn't return your greeting in the street."

"There must be something wrong with her mind," Shalin suggested.

"There might be," Granny Yin agreed. "Every Sunday before dawn, she hangs her things out on the clotheslines, everything

84

that can be taken out of her room, leaving no space for other families. Sometimes it turns overcast or rains after she has left and her things will be damper that night. If those things belonged to any other family, one of the neighbors would gather them in. But don't touch hers, remember. She will blame you for that. One day she hung out her things and left to go shopping. It began to rain. Jinli gathered in all the things on the lines. In the afternoon Chunlun came back and yelled in the courtyard, 'Who has stolen my washing?' Jinli was not at home and she kept yelling and cursing. Driver Wong happened to come back and gave her a heavy slap on the face. That stopped her yelling."

Granny Yin lowered her voice when she continued, "I don't think she was always as eccentric as she is. Driver Wong curses and beats her all the time. That has broken her. When she's alone she sings very nicely. She sings in the toilet."

Chunlun walked with a swing that reminded me of some creature between an ape and a boxer, a result of her imbalanced mind. As big as she was, she didn't arouse notice among us. Even if I saw her passing through the courtyard, my mind did not register the fact. I once went into her room to borrow some matches from Driver Wong. Their room was as depressing as the expression on Chunlun's face. The east wing stood a few feet in front of the north row. The Wongs' room would get a bit of sunlight only in late afternoon. Despite the higher elevation of the north row, their room was dark and damp, giving out a dank smell mixed with that of old cooked cabbage. I could not blame Chunlun for sunning the things in her room so often.

15 · My Other Neighbors

Jinli and her husband, Carpenter Shen, had the westernmost room of the north row, by the entranceway.

Jinli, still remembered by old neighbors as Mrs. Ho, was similar in physical build to Mrs. Yin—tall, well-proportioned, and also thirty-five. Jinli was attractive to the opposite sex. I didn't know why at first. Both were nicely plump, giving no sign of two births each. But men in the neighborhood did not think of Mrs. Yin in the way men usually do of women.

"Carpenter Shen is almost fifty," Aunt Kang told us at our card table one Saturday evening. "They still go for it every night. Think of Carpenter Shen's sick heart and that paralyzed leg! Their bed is against our wall and Kang Ping's is just on the other side of it, separated only by a thin layer of bricks. They bang and flap on the bed so noisily that Kang Ping is often awakened. I don't understand where they get so much pep. Well, even if they have extra to spill, they should restrain themselves a little bit for the sake of the two boys. They are growing up to understand things. Pooh, at such an old age doing that!"

Mr. Yin chuckled and Driver Wong laughed gleefully. Mr. Chang and Mr. Yu smiled faintly. I didn't know whether I should laugh or not. I was new in the courtyard and wanted to give the neighbors an impression that I was a decent person brought up by a decent family. On the other hand, I didn't want them to think I was aloof.

Jinli's first husband had worked for the Bureau. Granny Yin said that he was still alive, offering no more information than that. They had two sons, nine and eleven, who had changed their surname to their stepfather's. The boys slept near the door on a makeshift bed of loose planks supported by a bench on either end. At night a partition of cloth was drawn between the two beds. They must have realized what their parents were up to at night. Shen Rong complained to Mr. Yin, "They stay up late and make irritating noises. When I am just about to fall asleep, the old chap starts to snore." The boys refused to address Carpenter Shen as father.

I often noticed that when Jinli passed by the Yins' room on the way to the toilet, Mr. Yin would look at her with yearning in his eyes. Once he tried to touch her protruding breasts, saying, "I would like to catch fish in the stream between your mountains."

"I'll tell Mrs. Yin and see if she agrees," Jinli said in a mock serious tone and brushed away his hand. But I knew she enjoyed the flirtation.

The Kangs had the second room of the north row with their son Kang Feng, nine, and daughter Kang Ping, seven.

Cook Kang had only one eye. He lost the left one as a boy, falling from a ladder trying to catch baby sparrows in their nest under the roof in his home village in Henan Province. Forty years ago, a flood along the Yellow River drowned half a million people and chased away the stronger ones to beg in other parts of China. Kang, then 15, fled to Beijing, working at a public bathhouse which gave him two meals a day and a plank of wood on the floor to sleep on. All the hands there worked fourteen hours a day. If the boys were lucky, the owner might give them each a few dollars at the end of the year, from the tips left in the bamboo cup on the cashier's desk. The money was counted daily, but distributed just before New Year's among the bath house workers, barbers, pedicurists, masseurs and tea boys.

In 1953, Kang apprenticed at the newly established Bureau kitchen and began to earn a real salary. But he spent too much on fiery Erguotou. Besides, he had only one eye. He knew his worth and didn't think about marrying. In 1958, however, he became homesick and went back to Henan. He didn't meet any old acquaintances, but found an old maid, five years his elder, and brought her back to Beijing. The Bureau gave him his room to breed a son and daughter. The latter was the apple of the couple's eye.

Cook Kang drank less, though still every day. Aunt Kang had restrictions on how often and how much. After she had smashed two of his wine cups on the floor, he decided to conceal five yuan from his salary of sixty-two, and use the money at a street corner wineshop for a quick shot.

Kang Ping, like most of the young children who were caught in the economically difficult years 1960-63, was thin and small. She was beginning to grow when we moved in. Her brother Kang Peng was a robust boy. They were as simple-minded as their parents, but with less coarseness. Shalin and I liked the Kang children.

Next door to the Kangs were a couple with an adopted daughter. She began to inquire where she had been picked up. The parents were afraid she might learn the facts from the neighbors, so they moved to an apartment to be insulated from the intimate atmosphere of a courtyard, though they suffered the inconvenience of sharing a small kitchen and toilet with another family. I could not conceive of being cooped up in a tiny concrete enclosure with one or two other families.

Two months after we moved in, they left very quietly on a weekday morning. The neighbors had no idea they were moving out. "A queer pair," Mrs. Yin commented.

"They are not queer," Mr. Yin said. "They are just too conceited. He is a section head and has a high school education. So he thinks we are all numbskulls."

I should have asked the Housing Office to give me their room. It was larger, dry and, more important, sunlit. But the family made private arrangements with Gu Fu. His wife, Suyan, came from a country village a half hour walk from mine, but she could calculate. When the job placement program was suspended at the end of 1966, Suyan grabbed the interest of three veterans. She maneuvered among them and finally chose Gu Fu as her suitor. She was sure she could make him successful.

The Changs had the room on Gu Fu's right. Mr. Chang would have been at least a department chief if his education had gone beyond second grade; or if he had, like many other illiterate or semiliterate army officers who joined the revolutionary war in the early days, taught himself how to write annual reports. He had not learned anything of letters during his twenty years of service except that he could tell of brutal battles and horrible scenes of death. For many years Chang felt indignant that he had been given the low position of section head after his demobilization in 1964. Many of his subordinates had climbed far above him. "I fought for the new regime with my life," he used to say, "and they enjoy the fruits of victory."

Mr. Chang had a pretty wife, Muchun. Fifteen years his junior, she looked much younger than her thirty-two. She worked at a small radio factory soldering wires, but in the street she would pass easily as a dancer or film star. Even during the height of the Cultural Revolution when any clothes fancier than the standard uniform were denounced as bourgeois, she could always manage to dress differently. She liked to come up to our card table and stand in a stage posture to chat with Driver Wong. For this distraction, Driver Wong often dealt out a wrong card, which angered his partner, Mr. Yin.

The worst room at 6 Tanyin Alley was the one in the southwest corner next to Dian Wen's. At least the other rooms in the south row got sunlight reflected off the north row. The corner room was totally blocked off by the west wing, only four feet away. Shortly after I moved in, a young couple, an art designer and a translator, came to look over the room. They stared at

---

89

the shattered window paper for one minute and left. The woman looked around the courtyard as she was walking out. She must have thought, "What kind of people can live in such a place?"

"Of course this courtyard is not for college people," Dian Wen observed. "They don't want to mix with us uneducated. You should have seen him before the Red Guards shaved long hair off people. This chap, I didn't bother to learn his name, had his hair too long. He swaggered in the corridor, brushing his hair. Humph! He carried a horn comb in his jacket pocket."

When Dong Sen and his wife Guangfen moved in, Dian Wen and I helped them clear out two bucketfuls of debris the mice had dug out of the walls and floor. We fixed this room as we had mine.

Dong Sen, a veteran too, and his wife were known for their vicious quarrels even before they were married. They would curse, shout and hit each other for half an hour, then quiet down. The quarrel would have delayed cooking supper, so they would eat out. They might spend ten yuan for a meal at a restaurant, an extravagant sum for any of us. They did not borrow money from others, however. The last ten days of the month they subsisted on plain noodles with brine pickles or fried bean paste.

They never quarreled with the neighbors and got along with us very well. Another "queer pair" to Mrs. Yin.

The Yus had the two spacious rooms of the west wing, which was an extravagance for four people: the middle-aged couple, a son of thirteen and a daughter of ten. Well, Mr. Yu was the biggest official in the courtyard, deputy chief of the General Affairs Department. I wondered why he didn't move to a modern suite in one of the Bureau's apartment buildings. He could easily have gotten one. The Housing Office was under his jurisdiction.

Forty-one now, Mr. Yu had already held the post for twelve years. He had joined a Communist-led guerilla group at the age of eighteen in a village in Shandong Province. A handsome lad and clever, he was chosen to work for the group commander. Soon the Communists were taking over north China from Kuomintang rule. Many young Communists were eager to see real battles, but not young Yu. His commander was setting up local Communist governments behind the advancing army. Young Yu, now a secretary, had the attention of all the village girls. His former commander became the magistrate of one of Beijing's six urban districts. Mr. Yu chose his bride and brought her along to Beijing.

First he worked as a section chief under his former commander. In 1955 he transferred to the Bureau to strengthen the political force in this nest of intellectuals. Many of the staff members, left over from the old days, were not trustworthy politically, and needed supervision.

Mr. Yu survived many political campaigns and inner Party purification drives with ease. Those who had no personal interest entangled with his said he was a nice guy; those who worked under him or had dealt with him in business said he was a slicker whom no one could get a hold of. He thus earned the nickname Roly-Poly, a toy that anyone could nudge but no one could bring down. Chairman Mao called on the leaders to side with the revolutionary Red Guards; Mr. Yu took a month of sick leave. He took no sides and stayed safe at his position, unlike many officials who had been dragged into factional disputes and became subject to public criticism.

Everyone needed a place to live and many wanted better rooms than they had. They came to Mr. Yu's home to appeal, and of course brought gifts. And of course those who brought better gifts deserved better consideration. Mr. Yu would chide the visitors and tell them not to bring any gifts next time.

Mrs. Yu had preserved much of her country charm, enhanced by maturity. She did not have a job. With her husband a Communist official, she felt it was her obligation to do something for the proletarian cause. So she volunteered to work for the Neighborhood Committee, which was responsible for order, security, sanitation and a thousand and one matters. To the neighbors, Mr. and Mrs. Yu were good people. We in the courtyard liked them too. On their turn to clean the lavatory and sweep the courtyard, they would get up half an hour earlier and do the job thoroughly, while the Yins, Shens and Kangs let their children do that duty.

16 · Worshipers of Mao Zedong

There is no real spring in Beijing. The numbness I felt from riding my bike to work against the snow and northwest winds was still lingering on my face and fingers when people at 6 Tanyin Alley began to eat their meals in the courtyard. The Yins were the first to move their table out. Others soon followed. Each family had small stools and a low table three by four feet which they put in front of their door. Supper was cooked on the stove under the eaves, very handy for serving. I asked an old schoolmate to build me such a table. I didn't want the neighbors to think that I wanted to join the ranks of intellectuals—office workers with college educations who thought eating outdoors ungainly. The only family in the courtyard that didn't eat in the open was the Tongs.

At supper we swapped samples of each family's special dishes. Since our table and the Yins' were separated by only a brick-paved path, we did the most swapping together. Dian Wen could never sit through the meal at his table. Having made sure his mother had everything within her reach, he would shovel a portion into his rice bowl and go around the courtyard from one table to another. His humorous remarks whetted our appetites. Each family would welcome him to sample their food. Mr. Yin would greet him with, "Hello, dinner inspector Dian. Please try my stewed spareribs."

Another person who did not eat at his own table was Driver Wong. He was a good cook and, as a driver, he had many contacts with store assistants and could get such scarce items as fish, eggs, pig feet, pork liver and fresh vegetables. He liked to show off his skill and privilege. He would put a large portion of his dish into his huge rice bowl, twice the normal size, and make the rounds. But he was not very well liked in the courtyard. "He's too clever," Granny Yin remarked. I thought he was nearsighted, like most country villagers were who cared only for the benefits immediately under their nose. He and Mr. Yin were partners at cards and opponents in chess. He would usually stay at the Yins' table to finish his supper, squatting down, spreading his thighs like a frog and balancing his rice bowl by putting his left elbow on his knee. Mrs. Yin did not like it, especially when the younger man wore shorts with wide legs. But we liked the rumors he collected during the day. After five minutes, if he showed no intention of leaving, Granny Yin would tell him to pull up a stool.

I envied the way Mr. Yin and Driver Wong lived their lives. After several hours of work they could forget all about their jobs and enjoy the rest of the day. Manual labor gave them a lot of exercise and a big appetite. They could gulp down two or three bowls of noodles at supper. It seemed that everything they ate was delicious.

"These country rats," Driver Wong said vehemently after he had settled down on a creaking stool by the Yins' table. "They are everywhere. They swagger in the middle of the road. I honk and they stare at me sheepishly, but don't move out of the way. If I could get away with it, I would run a couple of them down."

"No," Mr. Yin said "you'd better be patient. Last week a bus driver dashed off from a bus stop with four country boys hanging onto the doors. One was thrown off and run over by a truck behind. This poor driver, in his early thirties, happened to be born to a former store owner. He was denounced as a class enemy trying to avenge his defeated class, and he was shot. The Red Guards are guests invited to Beijing by Chairman Mao himself. Every work unit must provide free meals and living space for them."

"They don't know traffic rules," Driver Wong complained. "I told the Bureau chief I would drive no more."

That was a bluff. Driver Wong spent at most one-tenth of his driving time on official business. Most of the time he lent himself to stores and personal contacts who gave him things free of charge.

"You can't blame them," Mr. Yin said, biting on a stalk of scallion and munching contentedly. "Most of them perhaps see a car for the first time since they were born." Mr. Yin chuckled coolly, "They understand my rule. I ride through them and kick those who get in my way."

By June, Chairman Mao had appeared on the tower of the Imperial Palace Gate in Tiananmen Square five times to review the Red Guard on parade, one million strong. He stood taller than any other leader, in his olive army uniform to indicate that he was the Supreme Commander of the armed forces. He waved his powerful arm, showing the Red Guard armband. The Red Guards, the majority of whom were middle school students, shouted to the pale green dot far above them, "Long live Chairman Mao!" "Long live Mao Zedong Thought!" "Long live the Great Proletarian Cultural Revolution!" "A long, long life to our great leader, great teacher and Great Supreme Commander Chairman Mao!" Quite a few passed out from overexcitement.

The Bureau asked each department to send one person to look after a group of Red Guards. I was young, politically reliable, and had little to do in the office. So I was sent over. Six of us took care of four hundred middle school students staying in one of the compounds of the Friendship Hotel, a sprawling cluster of buildings in the western suburbs built in the 1950s for Russian advisors which, after the Russians left, were converted to living quarters for foreigners working in Beijing. The students came from Guizhou Province, picked as the best in their schools. They were very proud to be in Beijing and looked anxiously forward to the day when they would be reviewed by Chairman Mao.

They were small of build, with fine, small features, and looked younger than northern children their age. During the five days before the parade, I took them to visit schools where big criticism posters were displayed denouncing China's biggest scab, renegade, Capitalist Roader, the former president Liu Shaoqi.

Every morning I gathered the fifty or so in my charge to begin the morning study session of the little red book, *Quotations from Mao Zedong*. I chose several quotations and led them in reading in unison. I had always wanted to laugh at such study sessions as foolish. I was reminded of the first year I was sent to school in my village. The old teacher had led us in reading aloud from our text, "A man has two hands. There are ten fingers on the two hands . . ."

I had dared not laugh. Nor would I here. Everybody was required to start the day by reading aloud some parts from that little red book. Refusing meant an unforgivable act of profanity. However, the sincere and innocent expression on the children's faces made me wonder if I wasn't disloyal to our great leader and to feel ashamed for the cynicism which had been building up inside me. Their total devotion to the great leader was pure and noble. I shuddered at my profane thoughts which often popped up; I was afraid I would one day say them aloud. Not a few people had been beaten to death by Red Guards for disrespectful remarks about the Chairman.

The night before the parade the youngsters were excited. We had to be up long before dawn to go by truck to the east end of Chang'an Boulevard and wait there until nine or ten o'clock. The hotel issued each a package of bread and sausage for lunch. I urged them to go to sleep early for a good rest.

They slept on a single layer of blanket on the bare floor. In one room I saw a girl with flushed face. I squatted down in front of her; she retreated toward the wall.

"Are you ill?" I asked.

She seemed panicked. She looked about thirteen, but I knew she must be over fifteen.

"I'm all right," she said hastily. "I've taken medicine."

"We'll do a lot of walking tomorrow, you know. We have to

walk back to the hotel after the parade. That may take two hours."

The kids' rooms were stifling and the air smelled stale of many bodies and washed underwear which hung all over. I felt the stares of other girls. Suddenly I realized I was not yet thirty. My presence in a girls' room caused embarrassment. I returned to my room and lay down in bed. I picked up *The Short Stories of Jack London* and settled in with the adventures.

We set off at half past four next morning. It was chilly as we rode in open trucks. The children, coming from the warm southwest, had not brought extra clothes. I noticed the sick girl shivering. I gave her my jacket. She returned it to me as soon as we arrived, even though the early morning air was damp and cold. We sat on the sidewalk to wait.

About nine o'clock the loudspeakers cracked and blasted the order to march. We stood up. The whole of Chang'an Boulevard began to pulsate forward, human bodies like waves, leaving the crumbled newspaper we had sat on to swirl under our feet until tramped into dirty shreds.

We were commanded to catch up with the formation ahead of us. My eye caught the fevered girl stumbling. The human torrent surged on. I ran over to her. Before I could grab her arm, she picked herself up and ran two more steps, only to fall again. I half dragged her to the sidewalk and a doctor from a first aid post ran over. I shouted to one of the other group leaders to look after my children as well. As the doctor examined her, I began to think I would be spared the two hours' strenuous march down Chang'an Boulevard. The girl seemed to need intensive treatment and I would have to escort her to the hospital in a car.

The doctor listened with his stethoscope at the girl's chest and back. "She's very ill. I'll send her to Ritan Hospital right away and you will go along." It didn't take him long to decide she had an advanced case of pleurisy. Twice a nurse inserted a huge needle in her back and drew out fluid. I winced each time.

From the time she was put in the ambulance she began asking me if she was still going to see Chairman Mao. I assured her she would see him next time.

"Next time?" she gasped and began to sob silently. "I won't have a next time to come to Beijing. No one from my village has ever seen the county seat. I must see the Chairman this time. My parents are waiting for me to tell them all about him."

Suddenly I remembered the portraits of Chairman Mao in peasant houses I had visited during my years in the service. My unit was often stationed near remote villages. Those folk worshipped Chairman Mao as they did their kitchen god. They burned joss sticks to the Chairman during festivals.

In the hospital she begged the doctor to quit the treatment and send her to Tiananmen Square. The doctors and nurses were moved. We who had lived in Beijing a long time had forgotten the excitement of seeing the great leader. The doctor suggested we go upstairs to watch the TV broadcast of the parade. I carried the girl on my back. She was very light. She wept all through the hour of Red Guards demonstrating their deep and absolute loyalty to Chairman Mao, their beloved Supreme Commander.

The girl did not return home with her group. She stayed in the hospital for three months. A doctor told me she was lucky to be in Beijing. "In her mountain village, her illness was not diagnosed, though it has been serious for two years. It is possible that no one would have identified it until her death, which would have come soon."

17 · Beijing Is Getting Hot

The neighborhood stoves were lit in early morning to cook breakfast. Wisps of dirty gray smoke rose lazily up from the crowded courtyards to befog the Great White Pagoda. We felt the late July heat more intensely than other parts of Beijing because our area was more densely populated. The low, crowded rooms were like the bamboo steamers Granny Yin used to cook pork and leek stuffed buns. We recalled with nostalgia the previous winter's whirling snow, the whistling northwesterly winds and icicles hanging down the outer end of the stove pipes. Forgotten were the moments of reddened hands washing clothes in the open, fear of creeping at bedtime into the cold quilts that needed half an hour to warm up with body heat, and riding bicycles through slippery frozen streets.

"At least you can keep yourself warm by putting on more layers of clothes or burning more coal in winter," Cook Kang groaned. "In summer it would still be hot even if you could shed a layer of skin." He was stripped to nothing but shorts, a dark patch apparent at the crotch. Working in the kitchen in summer was killing him. To make a compromise, he asked for the morning shift from 5:30 a.m. to 2:30 p.m. As soon as he got home, he would put on shorts and come over to the narrow strip of shade under the south row eaves. It was the gathering place of the whole courtyard on Sunday.

Driver Wong and Mr. Yin were arguing over a poor move Driver Wong had made. He was demanding his lost knight be given back. Mr. Yin was unyielding. Mrs. Yin, who was winding woolen yarn with her two daughters, said in annoyance, "Can you two be more civilized?" She turned toward them in irritation. "Hey, I say," she raised her voice directing it at Driver Wong. "I've told you several times to dress more decently."

Driver Wong was bare on top, greasy skin wet with sweat. The wide-legged shorts were of thin material. His limp testicles could be seen in a patch of dark shadow.

"What do you mean dressing decently?" he asked jokingly. Everyone knows what grows on the body of anyone else. Isn't that true?"

"If that's so why do you bother to wear anything at all?" Mrs. Yin retorted.

She stood up and walked over to the chess table. "I tell you what, you son of a rabbit. If you don't put on something to cover that damn thing of yours properly, I won't let you come near my room! Get out of here!"

"All right," Driver Wong stood up hastily. "I'm going to change, my dear sister-in-law."

Water splashed in the toilet and flew out from under the door. The dry ground hissed as it sucked in the water greedily. A low bank of shimmering fine dust rose at the head of the spreading water. "Ladies," Mr. Chang called out from inside the toilet. "I'm coming out. Please turn your respectful eyes the other way!"

"Who's interested, you old devil," Muchun, his young wife, answered. "Hurry up!" Turning to Mrs. Yin she said, "Taking a bath in that smelly place! Only he could do it."

Mr. Chang stepped out, his wet underpants sticking to his bony buttocks, jumped over the pool that had accumulated at the door, and scurried across to his room. He held out the towel at his left thigh, pretending to block the view of the people in the shade. We laughed.

Driver Wong returned to the chess game in a pair of shorts with longer legs.

"Think of those in Number 7 and Number 9 courtyards," Cook Kang said, scratching his side, skin drooping down to a pile upon his thighs. "Their courtyards have all been taken up with lean-tos and shacks to sleep in. At least we have a place inside the walls to cool off. They have to go to the street to find an airy place."

"We haven't had rain for a whole week," Granny Yin observed.

It was said there might be rain if there were clouds in the northwest at evening or in the southeast at dawn. We looked up, but the northwest was a dazzling immensity of clear sky.

"What's the matter with Dian Wen," Mr. Yin asked. "What important business does he have on a Sunday? Otherwise we could have a card game to wile away the day." He must be bored playing chess with Driver Wong. Card games involved four people and spectators. With Dian Wen and Mr. Chang cracking jokes and everybody supervising, it was more fun.

"Hu Bon and his men are investigating the case of Li Sunro," Driver Wong answered. "They still believe she was killed by the Red Alliance people."

"They just don't have anything better to do," Mr. Yin said. "Li Sunro has been dead three months. Why bother with her now? There are so many deaths these days. They dredged three more corpses from Houhai Lake yesterday morning. People are killed by others and by themselves. What's the difference?"

"Hey," Mrs. Yin called out. "Are you at it again? Can't you keep your mouth shut? They won't let you in the card game, even as a dummy."

Mr. Yin grinned and began to put the chess pieces in a cloth bag. He took very good care of his set. "Let's play cards."

Mr. Chang had changed into a pair of tailored shorts and sleeveless T-shirt. "Longsen," he beckoned to me. "Join us. Don't always gnaw at books."

The courtyard card club was composed of Mr. Yin, Mr. Chang, Driver Wong and Dian Wen. Mr. Yu and Muchun were alternate members. Playing cards was time-consuming and now I was resolved to build a foothold in the office professionally. I had to read a lot of books before I could feel secure there; and I would feel better when I would be recognized as an equal by my college educated colleagues.

"Come on," Mr. Chang urged, "Muchun will help you."

I moved my stool over to the card table and sat opposite Mr. Chang, knowing that Mr. Yin and Driver Wong were permanent partners. Muchun stood behind me so closely I felt my back muscle tingling with the static from her bare legs. The lower hem of her shorts flirted with my skin. When she bent over to take a card out of my hand, her breast literally pressed against my head. My will power was being tested. I kept my eyes straight at the cards in my hand or at the table, afraid I might touch her nipple if I turned my face. The tension was so great I gave up after three games. "You take over," I stood up and spoke to Muchun. "I need to catch my breath."

Dian Wen, Hu Bon and his girlfriend Big Beauty, and Lu Fen and his dark-skinned girlfriend, nicknamed "Sooty," came around suppertime. They brought beer, cooked meat and some noodles. None of them had married and they all lived in the singles' dormitory. They often came to Dian Wen's home for Sunday dinner, for wild drinking and eating parties at the Red Flag Detachment headquarters had caused too much talking.

Hu Bon never failed to bring inner-circle news such as who in high places was going up and who was being dragged down. I learned from him that Chairman Mao and Jiang Qing had not lived together for years. Also, a young woman the Chairman met on a train trip was now looking after him; Lin Biao, the defense minister and heir apparent of the Chairman, had a dreadful fear of drafts; Qiu Huizuo, a strong man under Jiang Qing, had slept with at least a dozen army nurses. Hu Bon's news and the food they brought were equally entertaining.

This time Hu Bon did not pass around the gossip. After a couple of glasses of beer, Hu Bon began a solemn speech.

"It's homicide." He had picked up quite a few judicial terms. "It is totally impossible to die from jumping from the second floor. That policeman Chao knew it and the coroner knew it. They didn't say it only because they were afraid of causing trouble for themselves. It's much easier to put the blame on the dead. Suicide settles everything; no one else is involved."

———

102

The two Red Guard organizations in the Bureau had been keenly sensitive about Li Sunro's death. The Revolutionary Rebels had insisted she was killed with a purpose, while the Red Alliance had avoided the subject, which provoked stronger suspicion.

"It must be the Red Alliance people who killed her," he continued. "She knew some secrets about the organization which made her uncomfortable. She had talked of withdrawing from the Red Alliance. That was the reason they killed her. We've already found traces of suspicious activities among some Red Alliance leaders. From the photos taken at Li Sunro's autopsy, we can be sure she was beaten before she died."

Hu Bon told us his conjecture about the murder: Li Sunro was returning late that night and was stopped at the back gate of the compound. Two young zealots from the Red Alliance, took her in to the garage next to the gate. Two others were waiting inside. They gagged her, wrapped her in canvas sheets and beat her. The motivation: to silence her from revealing inner-circle activities of the Red Alliance. This hypothesis was very convincing among the Revolutionary Rebel leaders.

Lu Fen produced a stack of color photos and passed them around. They were of Li Sunro, naked, on her stomach and back, from above, with details of chest, sides, legs, broken ribs, internal organs . . .

As Lu Fen enumerated, matter-of-factly, the process of autopsy he had witnessed for the first time in his twenty-eight years, I started to wonder: what is the Cultural Revolution doing to people? Especially to the young? Middle school students of thirteen and fourteen are beating people in the streets with their leather army belts capable of slashing heads open; college students drag old people in humiliating parades, forcing them to kneel and eat dirt; young workers in factories and offices fight equally brutal factional battles in the name of defending the purity of the Great Proletarian Cause.

Lu Fen, a demobilized soldier, had been in his second year

at college when he joined the army to defend the motherland. He sacrificed a secure office job that would be waiting for him upon graduation. He was slender, nice looking, and had a "scholarly" bearing. But I had seen him beat an elderly man with a stick at a public meeting. He continued even when the man's nose bled. His handsome face never changed expression; there was only an excited flush on his fair skin. Now he was showing pictures of a chopped up woman.

I looked out the window. Muchun was walking to the tap at the entranceway. Her figure through the window glass lengthened one moment and shortened the next. In the distortion of the uneven glass she looked grotesque.

18 · I Witness a Brutal Beating

Beijing's summer is not so bad compared to China's four furnaces: Nanjing, Wuhan, Chongqing and Changsa. After two or three days of sultry weather, a rain would cool the air down for a day. But during the summers I lived at 6 Tanyin Alley, it seemed the weather was always stiflingly hot.

In late July, 1968, Beijing did not see a drop of rain for ten days. Every night I took a stand-up bath in my underpants near the drainage grill, hidden from broad view behind clusters of sunflower stalks. Then I sat by my door with my feet in a pot of cold water. It did not make the thermometer drop, but it did give psychological consolation. My brain refused to think of anything. So I watched the sky, wishing clouds to appear in the northwest. I listened to the leaves of the two gigantic jujubes, hoping a breeze would rustle by. I sniffed the air, for when it was going to rain, the drain in the middle of the courtyard would give out a foul odor. The stronger the smell, the sooner the rain would come.

For a night, I was fooled by the shimmer of lightning in the northwest. Around midnight, the jujube leaves began to whisper little sounds from time to time, and the courtyard was drenched with that unpleasant smell. I even felt the air around dissolve. I rolled up the bamboo curtain in the doorway to let some imaginary coolness into the room where Shalin was sleeping fitfully in a membrane of perspiration. The rain came, in big drops, kicked up the dust and moved on in an instant. I was left to smell the dusty air.

If I had had my way, I wouldn't have gone to the office during the day, but would have napped under the eaves in the cool morning. However, Shalin said we shouldn't be like others who "receive the government pay, but don't work."

Suddenly the rain broke out in torrents. White slanting sheets obliterated everything. Rivulets spread to merge into an ocean in minutes. People in the office building were overjoyed in anticipation of relief from the heat. Then I remembered my home and hurried to the Red Flag Detachment headquarters to find Dian Wen. "Our rooms will be flooded soon." I told him. "Let's go back."

We struggled through the submerged streets. Some places were already a foot and a half deep. We had to push our bicycles for forty minutes. Boys were splashing and yelling with great delight in the pouring rain.

Water from the alley was cascading down the brick steps at our gate. Only a narrow strip of ground was still showing, at the foundation of the north row. The whole courtyard was a fish pond. Heavy rain drops knocked dimples in the surface. Granny Yin was desperately clearing away leaves and a variety of rubbish from the drainage grill. The plastic scrap around her shoulders gave little protection. Dian Wen and I waded over to her. "You go inside. We'll take care of this," I shouted in her ear.

The drainage pipe was too small to accommodate the deluge. Very soon the water would flow over the thresholds of the south row. Our labor had little effect as the rain kept pouring in bucketfuls. Dian Wen and I began building a semi-circular dam around each of the doors to keep the water from inundating our rooms.

The rain lasted until next morning. The flood in the courtyard subsided. The air became easier to breathe. We thought we would sleep well for a couple of days before it became hot again. However, we in the south row still couldn't sleep peacefully at night.

A nationwide campaign was carried out in 1958 to eliminate the four pests: mosquitoes, flies, sparrows and mice. During the Cultural Revolution people were too busy fighting human pests and let the lesser ones be. Neighborhood Committees had stopped inspecting the cleanliness of each house. The sparrows, whom the authorities had privately admitted were wrongly condemned, were reluctant to return, but not the others.

Now the mice were forced to migrate from their flooded underground tunnels through the cracks in the walls to the space above the ceiling. They would scurry all night long, squeaking and gnawing at the rafters. The noise was nerveracking. I banged the ceiling with the handle of the broom. The noise stopped for two minutes, only to resume again. I could see them in my mind's eye—standing still, their beady eyes staring in the dark, ears pricked up, wondering why I should disturb them.

In the small hours I was awakened by Shalin's shrieking cry. "Look! What is that?" she said urgently, pointing a flashlight at a fat worm on the floor. I turned on the light. She was barefoot. "I stepped on it and was scared to death."

It was like a giant snail without a shell. I looked around and saw several more. I picked them up one by one and went out to throw them in the drainage grill. In the morning I saw whitish trails of dried secretion on the floor, furniture and walls they had traversed during the night and I collected a dozen more under the threshold. No one in the courtyard knew what they were. They could constrict their bodies to creep through the tiniest crevices in the floor. I sealed all the cracks in the floor with cement and lined the base of the wall with raw lime. Still the nasty, soft-bodied trespassers would appear, making the summer nights more intolerable. Shalin had to turn on the light when she got out of bed to relieve herself.

I had not fully awakened from my midday nap around two o'clock. My neck was sore from the awkward position of sprawling over the desk for twenty minutes. My colleagues could sleep like that comfortably for an hour. My mind was sluggish, shrouded with staleness. The sleepless nights were getting to me. I felt queasy the whole day. Hu Bon came to the door of my office and beckoned me out—he was not liked by my co-workers and he knew it. He asked if I wanted to take a car ride to relax.

Hu Bon, Dian Wen, Lu Fen and I rode in Driver Wong's car.

Lu Fen's girlfriend Sooty, Big Beauty and a young man from the Red Flag detachment rode in another car. We entered the city, threading through old streets. We were going to Beijing Geography Institute north of the city. I asked Hu Bon why we didn't take the new roads outside the city to avoid the traffic. He began to explain. His group had intensified the investigation of Li Sunro's death and interrogated several suspects. One of them was kitchen accountant Ren Rong.

"Are you serious?" I asked. "He and I walked downstairs together and saw Li Sunro that night."

"You were fooled by them," Hu Bon smiled. I did not like his know-all attitude. He was two years younger than I but always behaved like a person of great authority. "They planned it that way, to get a couple of witnesses on the scene to prove their innocence."

I didn't argue. The whole Cultural Revolution was a dream— neither comedy nor tragedy. I was an indifferent spectator. I participated in some of Hu Bon's actions to escape boredom and gain a light Red Flush, politically. Shalin had been complaining that I had gotten too close to Hu Bon's group.

"You used to detest their doings," she said. "Now it seems you've become one of them. You'd better be careful. Theirs is not your cup of tea."

I explained that we were all from the army and now worked in the same building. "If I keep too distant from them, other army veterans may think I'm ingratiating myself with intellectuals. Don't worry. I won't join them in beating people or ransacking anyone's home."

But one motive I had not told her was that the Revolutionary Rebels side was gaining the upper hand at the Bureau. The Military Control Group, which had been sent to the Bureau by the central authorities in early July, had a liking for the Revolutionary Rebels. I had been a "political loafer" and now I might need a tinge of red to camouflage the "white" pursuit of my profession.

———

The car squeezed through Xinjiekou Street and out of a gap in the north wall of the city. The traffic here was light. Young poplar trees were luxuriant and the air was cooler. Occasional vegetable plots appeared in the open lots between buildings.

"We keep three suspects in the Geology Institute," Hu Bon was briefing me. "They are the most likely involved and all of them have political flaws that we can grasp as tails to swing them with. Even if they are found innocent, the Red Alliance will not dare protest."

"I had a transformer set up," Lu Fen said. "I tried it on Wei Shu. It is only twenty-five volts, but he shivered. He was really scared."

"Don't you think Wei Shu has gotten a little too much?" Driver Wong put in. A cigarette dangled from one corner of his mouth. Looking very smart in his faded army uniform, he reminded me of a Kuomintang army officer in a movie.

"That might be," Lu Fen said. He might become a wronged ghost. But for the time being, we have to work on him. We need a breakthrough."

"Yes, we need a breakthrough very soon," Hu Bon said reflectively. "We must solve this case and can't afford to get stuck in it. Otherwise the Red Alliance will have an excuse to get on us."

Driver Wong stepped on the accelerator. The speedometer shot up to 70 miles an hour. I felt nauseous. We made a sudden turn at a crossroad and were going back to the city. I was puzzled.

"The Red Alliance is trying to find out where we keep their people," Hu Bon explained. "They often follow us. So every time we go out there we take a different route."

I felt the same sense of mystery and anticipation I had reading *The Godfather*.

We entered the city by West Gate and came out on Xinjiekou Street again. After half an hour on a quiet, tree lined road we arrived at the Institute.

The school was deserted. Both faculty and students had left for home for a long, indefinite vacation, except for a few zealous students who had joined others to agitate revolution in factories. We entered a huge lecture room, one of a dozen flanking an empty corridor. All the desks and chairs had been removed. In this room I witnessed the brutality I had heard of so often since the Cultural Revolution began.

Three men were brought in from separate classrooms where they were imprisoned under guard by the Red Flag Detachment. Hu Bon sat cross-legged on the bare concrete floor. Sooty and Big Beauty stood by the window, looking out at the drooping willows in the courtyard, and chatting. It was obvious they had attended interrogations before. Hu Bon and his lieutenants Lu Fen, Dian Wen and Wang Pan decided to begin with the youngest and toughest looking of the three. Hu Bon waved his stubby arm at the man, beckoning him to stand in front of him. The man obeyed, stiffening his neck.

"How did you kill Li Sunro?" Hu Bon asked, his voice deep and flat.

"I've told you I didn't kill anyone," the man's voice was low, but stubborn.

Hu Bon signaled Lu Fen and Dian Wen, who pulled up a bench from the corner and set it in the middle of the room. They pushed the young man forward and forced him to bend over the bench.

"I'll give you a hundred lashes," Hu Bon said in his mildest tone. "If you can stand them, you are off the hook."

The man tensed his muscles and said, "I had nothing to do with Li Sunro's death. Go ahead with your beating."

"We'll see how tough you are," Lu Fen said. It is said that if someone doesn't raise his voice when he makes a threat, he means it. Biting dogs do not bark. Lu Fen's smile never left his face.

He and Dian Wen each picked up a piece of rubber hose and began to beat the man methodically, the hose making a sucking sound when it hit his buttocks. The man clenched his teeth and refused to utter his pain. I waited to see what would come of this kangaroo court.

The beating did not seem as horrible as described in novels. The hose was soft. It could not even damage the fabric of a man's trousers. In novels, raw flesh and blood would fly when a person was beaten with bamboo strips in the imperial magistrate's court. What I did not know then, was that in modern times tormenters were smarter. They inserted an iron rod in the tubing, which would only cause injuries beneath the skin. A beaten person would seem to have nothing worse than swollen limbs. But he could be suffering internal hemorrhaging or serious muscle damage.

When the count reached forty-five, there was a foul smell in the room. I sniffed around and found the source at the young man's feet. He was still holding on. I went over to Hu Bon and said that something must have gone wrong. He sniffed too, then we saw liquid dripping from the bottom of the man's trouser legs. He had lost control of his anal sphincter.

He was led to the toilet. The two other prisoners looked away as if condemned. Hu Bon wanted to go on with them. I told him I had had enough for the day. "Furthermore, the room is too smelly."

19 · The Glorious Red Terrorists

For several months Beijing had been ruled by a "Red Wind" stirred up by the Red Guards. Youngsters were frantically wiping out the Four Olds—old ideas, old living style, old social norms, and old objects. Sanitation workers were meticulous when they emptied public or private toilets. Every day they collected piles of gold, silver, jewelry and precious stones thrown into the bowls or pits during the night by their terrified owners. Granny Yin and Granny Dian had several dozen silver coins with the head of Yuan Shikai, the first president of republican China, known to old people as "Big Head." But Mr. Yin and Dian Wen announced in the courtyard that if any Red Guards would dare to confiscate the silver, they would "break their legs." Mother, hearing this brave statement, transferred her three dozen silver coins to my place.

Former factory and landowners, shopkeepers, policemen, Kuomintang officers who had surrendered to the Communist army, anyone who had once worked for the old regime were living in fear. Many were taking their own lives. Several corpses had been dragged out of the inner city Lake Shishihai, which was barely three feet deep. Bodies were piled up without a scrap of respect in the crematorium. Workers there threw them carelessly in the mouth of the furnace.

One Sunday afternoon, Aunt Kang returned from outside. She did not go to her room to change into her "home outfit" but rushed over to the group of neighbors chatting and playing chess in the shade, pulling her blouse off, her limp, heavy breasts dragging the worn undershirt down to reveal fat shoulders. Her bound feet were firm and steady. She pulled over a stool and sat down. The woven rawhide strips creaked in protest as her heavy buttocks sank solidly onto them.

"Granny Yin," she said agitatedly, "two women in Number 7 courtyard are dead! That woman and her mother-in-law who had a little limp, remember? They were buried alive!"

"What!" Jinli was astounded. Aunt Kang was satisfied with the reaction from her good neighbors, and enjoyed it. Granny Yin looked at her inquisitively.

"Yes," Aunt Kang shifted her buttocks, and the stool groaned a warning. "As soon as they arrived at their native village the Red Guards there put them under arrest. The women kowtowed for mercy. You know those young country kids, tougher than the city Red Guards even. They beat them on the back, chest and head with shoulder poles. They say they were still breathing when they threw then into a pit and buried them."

We all listened attentively. "Why did they kill them?" Mr. Chang asked.

"Why?" Aunt Kang was pleased to have caught more listeners. She scratched her ribs under the right armpit. "You ask me why? They were wives of a big landlord family. The villagers demanded of our Neighborhood Committee that they be sent back for punishment. That's why!"

"But they shouldn't have killed them," Mr. Chang said, then grinned as if apologizing for asking a foolish question.

"Shouldn't they have?" Mr. Yin chuckled coldly. "This is called class struggle. Class struggle, understand? Chairman Mao teaches, 'A revolution is not a dinner party, or writing an essay, or painting a picture, or doing embroidery; it cannot be so refined, so leisurely and gentle, so temperate, kind, courteous, restrained and magnanimous. A revolution is an insurrection, an act of violence by which one class overthrows another.' If we don't knock down the enemy, the enemy will knock us down."

Driver Wong, Mr. Chang, Dian Wen and I all laughed. Mr. Yin had a good memory. He could recite long quotations from

Mao Zedong's writings. His tone conveyed irony though, when he recited them.

"Those two women didn't deserve that kind of cruelty," Granny Yin said sadly. "They had never lived a day of good life. I knew them well. The mother-in-law was a concubine of a landlord. He owned a lot of land, but his wife was a tigress. She came from a very rich family herself. The landlord dared not offend her. She ordered the concubine around like a house slave. Every time the landlord spent a night with the concubine, the mistress would make things more difficult for her the next day.

The younger woman's fate was even worse. She came from a tenant family to be the bride of the landlord's son who was suffering from tuberculosis. The boy was only fifteen, but the villagers believed marriage would cure him. It didn't, of course. The young woman was widowed in the bridal chamber. Because both the concubine and the bride were from poor families, they stuck together.

Before the old landlord and his wife were beaten to death by the villagers during the land reform of 1950, the landlord gave some money to the two women to flee for their lives. He knew his fate was hopeless. They came to Beijing, worked as house-maids and made matchboxes at night. Who would expect that these two poor women would die like that? Only last week I talked with them at the west end store. They had never dared to offend anybody, the kind of people who wouldn't step on ants." She sighed and waved her palm leaf fan slowly.

I looked at Granny Yin, trying to bring to mind the images of the two dead women. They were seldom seen in the alley, even during the hottest days. They shared a small room, as obscure as they themselves. And now they were dead. That's that.

"Lives are cheap," Granny Yin observed. "There must be many wronged ghosts in the nether world these days."

"Not that many, Granny Yin," Driver Wong said, flapping his big fan vigorously at his crotch. "Wanfujing Street is still as crowded as ever. I wish the number in that world were larger, so I wouldn't have to squeeze through such crowds when I drive."

"Don't talk like that!" Granny Yin scolded.

All this time Jinli listened without comment. Her first husband was still in jail. Although she divorced him almost six years ago and remarried Carpenter Shen, who knew if the Red Guards wouldn't pick up the old account. She still had fond memories of her first husband, a Kuomintang air force captain. He was imprisoned in 1961, thirteen years after he had left the service of the old regime. She never objected to neighbors calling her Mrs. Ho.

"All right," Mr. Yin said impatiently. "Let's get back to our game. The dead are dead. Let's leave them in peace. Those still living must carry on and try to enjoy it."

The game resumed. The women continued their chattering. Every misfortune was remote to us. 6 Tanyin Alley was a bastion of staunch revolutionaries. No one would bother us.

By the end of July, the Red Guards' attention had shifted to looking for documentary evidence against "bad elements"—a new campaign to follow the purification of class ranks. Several people from the courtyard were enlisted to help the Neighborhood Committee in the struggle against class enemies. Dian Wen, Mr. Chang and I were called by Mrs. Yu one day to a criticism meeting.

It took place in a back room of the courtyard where the Neighborhood Committee office was located. The accused had been a Kuomintang secret service officer before 1946. To strike terror into this seventy-year-old man, the windows had been covered with old newspaper and the room was dimly lit with a bare bulb hanging from the ceiling. The atmosphere reminded me of an episode from a Beijing Opera, in which a clever imperial court minister decorated his chamber in imitation of Hell when he interrogated a vicious corrupt official. The accused was so scared he confessed.

As before opening any meeting, study session, discussion, or even a meal, the Neighborhood Committee chairwoman, a middle-aged housewife barely able to read, demanded everyone except the accused open the little red book and she led the reading, "Make trouble, fail, make trouble again, fail again . . . till their doom; that is the logic of the imperialists and all reactionaries the world over in dealing with the people's cause, and they will never go against this logic. This is a Marxist law. When we say 'imperialism is ferocious,' we mean that its nature will never change, that the imperialists will never lay down their butcher knives, that they will never become Buddha, till their doom."

She had us turn to page 176 and read, "It is up to us to organize the people. As for the reactionaries in China, it is up to us to organize the people to overthrow them. Everything reactionary is the same; if you don't hit it, it won't fall. This is also like sweeping the floor: as a rule, where the broom does not reach, the dust will not vanish of itself."

The dozen voices echoing in the sparsely furnished room sounded funny. In the office we did this ritual every morning before work began, in front of a portrait of Chairman Mao. We called it "morning report to the Chairman."

"Down with the reactionary Fang Si!" a middle school boy with a Red Guard armband shouted when Mrs. Yu gave the signal, and others followed. "Down with all reactionaries! Long live the Great Proletarian Cultural Revolution! Long live Mao Zedong thought! Long live Chairman Mao!" The old newspaper sheets on the window rustled.

Mrs. Yu announced solemnly the opening of the meeting. "This man standing before us is an enemy who had hidden deep in our ranks. He is a tricky old fox and has deceived us for many years. He was a secret agent of the Kuomintang with the rank of regimental commander. A full colonel! You hear, comrades? Here is a big fish!"

I knew she must have found the information either by looking at the man's dossier at the police station or the police had supplied it to her.

"Today we have weeded him out. This is a great victory for Chairman Mao's thought specifically expressed in our neighborhood. We are here to expose his crimes, to rip off his mask which has cheated us for so long!"

Mrs. Yu turned to the old man and shouted, "Fang Si, confess your crimes!"

The old man shuffled his feet nervously and murmured feebly, "I'm guilty, I'm guilty."

"Louder!" we shouted in unison.

"Yes, yes," the old man coughed and said obediently. "I'm guilty. I deserve death ten thousand times for the crimes I committed in the old society. I should not have served the Kuomintang reactionaries. My crimes are as high as the sky. I have let the Communist Party down and let Chairman Mao down."

"Don't give us empty talk!" the chairwoman said to him sternly. "Tell the revolutionary masses what you did for the Kuomintang reactionaries!"

"Yes, of course, I'll confess my crimes," the old man straightened slowly and painfully. His back must be sore in that bent position for half an hour.

"Bend down! You bastard!" the middle school boy yelled angrily and stood up to push the old man's head.

Fang Si began to recite mechanically what he had done while serving the Kuomintang. He remembered events and dates precisely and told them in a tight logic so it was difficult to pick loopholes for further questioning. He must have rehearsed it many times.

The dozen housewives and retired workers, almost all illiterate, were serious throughout the meeting. Their questions were ridiculously illogical. If the former Kuomintang officer had had the freedom to talk back, he could easily have embarrassed them. I sat there, putting in a question here and there to show my support for the Neighborhood Committee's revolutionary actions. Secretly I enjoyed the frustration of the chairwoman who seemed unable to break down the old man's dignity despite his forced humility.

117

20 · A Mountain Harvest

The two jujube trees in front of the east wing must have been there since the house was built a century ago. The trunks reached over the eaves of the house. Their branches twisted and spiraled up high above the roof. It is said that once every few years the jujube's bark should be slashed with a knife so that it will bear more fruit. The gnarled trunks showed many scars.

These trees put out their leaves very late. By the end of April when the old locust in the corner near the toilets was blooming with strings of tiny fragrant flowers, they would not yet have shown any sign of awakening. Beijing's spring is very short. We could still remember the dust and winds of April, when young girls had begun wearing light woolen sweaters.

By early May, when the poplar, willow and locust had grown a full crown and lilac bushes were bursting with fragrant lavender or white blossoms, the jujubes hurriedly leafed out. In July greenish blossoms appeared amidst the dense foliage and soon we could discern tiny berries. By August, the date-like fruit was ripe enough for children's impatient mouths. Mr. Chang, Dian Wen and Driver Wong selected a Sunday for gathering.

The whole courtyard turned out. Dian Wen, Driver Wang and the older boys climbed the trees to knock down the fruit with long bamboo poles, while the children and grown-ups alike scurried merrily in the bombardment, cheering and yelling in delight. Soon two dozen wash basins were filled with the glossy, red-tinged golden fruit.

By the end of September, while other trees were still luxuriant, these two began to shed. Leafing late and shedding early, it

118

seemed their only purpose in life was to give each family at 6 Tanyin Alley two basins of sweet fruit. Even their flowers were so tiny as to go unnoticed.

Before we knew it, autumn had set in. In the office, almost five days a week we spent the afternoon studying either Chairman Mao's new instructions and his five philosophical essays or attending criticism meetings. The number in detention had mounted to fifty-four. They were denounced in public meetings in turn. They were held on our floor in a meeting room with a heavy fabric curtain strung across it. The men on one side and the women on the other slept on boards. Early every morning the guards would wake them up and herd them to the courtyard to sweep the grounds. Then they came back to wash. Before they were led to the canteen for breakfast, they were lined up in the middle of the corridor in front of a large portrait of Chairman Mao to recite in unison: "I am guilty. I have let you and the Chinese people down. I deserve to die. I beg your forgiveness."

During the day they might be summoned to do some odd job; otherwise they read Mao Zedong's works. During the evening they would make self-criticisms to repent their previous "crimes" and would criticize each other.

I was assigned to guard them one night. That evening I heard their confessions polished by many recitations. Some were veteran Communists now labeled "Capitalist Roaders inside the Party." Those who had survived the many political campaigns were referred to as "experienced political runners."

"I'm very sorry that in 1963 I agreed with Liu Shaoqi's policy of giving commune land to individual peasants," the former director of the Bureau's Political Department criticized himself, working his facial muscles to express remorse. "Although I served in the revolutionary ranks for thirty-five years, I have not remolded my petty bourgeois ideology."

I found the monotonous recitations disgusting and left the room.

The next morning on the way to breakfast, as my charges were about to stop in front of Chairman Mao's portrait to beg forgiveness, I shouted sharply, "Move on!" I felt embarrassed when they stood there reciting the same words, so humiliated and stripped of dignity. The group dared not move on. They were surprised, knowing they would be reprimanded for forgetting to report to the Chairman in the morning. "I said keep on going!" No one showed any expression. They filed down the stairway.

With office function so disrupted, I was very bored. So when the Bureau was organizing a team of fifty people to help the peasants with their harvest, I was glad to have a change.

I liked the idea that school children, college students, office workers and sometimes factory workers had the opportunity to spend time in the outlying villages. In the factories there was no difficulty mobilizing enough people to go. The young workers would make the occasion an outing and in addition each was to be given one yuan a day for food subsidy. But in the offices, finding volunteers was a headache for the department chiefs. I, though, did not mind manual labor. A sweating was good for my sinuses. In the service we had often helped the local peasants. I had learned almost every kind of field work: transplanting rice, cutting wheat, plowing and threshing. I could smartly carry a hundred and fifty pound bag of rice.

I was put in charge of a group going to the Huairo Mountains north of Beijing in Miyun County, among which were two dozen detainees.

Shashi Canyon was a beautiful village of three dozen families on a hilltop overlooking the Great Wall at a mountain pass. A stream below gurgled through clear pools and reddish rocks. If the fortress-like village and its people were on film, they would be found striking. But the villagers were poor and their settlement dirty. Animal droppings were everywhere and the foul odor was repulsive in the crisp, tonic mountain air.

Four centuries earlier, this village had been a Ming Dynasty garrison against the nomads of the north. The Great Wall lost its significance after the Manchus crossed it in 1644. Families of the Ming guards became peasants, growing chestnuts, pears, and apricots on the mountain slopes. They also raised small plots of millet, potatoes, and beans. When they could sell fruit to the city, life was good.

In the Great Leap Forward, in less than three months, eight hundred million peasants were organized into communes. This village had been made a production team, one of a dozen of a commune spread over an enormous area of mountainous terrain. Draft animals and farm tools were pooled along with individual land holdings. A section of steel rail was the gong struck to mark the beginning and end of the work day. Older villagers went along in gloom, their thousands of years of household tradition broken. Yet the young people cheered, as they hoed the crops side by side, joking and teasing each other. Orchards were abandoned and the men were forced to reclaim forested mountainsides for grain, since the central government was demanding that each peasant family also provide its own food.

The first night at the village I called my fifty people together. "We are here among peasants. I hope no one will reveal another's political status. Those who made mistakes are here to receive re-education from the peasants. We shouldn't treat them differently. On the other hand," I looked at the cluster of detainees, "be obedient and do what the revolutionary masses and the peasants tell you to do!" I was not comfortable using this fashionable political jargon.

I felt pity for the the detainees. They were older than most of us. In their fifties, they had passed the required age for manual work. But here they were, swallowing pride as prominent professionals or high ranking Party officials. It felt bad to be the leader of the group.

I loved the scenery deep in the mountains as I went to collect chestnuts with a peasant group. The air was pure and refreshing.

The sky was clean with wisps of white clouds here and there. The tranquil environment made me forget both the harsh and trifling things going on in the world.

The villagers subsisted on millet supplemented with potatoes, and did not have enough of either. September was the hardest time. The work was exhausting, but they had consumed the summer harvest. Many families had to "borrow" grain from the production team against their later allotment. Some ate only potatoes mixed with the plants' vines for morning meal and roasted chestnuts for lunch. To city people, chestnuts were a delicacy. But as a regular diet, they were not so tasty. The peasants were glad for the steamed wheat buns I shared with them from my lunch. They wrapped the pieces in scarves to save for their children. They only had such treats two or three times a year, on major holidays.

In the village there was a girl of thirteen, slim and fair-skinned who stood out among the others, raw and dark. She wore clothes of cheap cotton, but they fit her figure perfectly. Nor were her manners as coarse. Her faded red blouse stood out amidst their gray and blue.

One evening on the single street of the village I passed her. She smiled nicely. Since we were standing outside her house, she asked me in as country custom required. Though I knew it was only a gesture of politeness, I followed. Her father hurried to greet me. To the villagers, all government employees were thought to be officials. And I was in charge of them all! Some of the younger people in our group liked to visit the villagers at their homes, flattered by the respect of the humble hosts. I preferred to spend my evenings wandering in the canyon. But I had a particular interest in the girl's family.

"Please come in," the father said. He looked in his late fifties, but if his daughter was only thirteen, he could be little more than forty. "Fengzhi, make tea for our guest."

"You see, our house is dirty and messy," he apologized to me. I did not think so. I had noticed that the courtyard was clean and the pigsty did not smell foul. The house was typically crude brick walls on a stone foundation, with a tile roof. In the room were only the most necessary pieces of furniture—a trunk on which we set a teapot and cups, two bottles of cheap liquor, and a pair of porcelain vases. Two stools flanked a clumsy table.

I was attracted by the elegant vases. They were a perfect pair, of blue and white design, reminding me of those in my grandfather's room. In the Cultural Revolution the Red Guards confiscated such treasures and smashed them in the street as a demonstration of "wiping out the four olds." Only then did I realize the value of these antiques.

The father asked me to sit on the only chair. I insisted on the bed, to show I wasn't pompous. The girl brought in two bowls filled with tea and set them on the window sill.

"We don't have good tea to serve guests," he said. "Our village is too far from the city." He did not say that they were too poor to buy good tea, for that would be understood as complaining about the good life of today, questioning the superiority of our socialist system.

"You have a fine daughter," I said. He smiled modestly. "Does she go to school?"

"Yes, she's in sixth grade. Now they have time off to help with the harvest."

She was two years behind city children, I calculated. I turned to her and asked, "How are you getting along in school?"

She looked at me directly and said, "Not well." Her eyes were big and bright. I wished I could take her back to Beijing so she could have a better education. She was being wasted in this backward mountain village.

I wanted to know more about this family. Where was the girl's mother whom I had never seen in the village? But it would be impolite to ask. A full third of the men in the village were bachelors. No girl wanted to stay here; they tried to marry into villages in the plains, whose girls tried to marry into the city. I assumed the girl's mother had either died or left.

I sipped the tea, which tasted like dried straw. I put a question here and a question there about their family life. Soon I realized the man was unwilling to offer answers and I said good-bye.

That night the Party branch secretary of the village sought me out to inform me that the man had been a rich peasant, one of the five categories of bad elements. I really did not care. At the time, I was politically safe. However, I did not counter the advice not to talk to that peasant again. But when the amateur song and dance troupe from the Bureau came to entertain the peasants, I asked a woman collegue of mine for her silk scarf, which I gave to the girl.

A few days before October first, National Day, we returned to Beijing in a pouring rain. I was glad to be home. My shabby room was more comfortable than before.

21 · Dian Wen Gets Married

In mid-September the whole nation was mobilized to celebrate the twentieth anniversary of the founding of the People's Republic. For this event, Beijing residents were issued extra coupons for pork, fish, sugar and eggs, plus special holiday rations of a pound of peanuts, two ounces of sesame oil and four ounces of sunflower seeds. Amidst the holiday excitement, Dian Wen announced he was getting married.

Dian Wen was indispensible to all weddings as the master of ceremonies. His jokes in innocent seriousness plus his popularity made the occasions enjoyable for everyone. But it seemed he had never thought of his own wedding. His sister, fourteen years older, whom we too called Big Sister, was concerned. He was still her baby brother, although he was twenty-eight. She had had her eye on a girl, four years younger, named Erfeng. Big Sister called a family meeting of Big Brother, Dian Wen, and their mother.

"I think Erfeng suits Dian Wen fine," she said, the skin around her eyes and under her chin showing the hard work of her life. "She's not pretty, has three younger sisters and a brother, and her father does not earn much. But I watched her growing up and I like her because she is obedient, honest, and has common sense. She will be able to take good care of Dian Wen."

Big Brother did not object, but said it should be Dian Wen's decision. He was five years younger than Big Sister and had his own daughter and son growing up. What a big brother could do for a younger was to help him set up his family, not choose a wife for him. He would, of course, raise questions if he did not like Erfeng. The Dian family and Erfeng's had lived in the same courtyard for three generations.

Dian Wen had met Erfeng occasionally on his frequent visits to Big Sister. He did not disapprove of Erfeng, though he wished his wife would be prettier. He could not name what physical defects she had. Many thin girls were pretty. Some had big front teeth, but that only enhanced their feminine appeal; and girls with sloping shoulders were regarded as beauties traditionally. Erfeng had all these attributes, but she was plain.

"Pretty girls are often unfaithful," Big Sister advised. "You won't make it big in this world. So be content with a common girl."

Dian Wen was accustomed to listening to Big Sister. When she was fifteen, her mother had a stroke and she had to take charge of the household.

Mrs. Pung, Erfeng's mother, accepted the proposal readily. But one problem troubled her profoundly. It called for delicacy. The day after Big Sister's proposal, she went over to the younger woman's home. "Sister," she felt awkward this time addressing Big Sister in the way customary among Beijing neighbors. "I want to discuss how we are to address each other in the future," she said tentatively. For her, the way neighbors addressed each other was a vital matter. It was totally improper to call older neighbors by name. You called them by Aunt, Uncle, Grandpa or Granny, as if they were related. For twenty years, Erfeng's mother and Big Sister had called each other "Sister." Now Mrs. Pung would be Dian Wen's mother-in-law, so by custom his sister should address her as Aunt. She felt that was demeaning to Big Sister.

"Don't take it too hard, Sister Pung," Big Sister said. "We are old neighbors. We shall keep it the way it is. Erfeng will follow Dian Wen in calling me 'Sister.' Don't let this marriage disturb our good relations."

"If you think it is all right, it is all right with me," Mrs. Pung said, still uneasy but relieved. She had solved the most difficult problem of her oldest daughter's marriage.

Old Beijingers were fastidious about rites and protocol. The Dian and Pung families were typical. The women would not hear of a marriage declared by a piece of paper allowing the couple to sleep together. A simple wedding at which candies were scattered to noisy children and tea served to polite adults would even be a disgrace to them.

"We're working class families," Big Sister told the elders of the two families righteously. "We should not be afraid of being accused of adhering to old ideas. Our wedding ceremony cannot be too simple."

Her words carried a lot of weight.

"But we have to think about what people in our little brother's office will say," Big Brother said tentatively. "We'd better not put on too much show. If you agree, Erfeng will come to his place by bus, and there will be no sending-off ceremony on Sister Pung's side, no firecrackers—and we can't get them anyway. We'll invite close relatives and his good friends for a dinner."

Big Brother's idea seemed reasonable and everybody agreed, Big Sister reluctantly. And Mrs. Pung's words got stuck in her throat but she nodded her head.

Hu Bon's people came to help set up Dian Wen's room. Big Brother, a good amateur carpenter, had made a wardrobe. Hu Bon sent Lu Fen and Wang Pan to transport it by cycle cart from Big Brother's home in the eastern part of the city. They pedaled for an hour.

Big Brother and Big Sister each gave Dian Wen one hundred yuan for the wedding. Other relatives contributed their share according to closeness to the family and financial situation. With his savings from the army, Dian Wen bought a cupboard, a radio, and a new double bed, which he put in the center of the room. He also bought whole sets of tea cups, pots, glasses and bowls. There were more things than he would need for many years. He reminded everyone that gifts could not be used on the wedding day. They would be put on display. To me it was wasteful and thus ridiculous.

Four quilts with brocade covers and cotton lining, gifts from relatives, were piled neatly. Mrs. Rong from the next courtyard was invited over to arrange the bed.

"Don't you young men touch the bed articles," Aunt Kang brushed aside the hands of Lu Fen who was about to examine a flowered sheet. "The wedding bed should be made by a perfect person."

"Am I not perfect?" he asked, puzzled. "I have all the arms, legs, eyes, nose and ears. See, I have all the teeth, too."

"A perfect person," Aunt Kang explained solemnly, "should be one who has a husband and children of both sexes. It will be still more ideal if her parents are still alive. And it must be a woman of age and good reputation. Understand?"

The young men did not understand and Lu Fen asked, "If the woman was remarried, is she still a perfect person?"

"No, she is not. 'A good horse does not serve two masters; and a good woman does not marry twice,'" Aunt Kang quoted. Jinli would not like Aunt Kang's criterion for being a good woman. She was not there.

"Cut it out!" Kang Ping said to her mother. "That is nonsense. You'd better not spread feudal ideas. The Red Guards will come and get you!"

"I would like to see if they dare!" Aunt Kang gave her daughter a hard stare. "I could lend them some of my guts!"

Granny Yin brought over a small bag and emptied the contents onto the bed. There were peanuts, jujubes and *guiyuan*. As she put the fruit under the mattress, she explained, "The names of these three kinds of fruit are homophones of the words 'give birth to a son soon.'"

"But I want a daughter when I get married," Lu Fen said, in mock seriousness. "What shall I put in my wedding bed then?"

Granny Yin laughed. She was too shrewd not to appreciate the joke. "It is only an auspicious gesture," she said. "Nobody can guarantee that there will be a son or a daughter. My aunt placed almost a bushel of fruit in my son's wedding bed, and he has only two daughters. It is superstitious. You young people shouldn't believe it. It's just for fun."

We were impressed by the old lady's philosophy. Very eclectic, wasn't it?

Checking out the room, Hu Bon said, "Dian Wen must have spent all his savings to decorate this room." It was extravagantly decked out with the wardrobe whose full-length mirror reflected the new double bed and the four quilts, two red and two green, and its pink silk spread. A cupboard stood against the east wall. Behind its glass panels were a gold-rimmed tea set and two bottles of the best Maotai liquor—for show only, since Dian Wen never drank. On top of the cupboard were another fine porcelain tea service and four thermos bottles, two red and two green, each with calligraphy of a Chairman Mao poem. On the wall were four framed inscriptions of Chairman Mao's words. The desk, an old piece of Bureau property, looked out of place with its peeling varnish. Hu Bon spread a printed plastic sheet on it and moved the radio over from the cupboard. This radio, the latest model, was twice as big as any other in the courtyard. Hu Bon turned it on to the sound of opera. The tone was clear and resonant.

"*On the Dock* again," he turned the wave station selector back and forth quickly. "I'm really fed up with the Eight Model operas."

I knew he wouldn't dare make such a statement in any other place. Eight Model Theatrical Works were personally promoted by Jiang Qing, the head of the Cultural Revolution Leading Group, more powerful, then, than the Central Committee itself.

The only broadcasts were songs of strong political significance, lectures on Communist ideology, or revolutionary drama, besides the operas. Hu Bon turned the radio off. "It's a pity there aren't good programs for such a good radio! How much was it? A hundred and seventy? Wow! How are you going to live after the wedding? I hope the bride won't have to eat only noodles with fried bean sauce on her honeymoon."

"What's wrong with eating noodles?" Aunt Kang demanded.

"We could only afford noodles at my wedding dinner. Now you young people want to eat meat and fish all the time. You even borrow money to eat good."

Kang Ping did not like her mother's expression of backcountry folk ways. She interrupted, "Here you go again! Don't tell us how poor you used to be. We don't need political preaching at home!"

"Well, we like to hear old people recalling hard times of the past," Hu Bon said. We smiled, knowing he was never serious when he recited fashionable political jargon. "It is very important for us to remember the past," he continued in a flat narrative tone. "As Lenin, our great teacher, once said, 'Forgetting the past means betrayal.' How can you forget the past? We should follow the steps of our forefathers, especially the steps of our beloved veteran revolutionaries, to the end of our lives. We shall carry the revolution through to the end, to the day when we achieve Communism in China and in the world.

"So you see," he kept on talking, "we should not forget the sufferings of the past. Once in awhile we should recall the past by eating a meal of coarse food. But on the other hand, what did the veteran revolutionaries suffer for? They suffered so that we could have a better life today. If we always ate corn buns and brine pickles as Aunt Kang did back in her village, we would be letting our revolutionary predecessors down. In order to repay our debt to those who fought for our happiness, we should eat fish and meat as often as we can afford to."

Everyone burst out laughing. "You smart bastard," Aunt Kang laughed the loudest.

"Actually, eating meals to recall past sufferings is not a new thing," Granny Yin said. "Before Zhu Yuanzhang became emperor of the Ming Dynasty, he was a poor Buddhist novice. One day he fainted of starvation by the roadside. Two beggars came along and fed him kitchen scrapings they had collected. The food was delicious to Zhu. He asked what the dish was called. "Soup of Pearls, Emeralds, and White Jade," for the leftovers were a mixture of all colors.

130

"When he ascended the throne and had had too many delicacies from the sky, land and sea, he remembered that tasty meal. He issued a decree which was posted all over the country, to look for those who could prepare 'Soup of Pearls, Emeralds and White Jade.' Local magistrates were deadly concerned; nobody had ever heard of such a dish.

"As the deadline approached, the award went up tenfold. The two illiterate beggars heard people reading the notice on the city gate and tore it down. By custom, the city guards escorted them to the magistrate's office, who, seeing their tattered soiled clothes, wondered if he was in serious trouble or good luck. He had no choice but send them to the capital. The emperor ordered the palace kitchen to give full assistance. When the food was ready, the emperor summoned all his court officials and their consorts, princes and princesses for a banquet.

"The soup was terribly sour and smelly. The emperor understood the proverb, 'When one is starved, even grain husks taste as sweet as honey; when one is full, honey tastes flat.' He pretended to enjoy the soup so that others were obliged to finish their servings too. He kept saying, 'How delicious it is!' He looked sideways to see if anyone was expressing resentment. He wanted to know if all his subjects were willing to share his past hardships."

"That's what our Party leaders want us to do," Hu Bon said joyfully. "Granny, you're very politically conscious. We should invite you to our office to give a report on the bitter past. That will give us young people a profound education."

"You aren't making a fool of me, are you?" Granny Yin laughed. "If you make another joke on me, I swear I won't go to your wedding."

Hu Bon came up to her and took her bony arm in his strong stubby one with great affection. "How dare I make jokes on you, my dear Granny?"

Dian Wen had friends not only among the Revolutionary Rebels, but also among members of the antagonistic Red Alliance. The activists from both factions argued and fought over such matters as who should be put into the category of class enemy, which official should be denounced as a Capitalist Roader, and tried every way to win over each other's members. In daily life, however, many of them kept up casual friendships. Several leaders from the Red Alliance came to the wedding and were warmly greeted by Hu Bon and Dian Wen. They were ushered into my tiny room where the double bed had been removed and two tables set, on which were plates of candies and packs of cigarettes. Relatives of the two families were being received in the larger room of the Yus, where similar treats were laid out on borrowed tables.

Big Brother had set up an open kitchen area near the water tap under the locust tree. On each of the two stoves a wok was bubbling with peanut oil, in which meatballs and spareribs were being deep-fried. Most everything there was rationed, but Big Brother had contacts. His two workmates were helping him. The whole courtyard was filled with the aromas of the feast.

Huang Ching from the Red Alliance headquarters and two younger members arrived in an office sports car. He used it most of the time for his own business or for factional fighting. He was a well-known "flying driver" and on good terms with all the traffic cops in the west end. He had only ever had one accident: he bumped his brand new car into the concrete wall of a bridge on his way to fetch his wife home from her suburban factory. The office paid 2000 yuan for the repair.

"That's the greatest disgrace of my life," he would say, not meaning that he was discovered using an official car for private purposes; rather that the incident damaged his reputation as a skilled driver.

Huang Ching walked down the steps at the entrance, holding his head high. He had been discharged from the army one year earlier than I had, but he always wore a well-pressed uniform. For this occasion, he had a brand new one, complete with cap and a pair of officer's leather shoes.

"We sincerely and warmly welcome our Brother Huang Ching to Dian Wen's wedding," Hu Bon greeted him with a broad smile. "It's a great honor to have you here. I was wondering why the sky suddenly turned brighter and here you are, our distinguished guest. Now come in."

Solemnly Huang Ching shook hands first with Hu Bon and then with Dian Wen. "Come," he turned and commanded his two companions, who handed him the packages. "Here are our humble gifts. I feel embarrassed bringing so little. But as the old saying goes, 'Light though the gift, the good will is profound.'"

Ceremoniously he presented a wash basin and a set of tea things to Dian Wen, who accepted them with equal solemnity. One of Huang Ching's companions handed Hu Bon a plaster bust of Chairman Mao and two of his poems framed on silk.

"We are indeed flattered to have you here," Hu Bon said unctuously. "Come on in and allow us to serve you tea."

They all crowded into my room.

Huang Ching demanded loudly, "What kind of liquor do you have for me?"

"We have prepared the best for you, Brother Huang," Dian Wen replied. "We have Maotai liquor and Tsingtao beer. Today you must have your fill."

"On such a happy occasion, I surely will," he said in his most cultivated voice. "No one here is going to quit until drunk!"

"Well said, Brother Huang," Hu Bon replied, handing him a pack of Zhonghua cigarettes. "But you have to be a little more patient for your drink."

Huang Ching lifted his hand in refusal and turning to Dian Wen said, "Fetch your bride to light my cigarette."

"She's coming," Dian Wen smiled broadly at his factional rival. To a certain degree these two men were much alike—both hated to think out complex matters; both loved making life light and carefree; and both lacked "brains."

Erfeng came, showing no shyness with these people. She knew quite well what sort of friends her groom had, and she liked them. She liked almost everyone, if the word "like" was not interpreted too strictly. For the wedding she wore a light blue blouse of silk with a subtly embroidered pattern, a pair of gray trousers of light wool, and her hair cut one inch above the shoulder and lightly curled along the edge. Within the limits set by the Cultural Revolution, she looked fresh and attractive. As the old saying goes, "A horse needs a good saddle to look good; a person needs good clothes."

She walked over to Huang Ching and lit his cigarette. He had planned to make fun of the bride, whom he had heard was shy and quiet. He inhaled deeply, feeling disappointed. He had her unwrap a piece of candy and put it in his mouth. She did this with restrained dignity.

Dian Wen brought in two dishes. On one of them were slices of sausage, beef, pork, thousand-year-old and brine-preserved eggs, beautifully arranged. The other contained slices of tangy cucumber aspic garnished with a piquant sesame butter sauce, a favorite dish to go with strong drinks. Lu Fen followed with several bottles of Tsingtao beer and the Maotai.

"I'm sorry I can't stay here with you guys," Dian Wen said, when he had filled each glass with beer. "Please enjoy yourselves heartily."

"Don't bother with us," Huang Ching said broadly, even waving his hand like Dian Wen. "We haven't learned to be polite when there is good food and drink."

We started drinking. Hu Bon kept filling Huang Ching's glass and urged, "You are a great drinker and we all know that. Finish this beer and then you'll change to Maotai. Half of this bottle is yours."

Huang Ching gulped down the beer and standing up said loudly, "Fill you glasses with Maotai and I'll make a toast."

Everyone poured a little of the fiery spirit and looked up at him. "I would like to borrow this glass of Dian Wen's," he pronounced, his facial expression extremely serious, "to propose a toast to friendship. We have fought each other for almost two years. Of course, we all fight for the cause of the Proletarian Cultural Revolution. Am I right?"

All chorused, "Right!"

"So no matter how different our views on some issues are, we should respect each other and be honest. Am I right?"

We echoed cheerfully.

"This Bureau of ours is a small temple where many evil spirits dwell and a small pond where many turtles hide. Our common enemy therefore should be those bastards who have lived a good life since the Japanese occupation by virtue of tricks they play with their pens. Let's unite and fight against them!" He sounded as if he were shouting a slogan at a criticism meeting.

"You're right one hundred percent," Hu Bon responded warmly. It was hard to tell if he was joking or not.

"But Huang Ching," Lu Fen asked over the table, "why do you refuse to let us investigate Cheng Fan? He worked at a radio station of the Kuomintang in the forties. Didn't you know?"

"He's different, Lu Fen," his tone definitely not inviting antagonism. "He worked there only for two years and soon joined the revolutionary ranks. Why should we investigate him?"

"As far as we know, he did not join the revolution by his own will. When the Kuomintang withdrew from Chongqing, he missed the plane and was stranded. It happened that he knew a Communist who persuaded him to work for the new radio station for awhile, and now he boasts that he worked for the revolution for many years."

Hu Bon looked at Lu Fen to stop him from saying more and said, "Here we are celebrating a wedding and we are not to discuss political matters. I agree with Huang Ching that we should attach more importance to friendship among us and fight our common enemies. Let's drink to the health of Huang Ching."

We toasted and Huang Ching forgot the argument he was about to present. Happily, he was drunk and Hu Bon's group escorted him to the office dormitory where both factions had their headquarters. Driver Wong would take Huang Ching's car to the office next day.

22 · The Yus' House Is Rebuilt

In early summer, every government organization from the central down to the county level was looking for sites to establish May Seventh Cadres Schools, a kind of farm in the distant countryside. The name was derived from a call Chairman Mao issued on May 7, 1966 to urge all those working in offices to learn some manual skills. The aim was to purify white collar workers and students from the cities of their cravings for bourgeois comforts.

The two factions in the Bureau sent a joint team on a survey tour that found a swampy area in Jiangxi Province, a thousand miles from Beijing. The first batch of one hundred and fifty set off in June as a preparatory team to supervise local workers in construction of living quarters and to purchase furnishings and farm tools. These were healthy young revolutionary zealots, mostly from the Revolutionary Rebels faction.

In early August the second batch, three hundred staff members and their dependents, politically mixed, left not so willingly. Except for a dozen reliable leaders, in this group there were those who had political flaws in their past or were born into erstwhile wealthy families whose land, factories and shops had been confiscated by the new regime. The central authorities broadcast that it was of strategic importance to evacuate some city people to the countryside in consideration of the impending war.

The Soviet Union and China had had several military skirmishes along the northeastern border. Defense minister Lin Biao was calling on the nation to heighten vigilance and prepare for war. Beijing residents had been told to dig air raid shelters. Streets, playgrounds and courtyards were piled with dug-out earth. Beijing was drier than usual and the wind blew up dust that penetrated everything. Mrs. Yu mobilized us to dig a shelter in the courtyard. We removed the clothesline pole in the northwest corner, dug a hole six feet in diameter and six feet deep. The walls of compacted ash and cinder kept caving in. We dared not go on, so filled the hole up, which left a mound for the children to play on.

The evacuation involved hundreds of thousands of Beijing residents. They hastily sold what they dared to sell: furniture. They had either thrown their valuables into the sewage or buried them in secret places. Secondhand stores were busy buying hardwood wardrobes, tables, bureaus, chairs and beds with fantastic carvings, some even from the glorious days of the Qing Dynasty.

One Sunday morning, Dian Wen brought back an old sofa. "I got this for fifty fen," he told us. "You should go there and buy something. They are selling at throwaway prices." He advised me to buy a sofa too. Nobody in our courtyard had a sofa yet. Only the Tongs had even a stuffed chair. "A wardrobe sells for only fifteen yuan, and a brand new desk for ten."

"Well," I said, "If a war starts as the central government has said, why should I spend fifty fen on a sofa? I would rather buy half a pound of pork and eat it. I remember a story about Afanti, the legendary joker of the Uygurs. He had a fat ram. Several rich men wanted to make a fool of him, so they came to his house and said, 'The sky will fall tomorrow. We'll all die. What's the use of keeping that fat ram of yours? Let's kill it and make a good meal so we can enjoy ourselves before we die.' Afanti thought a little while and said, 'All right. I'll kill it.'

"The day was hot. The rich men went to swim in a nearby river, laughing over their easy success. When they thought it was time for their meal, they climbed up the river bank, only to be shocked that all their silk clothes were gone. 'Someone has stolen our clothes,' the rich men said. 'Oh, I took your clothes and burned them to cook the sheep. Since we'll all die tomorrow, what's the use of leaving the clothes behind?'

"You see," I concluded, "The rich men lied to Afanti. But our government has made it clear, a war between China and the Soviet Union is inevitable. They are fighting along the border; we in Beijing are digging air raid shelters. I am not going to add any burden on myself. When the war starts, I won't have to worry about my furniture, since I have none. Everything in my room belongs to the Bureau. Anyway, there's no space in my room for a sofa."

Driver Wong was untying the sofa from the rack of Dian Wen's bicycle. He said, "We should buy something, Longsen, especially old sofas, stuffed chairs or mattresses. Old Hong, a driver from the Geology Institute, bought a sofa the other day. When his wife was patching the holes, she found a pile of five yuan bills stuffed in the spring coils. Five hundred yuan! Hong only spent a yuan and a half for it! You see, rich people hide their money in the upholstery. Now if you spend ten yuan to buy five sofas, I bet you will find at least a hundred yuan in one of them.

We helped Dian Wen take the sofa down and turned it over. Driver Wong probed the seams and looked carefully at the springs underneath.

"You can have half of the money if we find any," Dian Wen told Driver Wong. "I bought the sofa for my mother. The straight-back wooden chairs are hard for her. Now she can sit comfortably."

He turned to me and said, "Many families have gone to the May Seventh Cadres School. Several rooms on Weigong Street have been vacated. Do you want to move? I know someone in the Housing Office. If you want one, I can talk to him. I would like to move, but my mother can't walk stairs. The courtyard is much more convenient. And the neighbors can keep an eye on her during the day."

I did not think I could either. We were going to have a baby and needed Mother's help. Weigong street was far out in the western suburbs.

Driver Wong and Mr. Chang didn't want to move. Their wives worked in the eastern part of the city.

Let's wait a couple of years more, then we can move together, Dian Wen suggested.

"Talking about houses, did you hear they're going to rebuild the Yus'?" Driver Wong said, having lost interest in the sofa.

"Aren't they going to rebuild the south row and the east?" I asked. Shalin and I had hoped the south row would be rebuilt so our floor would be higher, the window larger and ceiling higher. We could get more space and air.

Driver Wong replied, "The Housing Office plans to rebuild the south and east rows next year."

"Next year, humph," I said. "Next year? Who believes them? Everything they plan is only a cake drawn on paper to fool children." I lost interest in the sofa too.

After supper, Shalin and I went over to the Yins' to tell them the bad news. Mrs. Tong came over too. She seldom visited other families. We knew she was a gregarious woman, but Mr. Tong was too much the patriarch. All of us stood up and Mrs. Yin ushered her to the double bed. The amenities soon turned to feverish complaints on the common theme. "Our houses are in much worse condition than the Yus'," Mrs. Tong said in muffled anger. "But they only rebuild theirs. Look at the east wing. See that? The corner will fall any moment. And we have that cursed lavatory next door, only separated by a thin layer of brick. The flush tank leaks and water seeps through the wall. We dare not put anything against it. Also people often walk on the roof to pick jujubes. The roof leaked badly this summer. It may cave in any time, I'm sure. I have a constant fear that one night one of us will be killed."

Mrs. Tong sighed sadly, looking pitifully at Granny Yin and then at Mrs. Yin, who sighed to extend her sympathy.

"Your house really needs major repair even if they don't rebuild it," Mrs. Yin said. "Why doesn't Mr. Tong go to the Bureau to complain?"

Mrs. Tong said wearily, "You know what a good-for-nothing man I have." She tried to raise her voice but failed. "He can be tough only at home, shouting at me and cursing the children. When it comes to matters of this kind, he is totally hopeless. Every time I ask him to report the danger to his office he says, 'The house won't collapse and you won't die in it.' I went to the Housing Office myself after that heavy rain. They told me, 'We know and will take care of it. You go home and wait.' Then what? They haven't done anything!"

Granny Yin and her daughter-in-law gave their neighbor a lot of sympathetic comfort and Mrs. Tong left feeling better for "talking it out."

"It's indeed unfair that the Housing Office is only to rebuild the west wing," Mrs. Yin said to Shalin.

Mr. Yin commented coolly, "Of course it's unfair. The east wing should have been rebuilt long ago. Unfortunately, Mr. Tong has no official connections. So he should not complain. I'm content living in this little, run-down room because I know my place. If I were a big official, I would have you live in a mansion."

"Don't talk nonsense!" his wife snapped.

"All right," Mr. Yin said and sipped his tea. "I tell you, it is only common sense that officials have a better place to live. There are too many people in China and there's too little to share. Of course, those who have power get theirs first, and their share is, of course, bigger."

"Watch your tongue!" Mrs. Yin admonished.

Her husband chuckled. "Well, I'm a plumber, one of the working class. The working class is the leading class. Three generations of my family have been proletarians. The *Internationale* says *I have nothing to lose but my chains*. I'm Red inside out, even to the color purple. Ha, ha, ha . . ."

"You'd better not talk this way in front of the children," Mrs. Yin said. We understood her worries. The two girls were too young to know what they should not pass around.

"All right. I'll shut my mouth. Let me have another drink."

Granny Yin gave her son a disapproving glare, but said nothing.

We chatted on about other things. Driver Wong must have finished his meal and was calling from his corner, "Mr. Yin, how about a game of chess in my room?"

To this Mr. Yin cheerfully agreed.

"Go and take out the garbage first," Mrs. Yin ordered, and, turning to Shalin and me said, "He doesn't move a finger after he comes home. He behaves like an army general returning from a great victory. He drinks and plays. When no one plays with him, he buries himself in novels. If the garbage box were not so heavy and the collection point not so far, I would do it myself. I hate to waste my words on him."

We smiled, knowing she wouldn't. It would be left to Granny Yin.

The Yus' house was finished at the same time as the High Wall mansion—in nine months, making a record in production during the Cultural Revolution.

The stadium northwest of Tanyin Alley had been used as a place for criticism meetings against various class enemies since that program began. After the Red Guards turned to fighting against each other, the stadium was deserted. In the afternoon, children would climb over the wall to play soccer on the unkept court, which had become riddled with potholes. Tall grass was rampant in the corners and along the track. We had almost forgotten the stadium's glorious days when the spare time sports school cultivated soccer players and gymnasts out of wild boys and girls from nearby neighborhoods. Several had gone on to the city and national teams.

Early in May, soldiers came and pitched tents in the stadium and the adjacent bus depot. Heavy trucks, excavators and an assortment of machines arrived. Bulldozers pushed all the structures down, great power shovels loaded the debris and earth onto huge dump trucks and deep pits were dug. Work proceeded at a fantastic speed here while all production in the factories was sluggishly slow; many were producing nothing at all.

Before they built anything, the soldiers erected a wall around the whole area. Of solid brick, it was five feet thick. Above the height of ten feet, it was hollow in the middle. Holes were left near the top, which spectators concluded were peepholes from which sentries within could shoot at any saboteurs.

Residents of Beijing's old neighborhoods thrived on gossip. Living compactly in courtyards made a certain intimacy easy. It was inevitable that rumors arose about the mysterious construction site. Some said the place would be an army command post, a Chinese Pentagon. Some said it would be a nuclear weapons research institute. Still others believed a missile base. "That's why they dug deep pits. They are silos," Aunt Kang said with an air of authority.

"Would they build a missile base in the city?" Mrs. Yin was skeptical.

"Why not?" Driver Wong said. "Our run-down houses are the best camouflage. Even if the Russians know it, they may not want to throw bombs on us small potatoes."

The area was heavily guarded. Armed guards at three entrances checked and registered everyone passing in or out. In six months the place had changed beyond recognition. Construction debris had been cleared. Scaffolding for the walls was removed. Civilian workers joined the soldiers in constructing buildings inside. Local residents could catch glimpses of the gorgeous single story houses that were rising swiftly. Soon we saw the ground in the compound being leveled, flowerbeds built and paths paved. Trucks were bringing in expensive furniture and decorative articles instead of lumber and cement. Outside, a wide road was being built toward the west. It would be linked to the road above the subway when that project was complete.

Work began along the south wall of the fortress. This job was as meticulous as any. Workers dug up the garbage layer, more than three feet thick, and filled the ditch with lime, sand and topsoil. We were amused to find several live frogs at that depth. The place had been dry since the stadium was built ten years earlier. How had the frogs survived? Then tiles were laid and bushes and poplar trees planted. The ambience was imperial next to the pitiful low houses and narrow alleys that were built of broken bricks.

Across the road to the south of the mansion was the four-story Guanyan Middle School. One day a work team came to put steel frames on each window facing the high wall and covered the frames with steel sheets. The principal announced that students could have the lights on during the day. Since it was the only multi-story building in our area, and now its windows were sealed, no one could watch what was going on inside the wall.

The neighbors no longer thought it was a missile storage site, or any military establishment. It was too nice looking for the war effort. The expensive furniture trucked in created a new assumption: it must be for some big shot to live in. Many started investigating.

Driver Wong refused to reveal his source of information. "That place is built for Jiang Qing, Chairman Mao's wife," he told us. "Don't tell anyone that I said so—it's top secret. She's very smart to have chosen this place to live. Who would guess she lives in such an out-of-the-way slum? The houses are all gray, matching ours, and are hidden in trees. The wall is gray too. It's so well camouflaged, there's no way to spot the place from the air.

"You know, anyone up to mischief will be a sore thumb there. I even suspect that above the wall there is an invisible screen of high-voltage, so even flies and mosquitoes can't get inside. I heard an underground tunnel will link the compound with the subway, so when the war starts, Jiang Qing can get her ass out of Beijing into the mountains."

"But it's despotic to seal off the school's windows," Mr. Yin grumbled. No one commented, pretending not to hear.

So Driver Wong's information prevailed over rumors. Gossip shifted to other subjects. The open, clean space in front of the south wall, however, became a blessing for the several thousand dwellers of our overcrowded alleys. Grandparents, parents, big brothers and sisters brought their young charges to play on the mounds of sand left over from the construction. Sentries with raised bayonets gradually became accustomed to children running around under the wall and young lovers stealing kisses in the shadow of the trees. Young people's passion had to find a way to be vented. There was no privacy in their crowded homes and they felt safe under the high wall with armed guards around.

The mansion was soon to be known to us all as the High Wall.

The new structure would cause a nuisance for my mother to come to my home when the baby was born. My parents' home was on the northwestern corner of the High Wall and we were diagonally opposite. With the short-cut between the stadium and the bus depot blocked, Mother would have to take a long detour. Instead of ten minutes, it now took twenty-five.

23 · Shalin Gives Birth to a Son

The leaves on the jujubes quivered in the autumn breeze and one by one detached themselves to float down from the branches. A stronger gust would lift the amber-tinged leaves up a little from the ground and push them toward the southeast corner. There they would whirl around and pile up when the wind abated. Mrs. Yu found an easier way to dispose of the abundance of leaves. She would sweep up the toilet paper bits from inside the stalls, shovel the leaves onto the paper pile and light the paper. In five or ten minutes, they would be reduced to ash which didn't take much space in the garbage box. The toilet paper—mostly squares of newspaper and sheets of used notebooks—would catch fire easily. But they gave off a foul smell which assaulted my breakfast.

Toward the end of October, Shalin and I reshuffled the furniture in our room and took the opportunity to clean up. We swept the floor beneath the bed. Mice had opened several holes which we stuffed with Granny Yin's formula. We scraped off the old newspaper over the cracks in the door and window frames and pasted in a new layer. We replaced the thin window paper with more durable Korean paper. The table was moved into a corner to make space near the door for the stove. The Yins and Dians did some rearrangement too, in preparation for the coming of winter.

In the summer I had planted several sunflowers in front of our room, and saved the sturdy stalks. I built a shelter around the door with them and empty cement sacks, so that the north-westerly wind wouldn't blow into the room so directly. Mr. Yin praised me for my genius but did not build one for his door. "He's lazy," Mrs. Yin said.

Winter came to the south row at least a week earlier than to the rest of the courtyard. October turned to November and I moved the stove in and cooked with the door open. In mid-November we began to feel the bite of the winter winds. The window paper began to rattle and cracks to whistle during the night. After a day, everything in the room was covered with a thick layer of dust.

With Shalin advancing in her pregnancy, Mother said I should do all the cooking and washing. I borrowed a camp cot so Mother could take a nap during the day. The room was too small for an extra bed. I had to think of a way to make space for us to sleep after the baby came. The Yins had extended the bed by attaching a wooden board to it. I got a plank and hinged it to the edge of our bed, so that it could fold down during the day. We would sleep crosswise with the baby in between.

Mother told the neighbors she wouldn't mind whether the baby was a boy or a girl. "I have four sons. Any one of them can give me a grandson," she said to Granny Yin. I knew she craved a boy; my father was the first born and so was I. "A granddaughter will make my family livelier," she said. Mother was very considerate about the feelings of others. The Yins had only daughters.

I hated to stay home during the day as much as Shalin. If the wind was not too strong, we would ride slowly to the west of the High Wall where there were blocks of neat four- and five-story apartment buildings. The sun was bright and warm on the glass windows. It must be marvelous inside. We longed to enter one room to feel the comfort for a moment, and talked about what we would do with an apartment once we had one.

When Shalin became too big to go out, we would sit in the sunshine under the windows of the north row. A job I strangely enjoyed doing on Sunday mornings was scraping off the alkaline lumps growing on the floor of our room. In winter, they sprouted like nail heads on the cement tiles. I would spend an hour scratching with a knife, then spread hot coal ashes to suck out the moisture underneath. We never dared spray water on the floor, since it was damp year-round.

At night, the cotton quilt was stone cold. To get into bed was an ordeal. I had to grit my teeth to slip in. The coal stove did not give off much heat. The cold stimulated my bladder, so I would wake up around 4:45 every morning and linger, feeling the goosebumps. A little after five, I would hear the creaking of the Yins' door. I felt sorry for Mr. Yin having to go to work so early in such cold weather. A hard life it was for him. Office workers didn't have to get up so early. We could go to the office later than the expected eight o'clock even without an excuse.

As the soft creaking and whirring of his bicycle retreated toward the gate, I would shoot out of bed, throw a jacket over my shoulders, jump over to the stove and open the air inlet to start the room warming, relieve myself in the chamber pot, and climb under the quilt, shivering, teeth chattering.

Courtyard socializing was greatly reduced. Each family kept its door tightly closed to preserve any heat the small stove could produce. The after-supper chat was conducted only between the closest neighbors, often between the two families next to each other. Only Dian Wen made his courtyard-wide tour every evening. The card club had gone into half-hibernation. Occasionally a game would go on in the Yus' new house on Saturday evenings, or in Driver Wong's room when his wife stayed at her parents' home. I seldom joined them now that Shalin was in a clumsy state. She wanted to keep me at her side all the time.

On March 20, 1969, Shalin gave birth to a boy. Mother held the baby in her arms in the taxi I ordered, the first taxi anyone in my family had ever sat in. I gave the driver a bag of candies as a token of celebration. Our neighbors congratulated the new grandma who tried her best to conceal her pride.

It was still cold. I had to do laundry in the open, since there was no space inside the room to place the tub and wash basins. The stove was too slow to supply hot water for rinsing, so I used cold water directly from the tap. In minutes, tiny cracks would appear on the back of my hands and ooze blood. Now I understood the saying, "Only when you have your own children can you appreciate the hardships your parents have gone through for you."

Baby showers had been outlawed by the Red Guards. My friends would not listen to that. Also I still felt embarrassed over the poor wedding dinner I had given when Shalin and I moved in eleven months earlier. I wanted to make up for that, to save face. On the day Sui was one month old, four friends from Hill days and Hu Bon and his group came to celebrate. We regarded ourselves as born revolutionaries. Whatever we did would surely not fall into the category of "spreading feudal ideas." Our military service had provided us with impeccable political immunity. We drank, ate and made jokes about the pitiful intellectuals in the office.

Mother began to think about a second child; we ought to have a girl. "Have another one while I am still strong enough to look after it for you," she said to us. "One child is not safe. I gave birth to seven but only four survived. One will be lonesome, too."

Shalin and I didn't argue the point, but knew we would not have another. Taking care of one was already exhausting us physically and financially, despite Mother's help. Washing diapers in icy water was killing me.

24 · Death Jumpers

Because of increasing antagonism among civilian Red Guard factions, the central authorities decided to put all of China under the surveillance of army officers. Hu Bon had convinced this newly arrived Military Control Group that it was of strategic importance to rout out all those involved in the murder of Li Sunro. "They are like a time bomb hidden in the revolutionary ranks," he told Fang Jun, a Red Army veteran in his late fifties, "and can cause a lot of damage to the proletarian dictatorship when the time suits them." Eight members of the Red Alliance were in detention under Hu Bon's Red Flag Detachment.

In May, by agreement, Hu Bon and his two close aides Lu Fen and Wang Pan were married on successive Sundays. I had been too busy washing diapers to care about their business. The gatherings at Dian Wen's home became bigger and noisier than ever. I loved to join them. It was fun; and I wanted to hear rumors and social gossip, of which Hu Bon's group had a great store. At that time, people had little faith in either official newspapers or the documents which passed down through the hierarchy frequently. We preferred to get our information from rumors, which were numerous.

Shalin did not like my spending time with them. I was very irritated when she called me out of the revelry and asked me to take our baby son out to the High Wall for sunshine. "He needs more calcium and the pills won't be absorbed without sunshine," she would say. I began to wonder if I had made a mistake in marrying Shalin. The wives of Hu Bon's group never interfered with them. Actually they joined them in merrymaking. I didn't want to offend Shalin and always complied with her wishes, though I felt frustrated.

One Sunday morning Driver Wong came to Dian Wen's room and announced, "Another jumped this morning!"

"Who?" we asked in unison, surprised but not shocked. Within a month three had jumped to their deaths from the Bureau office building.

"Chu San," he said, sitting down by the table and accepting the glass of beer Dian Wen offered him. "I went to the office early this morning. As I was getting off the bike I noticed someone standing inside a window on the fourth floor. His body was too high up to be standing on the floor, and the window was open. Then I saw his legs. He must have been standing on the sill. I recognized him as Chu San and realized what he was going to do. I shouted out his name and yelled, 'Don't!' He seemed to have heard me because he turned his head a little. Several people walking by stopped and shouted at him not to jump. Chu San looked up at the sky, touched his hair with his hand, took a deep breath, and jumped, the way a diver does in swallow style." Driver Wong imitated the movement for dramatic effect.

"I saw his body fall. The people screamed. The body struck the pavement twenty feet from the building. Thump! that's the end of it. Just like that! I ran over. Ugh! his head was cracked, blood was flowing from his nose and mouth. I called the security guard on duty, who telephoned the police, asking me to keep an eye on the site. The whitish brain had spilled onto the iron bars of the fence and the bikes left there overnight. The policeman arrived with the coroner. They turned the body this way and that and said, 'All right, take it to the crematorium.'"

"They have really simplified the procedures," Hu Bon said.

"I talked with the coroner," Driver Wong continued. "He told me he is kept busy examining dead bodies. The hospital asked him not to send them there."

"You should see how they deal with the dead these days at the crematorium," Driver Wong said, twisting the chopsticks to catch a piece of slippery cornstarch aspic. "They just kick the body out of the truck and drag it along by the legs. This time, when we got there—damn it, I have driven two bodies there this month. Chu San's blood had not coagulated and it flowed onto the path. There were at least six corpses dumped on the floor in front of the furnace."

I felt the piece of sausage in my mouth go rotten and went out to spit it into the garbage box. Inside again, I took a long swig of beer.

"I would like to give a piece of advice to you young fellows," Mr. Chang looked first at Hu Bon and then the others. "You are young and inexperienced in political campaigns. I've gone though all of them and I think I know more than you do. As a Party member for thirty years, I shouldn't say this to you. However, I don't want you guys to get in trouble out of sheer ignorance. You think you're doing the correct thing and have support from above. But sea can one day turn into land and land into sea. You have done your share for the Cultural Revolution. It's time you withdrew from it. I like the way Longsen thinks about life. He goes to meetings but keeps away from radical actions. He concentrates on improving his English. Now all of you have jobs. You should spend more time there instead of wasting time somewhere else. The big intellectuals in our Bureau are a smart lot. They keep quiet. They wait. No matter which direction the wind blows, they are there. Every regime has to rely on the professionals to do the job. Understand me?"

"Yes," Hu Bon answered for all. "Perfectly." There was no sarcasm in his tone this time. "You are right. I've been thinking a lot recently. Longsen has also told me to withdraw." He paused. "We need time for a transition. We cannot withdraw too fast. That would cause suspicion. Sometimes I feel I am riding a tiger—unable to get off, for fear of getting devoured. Yes, I do have to withdraw."

"Well, well," Driver Wong said, bored with the seriousness of the dialogue. "Big Beauty," he called out to Hu Bon's wife. "Every time I see you with Hu Bon, I feel terrible for you. You're too pretty and tall for him. You were made for me. Come over and sit on my lap."

Big Beauty tossed the remaining beer in Driver Wong's face and yelled at him, "You son-of-a-bitch. How dare you tease your mother like that!"

"I think they are a perfect pair," Lu Fen raised his chopsticks and pointed them from Hu Bon to Big Beauty. "When they are in bed, the middle of them is always at the same level."

The men laughed and Big Beauty glared at her husband. "Their mouths are for pissing," she said to the other women. "Let's go over to talk to Shalin."

The fifth jumper was found the morning of June thirteenth. I heard the commotion before we had put our bikes in the shed outside the office building. Shalin didn't allow me to see the scene. "It's no fun. Someone is dead. And many want to enjoy the excitement."

She went to the library on the first floor. I went up to the second, turned and hurried along the corridor and emerged through the back exit into the courtyard.

At the western end of the dormitory building, two dozen people were clustered, mostly young, and I recognized the majority as Revolutionary Rebels. The body was covered carelessly with a canvas sheet from the garage. A leather shoe lay on its side near the base of the wall. Hu Bon was there, talking to the policeman. Apparently the coroner had already left.

Lu Fen filled me in. "Shang Wo got up around five o'clock. Our two guards heard him walking to the washroom and back to his room. Then he walked out into the corridor again. It was too late when they ran out. He was on the ground, dead. They saw only a few spastic twitches of his legs."

The verdict was suicide.

Mr. Yin had known Shang Wo from the fifties. "His fault was that he was too ambitious and too smart," he said at the card table. "He should have known his place. In the old days he had been a reporter for a newspaper that had attacked the Communists as 'red bandits.' He should thank his luck to have escaped the disaster in fifty-seven. He was hospitalized for stomach ulcers at the time. After he recovered from the operation, he found out that several of his colleagues with similar political histories had been sent as Rightists to the wilderness in the northeast. He only lost one-third of his stomach so he thought he could play the same trick in the beginning of the Cultural Revolution. He had some good ideas he was itching to show the young people. He really didn't do much, just copying criticism posters here and there, inserting several sentences of his own."

"It was his bad luck that he stayed at the Red Alliance headquarters the night Li Sunro died," Driver Wong said. "I don't think he would have dared be involved in a killing. But he must have known something about the death. Otherwise why would he take his own life?"

Everyone contemplated the question for awhile. Mr. Yin went back to refill his tea mug and Mrs. Yu called out to her husband to take the boiling kettle off the stove. Mr. Chang and I responded at the same moment, "Why?"

"Nowadays one just can't know why things happen," Mr. Yin returned with his big enamel mug, blackened inside and out. "I wanted to laugh when my wife told me they had paraded their manager today. She was an illiterate housewife before she started working in fifty-eight. Now she makes thirty-seven yuan a month, two more than my wife. And so she has become a Capitalist Roader, forced to kneel on a wash board and confess she had been echoing the arch-Capitalist Roader Liu Shaoqi. Such humiliation could drive people to extremes. Ha! we must keep class conflict going, and there must be enemies to struggle against. Chairman Mao says, 'Take class struggle as the key link, everything will fall into line.' See, we struggle, and people die. There will be more deaths in the Bureau, I assure you. Let's stop talking deaths. Don't you want to play another round or two?"

25 · Dian Wen Is Detained

Hu Bon, Lu Fen and Wang Pan came to Dian Wen's home for dinner one night in August. It was to be their last together. Mr. Yin, Driver Wong and I were invited to join them.

"Kuai Dafu was arrested yesterday," Hu Bon said, his tone less carefree than usual.

"Ha!" Driver Wong said gleefully. "How pompous he was! It is said he had several mistresses and made love to them all at the same time. He rode in expensive cars with two bodyguards. Now he's in prison? How unpredictable one's fate is!"

Kuai Dafu, a student from Qinghua University, was one of three or four Red Guard leaders who had helped initiate the Cultural Revolution. He had backing from the very top. For this he had aroused bitter jealousy from rival Red Guard groups who made up rumors about him. Recently, when the central authorities sent a Military Control Group and workers into the University, Kuai Dafu would not let them in. He led students armed with rifles, spears and broad swords to hold the buildings on campus. Several soldiers and workers were injured by his Red Guards.

"They say he is a 5/16 element," Lu Fen said.

"What is this 5/16 stuff?" I asked.

"It's a Red Guard group set up in 1968 on May sixteenth," Hu Bon explained. "They were very radical from the beginning. They got wind that Chairman Mao and Premier Zhou had differences. So they attacked Zhou. But seeing that Zhou has many powerful men behind him, they had to go underground. It's hardly more than a year now, but I don't think there are many members active left. It's hardly worth a nationwide campaign. The real purpose," he turned the untouched beer and stared at the few remaining bubbles on top, "is perhaps a warning signal for all the Red Guards. Everyone who is in disfavor with the Military Control Group will be called a '5/16 element.'"

Hu Bon continued turning the glass. The bubbles had drifted to the edge, flattened and disappeared. Hu Bon had never been this despondent.

Chuckling, Mr. Yin said, "I believe the Red Guards have fulfilled their historical mission by now. They will step down from the arena of history—if they are smart enough to know it. Unfortunately many don't. Kuai Dafu is one. A month ago a *People's Daily* editorial already gave signals when it emphasized Chairman Mao's instruction: 'The majority of the cadres are good or comparatively good.' It means that it is wrong for the Red Guards to try to bring down all the veteran Party officials and older professionals."

He sipped his liquor and chewed a pickle. "Those officials who dared to challenge Chairman Mao's correctness have all been dismissed from office. If the Red Guards were allowed to continue attacking Party leaders, they would hurt those who follow the Chairman. So the slogan 'Rebellion is right' has become outdated. Of course, by common sense the Red Guards should be rewarded for what they have done for the Cultural Revolution. But too many of them have become too ambitious. Ambition is a dangerous thing. Now the central authorities have lost their patience with the beloved Red Guard boys and girls who refused to be disciplined. So they must go."

Hu Bon sat there twirling the untasted beer in his glass. Hu Bon said very little through dinner, but I knew he had comprehended the danger in store for him. Dian Wen, Lu Fen and Wang Pan were too simple-minded to see it yet. They drank and ate as heartily as ever.

Outside the gate after dinner Hu Bon said to me, "Longsen, I should have listened to you and withdrawn a couple of months earlier. I've heard that the central authorities are planning a new campaign. What it is about I haven't the slightest idea. But, definitely, it won't be in our favor."

I raised my eyes and looked at him in surprise. He looked suddenly so dejected. "Yes, we should all have taken seriously your advice to concentrate on advancing in our professions. I'm afraid the usefulness of the Red Guards has run out. Fortunately," he laughed, "all our wives are pregnant. They haven't failed us. We don't have to worry about not having successors."

In October, without any forewarning, the Military Control Group changed leadership. Chan Kui replaced Cheng Shi. The army officers confined themselves in meetings for a week. Soon word leaked out that Cheng Shi made a self-criticism for having been manipulated and for failing to support the genuine Leftists in the Bureau.

We were followers of Confucius. He taught us to be obedient to the father, the superior and the emperor. Since those who had attended school had learned more about his great teachings, they were more obedient.

Another Chinese virtue was patience. Chinese intellectuals had learned how to survive, and had survived many storms. They had survived the initial shock of the Cultural Revolution, the campaign against the Four Olds, the campaign of Purifying Class Ranks, the arbitrary manipulation of the Military Control Group, and now they were prepared to deal with the campaign of ferreting out 5/16 elements. This new one was much easier for them, for the target was their former tormentors—the young zealots of the Cultural Revolution.

But they were experienced. They showed no sign of jubilation. When the workers from the Bureau printing house proudly marched into the office building to help the army officers in the new campaign, the older intellectuals remained quiet. The printers walked back and forth in the corridors, looking into each office for welcoming faces, seeing themselves as saviors. The white collar workers, too busy catching up with their work—or reading books—only gave polite but not inviting smiles to the newcomers. They regarded these workers, as they had us demobilized soldiers and the army officers, as another batch of intruders on their domain. Soon the printing house workers could only feel at ease at the end of the day when they became the real rulers of the Bureau. They stayed late, pored over dossiers and files of several dozen young people who were suspected by the Military Control Group as 5/16 elements.

In the last week of October, for three evenings Dian Wen was "asked" to stay in the office for a talk with Officer Bian Zhu. The third night he was not home by eleven o'clock. His new wife, Erfeng, wept in the Yins' room and they tried to comfort her. Mrs. Yin assured her that Dian Wen was a good person and was willing to help anyone and therefore would not be wrongly accused. "Good people will always be rewarded," she concluded with a proverb. Mr. Yin thought otherwise. "Good people never live long," he quoted another old saying. Granny Yin disagreed with that. "I'm sixty-five. It's long enough. Am I not a good person?"

"You're an exception," her son added hurriedly and immediately turned to Erfeng. "Dian Wen is a good person all right, but too simple-minded. He's happy to do anyone's bidding. I think they are trying to make a breakthrough with him. They are really after Hu Bon. So as soon as they get Hu Bon, your husband will be left alone. Don't worry, he'll get out all right."

The next morning when I got up to fire up the stove under the eaves for breakfast, Dian Wen was squatting at his door.

"When did you get back last night?" I showed my concern by asking.

"They want me to admit that I joined the 5/16 clique." He looked up at me. His face was haggard, eyes swollen. If I didn't know he was in real trouble, I would misinterpret his expression as one of his comedy routines.

"My advice is that if you joined, tell them straight. If you didn't, don't admit to it, no matter how much pressure they put on you. If you give a false . . ." I hesitated here. The word "confession," which I had so often used for others during the Cultural Revolution, suddenly sounded very provocative to me. "If you give a false admission, they will surely put more pressure on you to expose others."

"They won't let me go if I don't admit it," he murmured. "They told me as soon as I admit, they will let me off, no conditions attached."

"Do you believe them? They are baiting you." I was getting impatient with him. "They will drag you deeper and deeper until you implicate others. They will make you betray your friends!" I felt chilly in my thin clothes and wanted to go inside.

Dian Wen was to be held in detention. He told his mother that he had to go out of town on an official errand. The neighbors had great pity for Erfeng. A thin woman, five months pregnant, she had to help the old woman dress, undress, relieve herself and eat. Every morning she would be seen carrying a big wash basin, which seemed to be overpowering her with its size and weight, to the tap where she washed her mother-in-law's soiled sheets.

Mrs. Yin was not happy about her mother-in-law and husband helping Erfeng too often. Times were different. Dian Wen was a confirmed counterrevolutionary. If they still kept as intimate a relationship as before with the Dians, someone might report it to her or her husband's work unit. She had sympathy for the younger woman all right, but she had her family, especially her two lovely daughters, to think about. Her family was beginning to be better off. She wanted a peaceful life. Also she had a feeling about Erfeng she couldn't put her finger on. But she definitely didn't like it.

Dian Wen was detained formally. It seemed that Chan Kui and his army officers had just begun to round up the small fish. A dozen so far had been detained. Each night those singles living in the dormitory heard cursing and shouting and table-pounding as the printing house workers were in interrogation sessions. During the day, mostly in the afternoon and evening, group meetings were held to urge the detainees to confess their crimes. I sensed the danger to me because Chan Kui and Bian Zhu, the army officers in charge of my department, had become remote to me, and the three printers assigned to the department often gave me stares which conveyed a threat. My instinct kept warning me that I would eventually be dragged in.

Still Hu Bon's name had not been mentioned by the officers or printers. However, it became common knowledge he was considered one of the three or four principal ringleaders of the 5/16 clique in the Bureau. He had stopped coming to 6 Tanyin Alley and we did not talk to each other at the Bureau. When we met in the corridor we acknowledged each other by nodding. The hushed atmosphere was terrifying as well as mysterious.

One day Hu Bon came to my home. Shalin was out at the store. "I'll be here for only a minute," he said, apologetic for his untimely visit. "Dian Wen is not reliable and I suspect he has admitted he's a 5/16 element and might have told the Military Control Group what we said about the Cultural Revolution and the central leaders. I would not be worried if he tells the truth. But I'm sure they won't let him off so easy. They'll force him to make things up against us." He stressed the word "us" to include me. I said nothing.

"I know Dian Wen's character," he continued. "He'll say what he is told to say. We must be prepared for the worst."

He left in a hurry. The neighbors pretended not to see. I was glad he had left before Shalin came back. I didn't want to worry her more than necessary.

On Saturday afternoon I got home around four o'clock. Those who had small children could leave the office two hours earlier for the weekend. I had stopped at Mother's to fetch Sui. The autumn air was warm. The two jujubes stood in silence. They looked pathetic, a few leaves hanging limply on gaunt branches. The summer had been dry and the leaves had fallen early. Here and there, a single date clung tenaciously to a bare twig, brightly red in the setting sun. A long strip of shadow from the Great White Pagoda fell across them and the east wing roof.

Dian Wen came home, escorted by one of the printers. The neighbors had not yet come back from work or school. Erfeng must have been notified to meet her husband. Within a week Dian Wen had lost twenty pounds, looked ten years older, his face ashen. Erfeng came out, timidly, and said to the printer, "So you came. Would you come in and have a cup of tea?" He declined and said coolly, "Here is Dian Wen. He has cooperated with us very well. We have decided to deal with him leniently. From now on he will be treated as one of the revolutionary people. We hope you help him realize further the seriousness of his criminal activities during the past three years."

The printer left, declining once again her invitation for a cup of tea.

Erfeng looked at her husband, who stood with shoulders bent. He was no more the carefree, funny young guy. He twisted his mouth but said nothing. She motioned him to follow her into their room. Granny Dian was weeping in her bed. Although slow in wit, the old woman had realized what had gone wrong with her son. She had not believed it when others told her he was gone on official business. For the past two days she had not mentioned his name.

As Dian Wen crossed the threshold, the old woman struggled to raise herself from the bed. He hurried over and knelt beside her. He could only utter "Mother!" before tears choked him. He sobbed as his mother cried soundlessly. After a long three minutes he murmured, "I have committed no crimes. I'm not a couterrevolutionary. But they wouldn't let me come home until I said I was."

"I know, I know," his mother said. "You are a good boy. You've been a good boy always. How can they say you are bad?"

Erfeng fetched a basin of water for Dian Wen to wash his face, then went out to prepare supper under the eaves.

Dian Wen didn't come out into the courtyard Saturday evening. Around ten o'clock Granny Yin walked past our window to his room and talked in a low voice for half an hour. The next day Shalin and I took our son to my parents' house to avoid embarrassment. I would have as few contacts as possible with Dian Wen. I had a premonition that he had reported my warning to him, that even if he gave a false admission, they would drag him deeper in spite of their promises. In that case it was only a matter of time before Chan Kui would come for me. I was ready: to stick to the truth and never betray my friends.

26 · I Am Detained for Investigation

The following Wednesday evening, Chan Kui personally called a meeting. That meant something important was impending. Bian Zhu announced that Hu Bon, Lu Fen and Wang Pan were to be put under investigation. Hu Bon and Lu Fen tried to say something, but the printing house workers wouldn't let them, and pushed and dragged them out of the room. I lowered my head in embarrassment for my friends.

"They are proved 5/16 elements," Chan Kui spoke to the meeting, waving his right arm up and down for emphasis. I felt disgusted, every time I heard him talk. So pretentious! "Each of them has been confirmed by at least three other 5/16 elements through our patient work of persuasion. Among those who co-operated with us was Dian Wen. He has now returned to the ranks of revolutionary people. I hope he will further cooperate with us to expose the 5/16 counterrevolutionary clique. In this way he, and others too, will correct the damage they have done in the past. In this campaign we only punish the ringleaders. We'll do everything possible to save those who stumbled into the 5/16 cliques and pull them out of the mud hole."

Chan Kui cleared his throat in a stage manner and continued, "The Military Control Group will also start the investigation of the seven deaths over the past two years of those innocent people who were falsely accused of being responsible for Li Sunro's death. I hope all those who want to repent will come forward and tell us the facts. Our Party's policy, as everybody here knows, is 'lenient to those who confess their crimes and severe to those who refuse to confess.' Dian Wen is a good example to prove that we follow this policy."

I glanced toward Dian Wen who bent his head low in a corner of the meeting room. He must be ashamed now that it was actually him who had sent his friends to detention. I felt him shudder when those deaths were mentioned. Immediately I realized that the danger for him was not over yet. I had heard from those close to the Military Control Group that the officers believed all seven of the people who died during the investigation of Li Sunro's death had been murdered. Simple-minded as he was, Dian Wen must have realized that his total cooperation had not saved him. To the contrary, he had been taken in. Intimidation plus enticement had made him a coward. His friends and others were talking behind his back, calling him a betrayer of friendship.

"Some people," Chan Kui was talking in a sterner voice. I was startled. His right arm, his dark triangular face, looked menacing. "Some people sitting right here are pretending they have nothing to do with this great campaign. I'd like to give them a warning: You'd better be smart and come to us to confess as early as possible. We have the records of your crimes. We haven't come to you because we want to give you the chance to earn leniency. We have patience and time. But I want to give a piece of advice to one in particular: stop your conspiratorial activities. I tell you, Revolutionary Comrades, this one is very brave. He tells 5/16 elements not to confess. He's playing with fire. He wants to throw his eggshell head against a stone wall. He thinks he can stop the advance of history with his stick-like arms."

Chan Kui raised his thick arm higher, shook it a couple of times and said, "His arm is only half this thick," a tremor of humorless laughter swept the meeting room. Chan Kui was not very satisfied with this weak response; his dark face turned darker. "Those cold-blooded humorless stinking intellectuals!" I seemed to hear him cursing.

After the meeting, around eight o'clock, I found Shalin waiting at the gate of the office building. We walked our bicycles for awhile. Before I could tell her what had happened at the meeting, Dang Ming caught up with us and said, "Longsen, don't make hasty moves. Chan Kui did not mean you. Although I have been here only two months, I know you are a good person. The people in our department speak well of you. We all know you are different from Hu Bon and the other young men."

I smiled and thanked him for his kind words.

Shalin did not believe I was really in trouble, but was worried about my mood. Despite the late hour, she insisted we go over to the Yins for a chat. I understood she hoped Mr. Yin would be able to lessen my fear. "He never joined any Red Guard group," she told the Yins hopefully. "How can they frame him up as a 5/16 element?" She did not sound very confident.

"It's useless to worry too much," Mr. Yin said. He was not a man to say nice, useless words, and he understood me so well that he would not waste them on me, even if he knew how. "There might be trouble for Longsen, not only because he has been close to Hu Bon and this group—I knew all along they would get in trouble one day—but because he is too outspoken and disobedient. The power in China is absolute, which means those in authority cannot be disobeyed. Longsen is not the kind of person to follow orders easily. If he didn't get entangled with Hu Bon's case, it would be with someone else's. My advice is: before the time comes, which may not come at all, live as normally as possible, and at the same time be prepared. We all know Longsen has never beaten people nor confiscated property. The evidence against him might be only remarks he made against the Cultural Revolution and some central leaders. Even if he is detained for investigation, as long as he can stick to the facts he'll be all right. Don't be like Dian Wen and admit what they feed you."

To make the atmosphere lighter, Mr. Yin changed the subject by asking what the situation was with Dong Sen and his wife Guangfen. "We haven't heard them quarreling from their corner room for two weeks."

"Isn't that strange?" Mrs. Yin chimed in.

Indeed, the couple had been very quiet. Because I had been so absorbed in my own worries and their room was beyond Dian Wen's, I had not paid much attention.

Dong Sen was one of Hu Bon's Red Flag Detachment, but not very active. His name had not been mentioned among the 5/16 suspects. However, he was scared.

"Dong Sen is not a brave man," Mr. Yin said. "Well, who can be brave in such a time?" I said, and told the Yins that the Military Control Groups would not take him very seriously, although they might have listed him in the category of passive 5/16 elements.

"It's late," I said to Shalin. "Let's go to sleep. We have to live tonight and let tomorrow take care of itself."

"That's right," Mr. Yin stood up. "If it is luck, it won't turn into misfortune. But if it is misfortune, it won't be avoided."

I was getting more irritable and impatient, wishing it would come sooner so I could get rid of this anxiety. I could not bear the cold stares from the printing house workers and army officers. Dang Ming kept telling me the Military Control Group was not after me. His consolation only made me more irritated.

The time came a week after Hu Bon's detention. Chan Kui came to one of my department daily meetings and declared that I was the "chief-of-staff" of Hu Bon's counterrevolutionary gang. "He's elusive," he told my colleagues. "He has deceived many people. Yes, he never beat anyone up, nor searched a home. That shows he's smarter than many others. So he's more dangerous than those who did. He harbored a deep hatred of the Cultural Revolution. He provided evil ideas to Hu Bon's gang for their counterrevolutionary activities. In appearance he is neutral. But he's a hidden enemy and we should thoroughly expose him. Comrades, don't sympathize with him. He has deceived you with dirty tricks."

"You say I am a liar?" I shouted in a strained voice. "Chan Kui, you are a liar. You have been deceiving us in the Bureau since the first day you came. You are abusing the good name

165

of Zhou Enlai. You say you were sent by the Premier himself. But what have you done here? You've made over a hundred people counterrevolutionaries . . ."

I went on with my accusations. I only remember the darkening and reddening face and his yelling, "Take him away!"

I was escorted by two workers and three of my colleagues to one of the rooms in the back of the complex. Another investigation team was thus formed to see that I confess what the Military Control Group needed. As I walked down the stairs, I heard Chan Kui's voice booming in the corridor. I felt a certain satisfaction.

Although I had prepared for this day, the initial shock was great. I had anticipated humiliation which I could not define in specific forms, but I knew it would be painful. I did not know how I would react when the interrogators shouted or cursed at me. I might shout and curse back, as some others had done. That would make things worse for me, or even irredeemable.

However, I was left alone in the inner room of a two-bedroom apartment. Suddenly the heroism, which had been boosted by anger, evaporated. I was overwhelmed with shame and the hurt of being wronged. I began to sob.

The rooms were bare of any furniture except for a board bed and a desk in the inner room and four chairs and two beds in the outer. I was alone for two hours while the investigation team members talked in low voices in the next room. I suddenly had great sympathy for caged birds. Around ten o'clock, a worker carried my bed things and toilet articles to me. That night no one questioned me. I lay on the bed, fully dressed, looking at the ceiling, worried about Shalin who must be terrified, at the same time calculating how to deal with those bastard officers and workers. Around dawn I made up my mind; no confrontation with them, no admission of joining the 5/16 clique. I would give a confession of remarks I made or resentments I had against the Cultural Revolution and some of the central leaders. I was not going to implicate others—more for my own sake than for saving my friends. If they had only my confession against me, it would be easy for me to demand a re-examination when the situation changed. I had to pretend to be scared, regretful of what I had said, in order to win sympathy from my colleagues. I knew as long as I denied any organizational involvement and any beating of people, my case could only be proved to be an "ideological crime."

It was already ten o'clock in the morning and still no one had come to question me. Cha Gong from my department, and now a member of my investigation team, had brought a bowl of rice porridge, a piece of steamed bread and a huge slice of pickled turnip for my breakfast. The light rustling sound from the outer room indicated that only one guard was left. Outside the window, the early winter sun was warm and bright. I looked out, straining my eyes to distinguish the Great White Pagoda in the morning haze. Life is so funny. On October first, National Day, I had stood on the rostrum at Tiananmen Square to view the grand parade, a great honor for a Chinese citizen. In only two months, I had become a prisoner. I had not changed; the times had. Young political radicals like Hu Bon were no longer needed by the central authorities. So we had become their enemies.

I stood by the window, looking down at the courtyard four stories below. Flowers in a tiny garden were withering. Last year four people had jumped from this same building. I wondered what it would be like to throw myself out the window.

Not until three o'clock did Chan Kui come with the investigation team: two printing house workers and three from my department. Chan Kui did not look that fierce and affected when he talked to me.

"We know you are different from the others," he began. Since he was sitting in a chair, he did not wave his right arm as he always did at meetings. "What we want you to do is to clear yourself by writing down what you did from 1967 to 1969. Did you attend any demonstrations, meetings of any Red Guard group? We need your help to expose the enemies."

167

"I never attended public meetings or demonstrations," I said docilely, self-conscious for having so bravely yelled at this veteran officer only yesterday. "I only went with the office people on parades to celebrate Chairman Mao's new instructions."

"Well," Chan Kui sounded patient and understanding, "you just try to recall every detail. We won't do any harm to you. We know your mother is in the hospital and you want to see her badly. I'll let you go see her as soon as you can clear yourself. If you can do it in three days, we'll let you go in three days. At most a week should be enough for you."

A week without visiting my mother! She might die sooner than that!

I did not want to offer any leverage to Chan Kui and kept my face obediently blank. He shook hands with me when he left. I had had experience recently with his shaking hands with people in the Bureau; I did not trust him.

I thought hard, making a list of events I might have participated in. In a whole day I failed to come up with a list of any that could sound counterrevolutionary. I was in a panic, knowing that if I could not work out a decent self-accusation, they would not allow me to return home. I asked the guards to tell Chan Kui that I wanted to speak with him. He came promptly. I pleaded that I really had not attended any counterrevolutionary activities.

"Don't be in such haste to come to a conclusion," he said patronizingly. "You know the 5/16 clique was very tricky. They camouflaged their vicious schemes very cleverly. Sometimes innocent people might mistake them for revolutionary actions. Don't think that Hu Bon and his gang would trust you enough to tell you everything. You were used by them for your reputation as an outspoken man. They have been confirmed key elements of the 5/16 clique. Our great leader Chairman Mao and Vice-Chairman Lin Biao have ordered us to rout them all out. They are dangerous to the cause of the Party and the country. You must discard your concern for personal interest and help us eliminate them. You have been very close to them. You must have valuable information."

"I really didn't take any part in their actions." I stammered, ashamed of my weak voice and the pleading tone in it. Even before my detention, I did not believe Hu Bon and his group had done anything that could be categorized as counterrevolutionary. But after all, I was not with them all the time. How could I be sure they were not? They might have hidden something from me. Chan Kui might be right that I had been used as a smoke screen. If Hu Bon was really the 5/16 leader, I was in grave trouble. It would not be possible to deny I was a working member. No matter how clean I had been, I would not be able to explain; as a Chinese saying goes, "One who jumps into the muddy Yellow River cannot get out unsullied." Perhaps the best way for me for the time being was to go along with the Military Control Group.

That night I wrote out a confession. I stuck to my principles of not involving others. I confessed that I had slandered the military morning drills as destroying family life; that Lin Biao was a hypocrite; Jiang Qing had many lovers; and that I had doubted if those in power were really good because if they were not in power, they would not be called good.

The investigation team leader told me Chan Kui was pleased with my progress. He brought me a note from Shalin in which she said she and the boy were well, and urged me to cooperate with the investigation. That offered hope for a visit to my mother.

After three days, a message came from Chan Kui saying I had not confessed completely. I at once realized I had been cheated. Now I knew how Dian Wen had fallen into their trap. They had had no evidence against me at all before they put me in detention. It was I who had given the evidence to them against myself. With my written confession in their hands, they could put more pressure on me. Anger welled up. I was angry at myself. I had never yielded to coercion. I should have fought back and refused to write a confession.

I remembered the fights with older and stronger boys back in my village. One had ordered the kids to crawl on the frozen ground and let him ride them like a horse. He threatened that anyone who refused would be expelled from all the games in the village. I could not submit to such humiliation. I was seven, fragile and tiny.

And shortly after my family moved to Beijing, I had fought Erhu. That had established my position in the neighborhood.

At thirty now, I had to plead and beg mercy from such a low creature as Chan Kui. Even if they released me after one or two weeks as they promised, how was I going to live among my relatives and colleagues with any dignity. Deep into the night I stood by the window. It was dark beyond the Great White Pagoda. I could make out a large open area that had been the sports ground of a middle school. Now it was overgrown. I wished I could become a dragon. In legends they were capable of causing floods. And in the Bible, it says when God was fed up with greed and misconduct in the world, he started a deluge to drown all human beings and living things, except for one family. China was going to the dogs. I would like to see a flood clean up the dirty earth. I am not going to take my own life as many had done, I pledged. If I am to die, all must die with me.

After the fourth day, I did not add any new information to my confession. I kept a copy of what I had written. When asked for more confession I would alter the wording and hand it back. I also stopped mentioning my mother. It was the officer Bian Zhu who kept reminding me, "You must clear yourself as soon as possible. Remember your mother is still in the hospital looking forward to seeing you."

I had made up my mind to start a protracted war with them.

A month and a half later, I was released at a public meeting. I was not indicted as a 5/16 element, for no 5/16 suspects had mentioned my name in their confessions. I was cited as a model for making a clean breast of my counterrevolutionary activities and for my willingness to repent. Also at that meeting Hu Bon,

Lu Fen and Wang Pan were sent to prison. I returned home, agonizing over a guilty feeling that I had let my friends down. Shalin comforted me by assuring me that I had given no false information to incriminate them. The next day I reported to the office kitchen to sweep the dining room and make coal balls and chop kindling.

27 · Mother Dies

The Revolutionary Rebels became the pool from which Chan Kui ferreted out 5/16 elements. Most of those in 6 Tanyin Alley were inclined toward the unlucky faction. Dian Wen, Dong Sen, Driver Wong and I had been suspected targets. The neighbors were very careful about what they said aloud. In the evenings the courtyard was desolate. Everyone stayed inside except to go to the taps, the toilets or to cook just outside our doors. We greeted each other tersely. Even the children stopped making a lot of noise. When winter set in, each family stayed inside, close around the stove.

In 1970, Spring Festival fell on February 12. Mother insisted we take her home for the family reunion. Her liver cancer was terminal. Every day in the hospital people were dying. The groaning and screaming of agony which filled the corridor was too much even for healthy nerves. Since we knew there was no cure, why should we leave mother there to suffer? And according to my village tradition, we should take her home if she was going to die.

At home, we found her a doctor who practiced traditional Chinese medicine on the side. She was in less pain during the several days of celebration.

Two weeks after the holiday, she was dying. For the first time in her life, she asked for something: a set of burial clothes. I rode my bike all over the city. All elaborate funeral rites had been denounced as feudal and were abolished. Funeral parlors had been shut down. No store sold death clothes. Granny Yin gave me a silk jacket of her own.

"Take this to your mother," the kind woman said. "I won't need it anyway since we are going to be burned to ashes. Your mother still has her country folk ideas. You should let her die with an easy mind." We had not told Mother that she would be cremated, as required by the city government.

When I came back, I found Mother semi-conscious, breathing hard. I showed her the jacket and her eyes concentrated for a moment and flickered. I had a feeling that she was disappointed with the simple dress she was given to wear in the nether world.

Granny Yin came to my parents' house to help us. As Mother breathed her last Granny Yin commanded us urgently, "Change her clothes before the body becomes stiff!"

Shalin and my second brother's wife changed her clothes under Granny Yin's supervision. A neighbor called the crematorium for an ambulance. Since there would be no funeral, it was of no significance to keep the body at home for long—another thing Mother would resent in her other life. The crematorium sent an open truck over, on which there was another coffin and the family of the dead. The workers refused to do make-up for Mother, saying, "What's the use of that? She will be burned in an hour!"

"The times are different now," Granny Yin sighed deeply. "There is no respect for the living. And no respect for the dead either."

I gave a bottle of good liquor to each of the two undertakers as suggested by a neighbor, hoping that they would handle Mother more decently. That made them a little friendlier. "Take this woolen blanket back," one told me. "Why feed such an expensive thing to the fire?" I complied, tugging my father's sleeve as he started to protest. I had heard rumors that undertakers stripped valuables from the dead before they pushed the body into the furnace. If we did not listen to them our bribe would be wasted.

The morgue at the crematorium was clean and the several beds with dead bodies were draped with clean white covers. Mother was put on a trolley bed painted white like those in hospital wards. At the registration desk, a girl attendant asked me to return to the morgue to check the tag number which the undertakers had forgotten to write on the form. I was unable to find any attendant, nor the bed with Mother either. I entered an adjacent hall to find myself in the furnace room where the dead had been transferred onto crude steel beds ready for burning. White sheets were nowhere to be seen, the bodies in grotesque positions. A shoe on the foot of an old woman was missing, showing a waxy bound foot, toes crushed into the sole. A middle-aged woman's trousers had loosened to reveal her swollen abdomen a bluish color. Dumped on the wet cement floor was what once had belonged to a boy's body, apparently the victim of a traffic accident. Hurriedly I found Mother's body and memorized the tag number, adjusting her in a more respectful position. The attendant at the desk jotted down the number and told me tersely, "Come back for the ashes in three days."

I began to doubt if the ashes in the jar I bought would be those of Mother. I'd heard the furnace workers just shovelled them into a jar at random.

I didn't shed a single tear for Mother's death. I just could not bring any to my eyes. But I felt it unfilial for a son not to weep for his dead mother. I confined myself to our little room. Tears did not come there. I had wept when I was taken to that detention room two months earlier because I felt so deeply wronged. I had loved Mother, but there was only numbness in my heart, no tears. For a month and a half, locked in that room, I had thought about death, though fleetingly. Anger and a wish for revenge from deep within me had consumed my stock of tears.

Shalin and Sui were in the courtyard. Shalin was talking to the neighbors about Mother's death and the crematorium. She did not want to bother me at the moment, thinking I must be feeling bad.

It was getting dark. Shalin came in and asked if I would like to have noodles for supper. I offered to go buy them. I went to the store at the west end and waited in line. The passers-by on bicycles and on foot were hurrying home, carrying vegetables bought at roadside stands. A young man sped down the slope of the narrow street, ringing his bell loudly. A man in his late forties was crossing the street. The young man braked abruptly beside him, and the older man jumped aside, spilling his soy sauce. The sticky, brown liquid dripped down his jacket.

"Are you being chased by ghosts?" the man shouted angrily. "You must be going to your mother's wedding!"

The young man, balancing himself elegantly with one foot on the ground, smiled and said, "No, sir. I'm going to meet your daughter who is waiting in bed for me. She must be getting impatient with my delay."

The older man's face went red. In a flash he raised his right hand. The next thing the on-lookers saw was the deep brown soy sauce blooming on the young man's face. He threw his bicycle down and roared, "Fuck your mother, son-of-a-bitch!" He punched fiercely and blood appeared on the corners of the older man's mouth. Dropping his basket filled with vegetables, the older man grasped the other's collar. "Let's go to the police!"

"Let me go. Otherwise you'll be sorry."

In the struggle, the two men stumbled, falling on the ground and rolling in the dirt and litter. The street by now was solidly blocked. Children were shouting and cheering, encouraging the two to fight harder. The noodle line did not break, but the sales clerk stopped weighing. "The movies and operas are too dull," he said gleefully. "Fortunately we have street fights to watch. They are real and more fun, you know."

No one intervened. The two men, tired of fighting or perhaps realizing that spectators were watching them as they would a comedy show, stood up. Glaring at each other ferociously, they spat the filthiest phrases I had heard since my childhood in the ghetto by the old city wall: "residue of urine" or "borne by an unmarried woman." I admired the genius of those residents of Beijing's side streets who created such colorful vocabulary. As the population was better educated, slum swearing had almost died out, until the Cultural Revolution. The Red Guards revived the worst curses to denounce "bad elements." The plague spread quickly; as the saying goes, "It takes years to cultivate good manners; but bad habits are learned in a moment."

The children were not satisfied with the fighting. Several were still shouting, "Come on, beat the son-of-a-bitch!" No one knew which side they were supporting. "Do you only know how to shout, you cowards?"

The noodle clerk was still watching. An old man in his seventies pushed his way through the crowd and said to the two fighters, "You two, you're making fools of yourselves. Shame on you. Beat it!" His tone possessed such authority and his bulky chest indicated a history as a dominating figure in gang or underworld activities, that the two men gave each other a threatening final glare, and said the traditional good-bye of street roughnecks, "Don't let me meet you again."

"These days people are very short-tempered," the woman next to me said. "It is as if everybody has eaten gun powder. They explode at the slightest provocation." Turning to the clerk she said, "Comrade, would you please give me a pound of noodles? My husband and I have to go to a meeting after supper."

He looked at her annoyed, but softened to a smile. The woman was in her early thirties and looked very sweet. She got her noodles promptly. I felt an urge to pick a fight with someone, to get it out too. What was it? I didn't know exactly. Everything around was irritating.

Human beings had been fighting each other since the goddess Nuwa wrought them from the Yellow River clay. Nor were Noah's kin different. And what would be the end for them? The powerful, the weak, the evil, the virtuous—for all, the end was death. Everyone in Beijing would be delivered to the crematorium at Babaoshan Hill. But while they were breathing, they fought.

28 · A New Wave of Deaths

After two months of "sweeping the outer line," Chan Kui began to go deeper into the counterrevolutionary nucleus. Three older officials were named as the patrons of the 5/16 clique in the Bureau. Zhu Jia, head of the personnel department, was put under investigation. He had been a regional commander when he left the army in 1964, a Communist of twenty-five years. He liked us army discharges, since he had handled recruits in the service. He was angry when he was detained and had shouted at Chan Kui that he would report the affair to the Party Central Committee.

"All right," Chan Kui had said calmly. "Go ahead. But first you have to confess how you masterminded the counterrevolutionary activities in the Bureau. We have concrete evidence that you were involved in the murders. After you have made all this clear, I would like to go with you to Premier Zhou Enlai himself and tell him what a good Communist you are.

Zhu Jia could not tolerate the insults of the younger army officers. He escaped from the detention room and climbed up a brick smokestack ninety feet high behind the office complex. His guards were in a panic and Chan Kui called a fire engine to the rescue. Zhu Jia was, after all, not a common fish. His death would bring attention from the top and questions about Chan Kui's ability.

A crowd gathered under the towering chimney, holding several safety nets borrowed from a construction site. Zhu Jia in a thin shirt and trousers looked like a white scarecrow high above. Microphone in hand, Chan Kui delivered the most appealing, passionate speech he had made since coming to the Bureau.

"Comrade Zhu," he said, deliberately putting emphasis on the word Comrade, which was forbidden to be used to anyone under investigation. "Comrade Zhu. Please come down. We can talk over anything, no matter how serious it is. You and I, both Communist Party members of several decades, should be able to understand each other. If I, or any of my fellow officers, have done something wrong to you, we would like to correct it. If you think we are totally wrong, still you can explain. As a revolutionary, you should have the courage to live and work for the Party. Please come down. We won't blame you for anything."

"No," Zhu Jia shouted back. "I know your kind. You will put me in jail as soon as I get down. I'd rather jump to my death than be insulted by you liars."

He had climbed up the chimney an hour before his guards discovered him missing. That had been plenty of time to jump. It might be a bluff to scare the Military Control Group from further prosecution.

"We are not going to send you to prison. Why should we? You have committed no crime. There is no reason for that."

I knew he had already decided to send Zhu Jia to prison. A jeep from the Beijing Public Security Bureau was parked in the compound and three policemen were mixed in the crowd, all armed with pistols. The fire engine raised its ladder, like a gigantic arm stretching skyward. It had recently been imported from Germany, Driver Wong had said. Standing on the tip was a fireman with a megaphone. As the ladder slowly reached the top of the chimney, Zhu Jia threatened to jump and Chan Kui ordered the fireman to stand by while he continued to coax him down.

Whether it was because of Chan Kui's strong persuasion or because he thought he had achieved his aim with this early morning climb, Zhu Jia allowed himself to be grabbed by the fireman and brought down as the ladder lowered swiftly to the ground. Zhu Jia was shivering from two hours exposed to the cold. As soon as his feet touched the ground, the policemen walked over and handcuffed him. One of his guards put his woollen army coat on him, as a gesture of Chan Kui's humanitarianism.

Zhu Jia struggled and swore. It was too late. Once again he had been deceived by Chan Kui. The policemen were young, strong, eager to perform their duty, and expert at arresting people. Zhu Jia was thrown into the back seat of the jeep. He tried to sit erect to maintain his dignity, but the policemen knew how to shatter all a man lived for—they pushed him down onto the floor of the jeep and set their feet on top of him. They roared away. Chan Kui waved his hand to signal that the drama was over, and walked toward the office building wearily.

It was a Thursday, the only evening besides Saturday that there were no meetings at the office. I rode my bike home, tired from working long hours in the office kitchen. The superintendent had set me chopping kindling for two hours and making coal balls for six. The water was cold, the place drafty. My bare hands were chapped. I was unable to wash off the coal dust that had penetrated into the skin.

I found the whole courtyard was out, gathered in the southwest corner. Shalin came over to tell me Dong Sen was dead. He had drunk a bottle of DDT which we used to kill flies and mosquitoes. Despite having heard of so many deaths, I was shocked. It was near and real this time. Sadness dragged my heart downward.

"Guangfen came home around five o'clock," Shalin told me. "She found the room dark. Dong Sen had been notified to go to the May Seventh Cadres School and should have been packing. I heard her yell at him for not preparing supper. Then she screamed and ran out of the room. Mr. Yin, Mr. Chang and Driver Wong were already home and ran over to her. Guangfen could only point to the door. The men went inside. They found Dong Sen dead. His face was gray and his eyes half-open, saliva dripping from a corner of his mouth."

"He shouldn't have done that," I commented listlessly. I didn't go over to the Dongs' room.

Three policemen came. An army officer from the Military Control Group arrived with two printing house workers. They stayed in the courtyard for ten minutes and left. Around 8:30, a truck from the Bureau took the body to the crematorium. It was suicide, the police declared. Dong Sen was the third death since the campaign against the 5/16 clique began four months ago. One had hanged himself in the washroom of the singles' dormitory and one had slit his wrists. The hanged man did not receive much sympathy, having left behind a wife and baby daughter in his native village. He should have chosen a less conspicuous spot to hang. One Revolutionary Rebel leader had jumped from the fourth floor of the office building, but only broke his leg and jaw.

Shalin stayed with Guangfen that night. Guangfen sobbed and cried. She blamed herself for Dong Sen's death. "I was too harsh on him. You know both of us were short-tempered. Even before we married we quarreled. He wouldn't have thought of death if I'd been nicer to him."

Shalin comforted her, saying it was not her fault. But she did believe Dong Sen would have had more to live for if Guangfen had been good to him. After the baby was born she had become even more impatient with him. In the Bureau, fifteen people had already been detained and fifty more were openly mentioned as suspected 5/16 elements. Dong Sen's name had so far remained in the printing house workers' casual talk. He had been timid, all right. But to die called for great courage.

"Yes," Guangfen sobbed. "If I had treated him better, he would have lived through the campaign. For the last week he was restless, often in a daze. Who would have thought he would kill himself?"

Shalin and I were very sorry for Guangfen. Only twenty-five, she was widowed with a small baby. Shalin did not know how to comfort her.

The next morning as I was leaving for work Shalin said to me, "I wish Dong Sen had not been so rash. The most precious thing is life. As the saying goes, 'As long as the mountain is green, you don't have to worry about firewood.' In times like these we must take good care of ourselves. We have ourselves to live for. We'll show them that we can live, and live happily!"

I had not told Shalin about my thought in the detention room —that I was not going to die alone; when I died, the world would have to come along.

29 · Shalin Is Sent to the Farm

Like most of the demobilized soldiers in the Bureau, Mr. Chang had welcomed the entry of the Military Control Group and enthusiastically supported their work. He was the most pious follower of Mao Zedong in the courtyard and was willing to follow the Chairman's instructions without any trace of the cynicism which was germinating swiftly in the minds of many.

In order to buy the first copy of Volume Four of *The Selected Works of Mao Zedong*, he had waited outside a Xinhua bookstore from midnight till eight in the morning. He had eight sets, including two sets issued to each of us by the Bureau and two sets issued by his wife's factory. He had collected five hundred Chairman Mao badges which he pinned on four squares of velvet and displayed above the eight sets of books. He would tell every visitor to his home which badge he had bought where and which was a gift from what comrade-in-arms. He thought of himself as a proletarian revolutionary inside and out.

That was why he flew into a fury when the Military Control Group notified him to go to the May Seventh Cadres School. He stood in the courtyard and exploded, "If they suspect me of something, they should have the guts to tell me so!" His shallow chest heaved and fell like bellows, his thin arm shook. "I joined the Communist army at the age of fifteen and fought from the Changbai Mountains in the northern tip of China to Hainan Island in the south sea. I still have shrapnel in my body. These men in the Military Control Groups were in their mothers' wombs when I was a battalion commander. Now they have the cheek to order me around! I won't go to the farm; let's see what they can do to me."

Mr. Chang felt outraged that the adolescent officers were implying that he, a veteran Communist of more than twenty years, was degraded to the level of a counterrevolutionary element and was being sent to the farm for re-education! "Ha, that devil Chan Kui! He said to me, 'It's Chairman Mao's call on the cadres to do manual labor.' I fuck his mother! Me, re-educated! Outrageous! I know what that sly fox is up to. It is as apparent as a flea on a shaved head. He wants to get rid of all who disagree with him. I'm not a five-year-old he can fool. I fuck Chan Kui's mother!"

Mr. Chang began a deluge of curses. The swearing style of northeastern China was raw, coarse and straightforward, invoking parts of a woman's body and their function. Beijing style was comparatively more subtle and civilized. No one came out to interfere with him.

Shalin was also told to pack. I had known all along that Chan Kui would not let us go so easily. Merely confining me for a six weeks and having me moved to the office kitchen was not enough to satisfy his frustration. In the open, Chan Kui praised Shalin as a person of principle. Wives of other suspected 5/16 elements made accusations against their husbands to please the investigators. Shalin didn't. Instead she told Chan Kui that I had done nothing harmful to the Communist Party or the country. Chan Kui was very annoyed with her simple-minded stubbornness in spite of his constant hinting that she should provide some "hard evidence to help him realize his mistakes." He had picked her out, I knew it. When he had a chance, he would take it out on her. Now he decided that two years, or longer, on the farm was an appropriate retaliation for her non-cooperation.

I went to talk to one of the two officers of the first Military Control Group, who had survived Chan Kui's vigorous purge. In his early thirties, he had retained some sympathy toward the Revolutionary Rebels and was not harsh toward us minor "bad elements."

"Our son is only one and a half," I said to the officer. "He's too young to be separated from his mother. How can I take care of him while working in the kitchen? Especially since the kindergarten won't take children under three. Could you talk to Chan Kui and let me go instead?"

He hesitated for a minute. "You know I would like to help. But everyone has difficulties. We must do our best to overcome them. Especially people like you. It's a test to prove you take the revolutionary cause above personal considerations."

I had not expected the once friendly officer to talk in such a businesslike manner. He might be scared of Chan Kui too. The other officers from the first Military Control Group had all been sent to remote frontiers. It would be unkind to insist he talk to Chan Kui on my behalf.

"But I'll put in a word at the kindergarten so they will take your son for day care," he added.

"Don't plead with them," Shalin insisted. "It will only be two years."

I was irritated by her lightness. Two years! How many two years are there in one's life?

We packed and cleaned up our tiny room. The Bureau gave each person going to the farm a raw wooden box, big enough to hold half of our belongings. Shalin wrapped five dozen Chairman Mao badges in a rag and stuffed the package in a corner of one of the trunks under the bed. "Watch out," she said. Don't let Sui get his hands on these. We'll get in deep trouble if he is seen playing with them. Remember that young man in the Red Alliance who accidently hung an old newspaper upside down over his window? A photo of Chairman Mao was in the paper. He was accused of blasphemy, dragged to a meeting for criticism and then sent to a police station where he was kept for a night in an unheated room. Now the Red Alliance is on the rise and you are in trouble. They might do the same to you."

I nodded my head.

Despite outraged resentment, Mr. Chang allowed himself to go to the May Seventh Cadres School with the third group, which was mainly members of the Revolutionary Rebels. Driver Wong brought a pickup truck to the east end of our alley to take Mr. Chang's and Shalin's luggage to the railway station. "They have made their bed," Mr. Chang announced as we saw them off. "They will lay in it sooner or later. You'll see." Driver Wong comforted him, "I don't think Chan Kui will stay in the Bureau long. He has made too many enemies. There must be more than a hundred counterrevolutionaries and murderers in the Bureau, far exceeding Chairman Mao's estimate of three percent in any unit."

"Everybody is a counterrevolutionary now," Shalin said. "So the name doesn't sound that terrible any more."

A week after Shalin left, Dian Wen and three others were taken away in a jeep at night. "It won't be easy for him to get off this time," Mr. Yin said, slowly twisting his cup. Granny Yin and Mrs. Yin sat on the edge of the double bed, looking expectantly, as if waiting for the judge's verdict at a trial. "Dian Wen is a damned nitwit. He may think he will be let go as easily as the first time. I am pretty sure he will give more confessions this time. He must have been sent either to prison or a remote place, so he won't have any chance to reverse a confession."

"The human psyche is a queer thing," I said. "People cling to hopes even when they know it is hopeless. When I watch someone being slowly tortured to death in a movie, I always wonder why he didn't fight back in the beginning when he was able. At least he could have had a quicker death with less suffering. In reality, people tend to have an optimistic perspective; thinking, or rather hoping, that everything will come out all right. So they wait, right to the end."

"That's true," Mr. Yin agreed with me. "Especially us Chinese. We endure until death, a slow death. On the other hand, onlookers have a cool mind. They can see things objectively. Those in the middle can't."

After almost a year in the kitchen, I was sent back upstairs to do odd jobs; typing forms, delivering documents, cleaning the toilets. It made me wonder whether they thought it was dangerous to keep a counterrevolutionary around the Bureau kitchen. As if I might put poison in the food!

There was an advantage to being a counterrevolutionary; I did not have to attend the endless political study sessions and criticism meetings, except those of which I was the target. When my colleagues gathered in the meeting room, I was left in the office to study on my own. I was allowed to read only Mao Zedong's writings, but instead I read novels in English. I would substitute *A Tale of Two Cities* or *David Copperfield* for *Selected Writings of Mao Zedong*. I loved Arthur Miller's play *The Crucible*. How similar the situation of the Cultural Revolution was to the witch-hunts in the United States; McCarthyism was the American Cultural Revolution.

When I heard the clicking of the door knob I would put the English book in my desk drawer and pull forward Chairman Mao's which I kept ready on the desk.

I avoided everyone in the office, whether revolutionary or counterrevolutionary. After lunch I would ride my bicycle for twenty minutes to August First Lake to swim. I would undress, rub my body with a dry towel, do warm-ups and jump in the water. At once I would feel a pleasant numbness from the cold water. I would stroke forward, enjoying the graceful movement of my arms and legs. For a half hour I would swim across the lake and back. I would haul myself up the stone bank, dry off and put on my clothes. I would shiver for a couple of minutes as I jumped and stretched my arms and legs. Watching the floating fragments of ice, I would feel my mind purified of earthly worries. A half dozen older folks came to the lake for winter swimming too. They were a merry lot. I did not want to join them.

My tiny home became inhuman and chillier. I hated to eat at the office dining room. I hated to be with people, especially those in the Bureau. So I would buy a bun and a link of sausage from a small restaurant on my way home, and cook a simple soup to have with them. I would drink a large dose of strong sorghum liquor. The raw, burning liquid numbed my brains as the icy water did my skin.

Sometimes Granny Yin would push open my door and walk in with a bowl of wonton soup in her hand. "It's cold today," she would say. "This will warm you up." Sometimes Mr. Yin would pop in, calling, "Come over to my home and drink with me. Drinking alone is no fun, and makes you drunk too easily."

I was grateful for the neighborly gestures. I had cut almost all contact with everyone except the Yins. Their room was humane while the rest of the world was not. The two girls would take their bowls and move to sit on the bed, so I had a place at the table. Only at such times did I have a chance to talk. They would ask how Shalin was getting along on the farm. Mr. Yin and I would gradually come to the subject of the shifts of power at the top and the situation at the Bureau.

"Dian Wen and Hu Bon are fortunate," Mr. Yin said one night. "Chairman Mao has recently said, 'Treat prisoners as human beings.' Some people out of jail last year said the police tortured and beat prisoners. It's forbidden now. Also their grain ration has increased from six ounces a day to eight."

"How is Dian Wen?" Mrs. Yin wondered aloud. "It is two months."

"He's in the Number One Municipal Prison." I had overheard the information at the office. "They say he is a model prisoner. They knit socks there."

Mrs. Yin wanted to know more. I could not supply it. I was not interested in talking about prison. The Yins soon realized that and turned to other subjects. I knew they wanted to drag me out of the abyss for a little while by inviting me over to talk.

Soon I wanted to go back to the loneliness of my dark room.

The hardest pain was when I picked up Sui at the kindergarten on Saturday afternoons. Most of the time, I was the last to get there because I dared not leave the office early, as others did. I had to make an effort to keep the tears from flowing when I saw Sui standing alone in the large empty room waiting for me. I would put him on the cross bar of the bicycle, walk for twenty minutes to the market place in front of the zoo and buy a treat for him to eat. We would sit on the curb, he watching the traffic, and I watching him eat. Around six o'clock we would go to my father's house for supper.

Both my brothers had gone to live in our native village. Without Mother around to hold the family together, the house was as empty and cold as my own room. My father and I would eat and talk disconsolately. Then I would take my son to our pathetic home, where I would try my best to make the stove give more heat. The Yin girls and Kang Ping would come to my room to play with Sui. I would leave him with them and go over to the Yins to chat.

30 · Two Adulteresses

The atmosphere at 6 Tanyin Alley was depressing. The sight of the weeping Erfeng and lonely Guangfen was enough to stop anyone from talking happily. Dian Wen and Mr. Chang used to be our source of merriment. Without them, the courtyard was dismantled as a friendly community. The chatting before and after dinner had long stopped. Each family went on living as a closed unit. The neighbors were estranged more and more as the weather got colder and colder.

The only family in the courtyard which was benefiting from the present campaign was Suyan and her husband Gu Fu. Suyan had worked into the confidence of the army officers and was going to join the Communist Party soon. She was right now coaxing the Military Control Group to send her husband to study in West Germany.

"She doesn't know what shame is!" Driver Wong told Granny Yin about her doings in the Bureau. "She doesn't bother to put up any pretense when she kisses ass with the army officers. You know, she quarreled with some women in her office over a coupon to buy a sewing machine. It's very hard to get one, even with a coupon. But she managed to, and you know what? She gave it to the officer in charge of her department!"

"Look at that!" he indicated with a turn of his head as she walked to the toilet. "How complacent she is! She's going to be a Party member and her husband will study abroad. It is as if all the luck in this world had gone to them!"

Suyan stopped to greet them. "The weather is very nice today," she smiled at Granny Yin. "This woolen sweater is too warm." She was wearing a sleeveless cashmere sweater, two plump breasts rising nicely.

"It's really nice today," Granny Yin smiled back. "My room was even stuffy after I cooked lunch."

"You should ask the Housing Office to build a kitchen for you, too," she said, drawing the sweater down over her waist, conscious of Driver Wong's stare flowing from her open neck to her sturdy legs.

"Yes, we should," Granny Yin said, her tone encouraging the younger woman to go on to relieve herself.

"The Office won't build a kitchen for anyone who asks," Driver Wong said coolly. "We don't have influence." So far the Housing Office had built kitchens for the Yus and Gus, promising to build one for each family. We were not optimistic, however.

Driver Wong grinned at Suyan's back as she closed the toilet door. "Humph, she would sleep with any army officer to get what she wants!"

"Don't talk about her like that!" Granny Yin said. "If they build a kitchen for us, that's fine. If they don't, you are not to argue with them. You'll only get us in worse with the Bureau. They have been urging us to move out of this courtyard, since my son doesn't work at the Bureau any more."

"I won't quarrel with them," Driver Wong assured the old woman. "Mr. Yin worked for the Bureau for many years, they just can't neglect you. They'll build a kitchen for you. I'll bet on it."

"All right. If they build one for us, I'll treat you to a dinner with wine."

"That's done," Driver Wong said. "I'll win. You'd better not treat me to a cheap dinner."

Suyan came out of the toilet. Driver Wong sniffed at the foul smell freshly emanating. It was not kept as clean as before.

"You know, Granny Yin," he said, mysteriously gleeful, "Suyan is really clever with men. Several young officers are running around after her. Ha, ha! She knows how to take advantage of a situation."

I remained inside my room. For one reason, I preferred to keep away from people, and for another, I did not want to join Driver Wong in saying bad things about Suyan. After all, she was my "countryfolk." Also, I didn't think she was a "loose" woman. She merely wanted to be better off, as Granny Yin said. She had reported on nobody. People from our area were honest. Suyan was merely too nearsighted, and selfish.

Driver Wong should not be talking about her that way. He himself was not clean either. He had been making eyes at Muchun even before Mr. Chang had left for the farm. It had become obvious to the neighbors during the summer. Whenever Muchun washed clothes or vegetables at the tap near the entranceway, Driver Wong would go over to wash something too, and purposely brush her arm, occasionally her protruding breasts.

Muchun was thirty-two; Mr. Chang was already forty-seven. He was skinny and old; Driver Wong was young and vigorous. And she was beautiful and liked to show it. In hot weather she dressed extremely scantily—a semi-transparent knit top revealing white shoulders and a strip of abdomen, two sturdy nipples protruding. Her shorts scarcely covered her buttocks. Sitting cross-legged in the shade of the tree on a drowsy afternoon, her slim legs and the contour of her breasts, firm and round despite two births, were a powerful magnet to any man. Driver Wong would stare in her direction from his corner for as long as he could.

Now Mr. Chang was a thousand miles away at the May Seventh Cadres School and came back for short visits only on major holidays. Muchun made herself more attractive, and intentionally more appealing to Driver Wong. First they found more chances to talk in the courtyard. They used a tone unnaturally loud—for the benefit of the neighbors, to show that they had become friendly neighbors, laying the foundation for visiting each other's rooms. Driver Wong took as his obligation the buying of grain, coal and other things for Muchun, and playing with her sons. Driver Wong's wife, Chunlun, was afraid of him, for he often shouted at her and sometimes even beat her in the courtyard. She dared not intervene in her husband's flirtation. The neighbors were not as willing to meddle in such things as they would have been several years earlier.

Two weeks after Mr. Chang left, Driver Wong began to come home early and would spend an hour in Muchun's room. Muchun always forgot to draw open the curtain in the morning. But it was hung a bit below the two upper panels of the window. The boys would climb up to the roof of the south row and strain to see what was going on inside. They could not see much.

"Why bother with others' business," Mrs. Yin said to Carpenter Shen's wife, Jinli, giggling over the boys' fantastic descriptions of two shimmering bodies in Muchun's room. "The best way to protect yourself today is to follow the ancient wisdom: 'Sweep the snow on your own doorstep, not beyond.' It seems nowadays everyone bears a grievance against someone. Since nobody wants to step out with honest words, Driver Wong and Muchun dare behave so openly."

We also noticed that Dian Wen's Big Brother came to visit Erfeng too often these days. When the Yins told Shalin and me about their suspicion, I felt my face burning. Dian Wen was my best friend and I hated to hear people talking badly about his wife.

"Erfeng has sent the boy to live with Big Sister," Mrs. Yin analyzed. "She said it was too much to look after him alone. Dian Wen's mother moved over to Big Sister's home too. Erfeng got rid of them to make it convenient for herself and Big Brother. Think of it, sleeping with his younger brother's wife!"

I could not bring myself to believe the fact. Shalin did not want to believe it either. Erfeng was an honest woman. How could she betray Dian Wen so soon? Seven months? At most eight months since Dian Wen was taken to prison!

"Big Brother came here last Saturday night," Mrs. Yin said. "It was already after nine o'clock. We saw him come into the courtyard, walking very lightly. He went into Erfeng's door without knocking. Both of them left around half past ten. The next morning I heard a cat mewing in Dian Wen's room. Erfeng must have gone to her mother's home and locked the cat in. I have a key to the room; Erfeng left it with us to look after the stove during the day. I opened the door and went in. You know what I found? The bed was all rumpled and the chamber pot half full. It doesn't take much imagination to figure out what they'd been up to!"

Shalin laughed self-consciously. "I always thought Erfeng was an honest and simple woman," she said. "She talks little, never quarrels with others, even walks with her head bent. Who would have thought she could become like this."

Mrs. Yin licked her lips and said, "Human beings are the most unpredictable creatures under heaven. I was not surprised Driver Wong and Muchun were carrying on. They are birds of a feather. But Erfeng . . ."

"You know," Mr. Yin said to Shalin and me, "my wife didn't believe that the decent-looking, obedient Erfeng could do such a thing. I told her, 'You'd better work your simple brains a little harder.' I have sharp eyes. Wasn't I right when I told you in the summer that Driver Wong and Muchun were flirting and that when they stopped flirting in the open they would do the real thing inside? Now you can see, they have stopped talking in the courtyard. If you pay more attention, you'll notice almost every afternoon around two-thirty Driver Wong slips into Muchun's room. She is off on sick leave and he has the convenience as a driver to come back any time to meet her. From the way Big Brother and Erfeng talk to each other I know they are no longer simply in-laws."

Although Mrs. Yin ardently disapproved of Big Brother taking advantage of his younger brother's wife, she herself must have felt more secure. As simple-minded as she was, Mrs. Yin could not have missed noticing that her husband had become enthusiastic about helping Erfeng with household chores. Now that Big Brother was taking care of Erfeng, she didn't have to worry about her husband any more. She only felt sorry for Dian Wen. Mrs. Yin wanted to tell Big Sister about the affair. "You idiot!" Mr. Yin said. "You'll only mess things up more and make an enemy of both Erfeng and Big Brother. I doubt that Big Sister would believe you anyway. They are brother and sister, remember. And when Dian Wen returns home, he'll surely believe what Erfeng tells him, not you. Forget it!"

31 · Shalin Comes Home for Spring Festival

Except those convicted 5/16 elements and a small number of their guards, people from the May Seventh Cadres School were coming back for Spring Festival in 1971. As usual, the newspapers, radio and the leadership at each unit began to laud the great achievements of socialist China and urge civilians to pay more respect to the army, and the army to love the people more deeply. The *Beijing Daily* once again assured residents that each would be supplied with two pounds of pork, one of eggs, half each of peanuts and refined flour, two of refined rice, one of good quality fish, and two ounces of peanut oil more than the regular five. "We will celebrate this Spring Festival amid greater achievements and ever-improving prosperity," the newspapers repeated again and again.

"Have you bought your rationed goods yet?" Jinli asked Muchun.

Jinli had just come back from the west end store with her basket filled.

"Not yet," Muchun said. "I hate to get up so early and wait in line for two hours. Driver Wong said he is going to buy my things for me. If he can't, I'd rather eat cabbage for the holiday dinner."

"It really is not easy to buy them," Jinli said, proud of her morning accomplishment. "I got up at six and went over to the store. Me and Mrs. Yin each took a line at the fish counter and the meat counter. Even so we waited over two hours. And the pork is very fatty. Is Mr. Chang coming back for the holiday?"

"No. He said the train is too crowded right now and he's afraid he won't get a seat from that small station. He can't stand

---

195

all the way to Beijing with his poor health. He said he will come back after the holiday."

"That might be better," Jinli smiled. "Then he can stay home longer."

Jinli immediately went over to the Yins and reported that Mr. Chang was not coming home for the holiday. "Of course Muchun doesn't want him to come back," Mr. Yin said. "She has that man with her. Ha, ha! He's more enjoyable."

Mrs. Yin glared at her husband and pursed her lips toward where Yin Ying and Yin Rong were knitting on the single bed.

Mr. Yin caught her meaning and changed the subject. "Long-sen and I were just remarking that the newspaper is bragging again. It gives an impression that holiday supplies are abundant. The devil knows how abundant they really are."

"Shit!" Jinli pitched in.

"The big officials have a special store to get what they need," Mr. Yin continued. "And their things are the best, and cheap. They don't have to wait in line for hours on a cold morning to get them. Their servants will bring them in cars. Last November Jiang Qing called a big meeting in the Capital Stadium to denounce back-door practice and special privilege. Six thousand people attended. Of course Jiang Qing wanted to generate public resentment, to smear the faces of some Party officials who were against her. That meeting offended quite a few of her rivals. I heard that they went to Chairman Mao to protest. So he said something like back-door trading is a trifling matter that cannot do much harm to the great cause of the proletariat. We criticize the Soviets for having a privileged class. Don't we have one too?"

"You'd better stop your gabbling," Mrs. Yin said. She did not mind much if her husband talked only to me in that way, but did not like him to talk to others with such openness. She said, "I spent the whole morning buying meat and fish. It's your turn to buy the rationed groceries. If you are late, they will sell out of peanuts."

Mr. Yin stood up and said to me, "Have you bought your things?"

I told him I didn't want to spend hours merely to please my stomach.

"You know what?" Mr. Yin said, picking up the ration book from the table, "I wish I had a son to become a doctor, a son to be a shop assistant and one to be a driver. Then I could sit home and enjoy life. You get free medicine and prompt service if you know some doctor; you get goods in short supply if you have contact with a shop assistant; and you can go everywhere if you are on good terms with a driver. It seems like Driver Wong owns that office car. He can use it any way he wants. Ha! Tell you what, the best position of all is to be a big, big official so you can order people around. In capitalist countries, one has to have money, In our great socialist China, one only needs power."

"Can't you stop that nonsense!" Mrs. Yin was really annoyed. She threw a basket at her husband. "Get moving! Right now!"

"All right, I'm going, I'm going, Madame."

"Longsen," Mrs. Yin said to me when he had left, "don't take trouble to prepare meals for the holiday. You'll eat with us."

Guangfen decided to go to Dalian to live with her parents. They had found a job for her there. She had had a hard time since Dong Sen's death. The Bureau refused to give her any financial help, since her late husband had been a counterrevolutionary. She had lived on her monthly salary of thirty-nine yuan. It cost a lot to raise a baby. The neighbors collected old rags and cut them into diapers, and old clothes to be reshaped for the baby. Fortunately, Guangfen had enough milk to breastfeed the baby, thus saving the ten yuan a month that cow's milk cost. Young mothers needed chicken, pig's feet and eggs to restore strength and generate milk. But none could be found easily in the market. Driver Wong offered to help, and the things he bought were cheaper than market price.

Four days before Spring Festival began, Guangfen was ready to leave. Driver Wong borrowed a minibus so more people from the courtyard could see her off at the railway station. The women passed the baby around and kissed his plump cheeks. The baby was liked by everyone. He seldom cried, smiled sweetly, growing more and more like his father. He had a big voice when his mother was slow to provide milk—a short-tempered creature like both his parents.

"I don't know how to thank you all," she sobbed. "Without you nice neighbors I don't think I could have lived through it all."

"Don't cry," Granny Yin scolded. "It will slow your milk. We are neighbors and should support each other."

Guangfen burst into tears several times before she boarded the train. We saw her face pressed against the glass. When the train moved, she raised the baby for us to see. The women cried. Driver Wong said, "Stop your precious tears. We should celebrate. Guangfen is the only one from our courtyard we have seen off neither to prison nor the farm."

Shalin came back from the May Seventh Cadres School two days before the holiday began without telling me first. "I thought they wouldn't let me come back," she said. "There had to be some people to look after the place anyway. So I didn't ask for leave. Then Fang Hun came to me and said I could come back if I wanted. So here I am."

She seemed less restrained than before. "The 5/16 elements on the farm give me a lot of help," she said happily. "Coal is rationed to each person. I live alone in one room and the coal is not enough. They steal coal from the kitchen for me. Actually, we don't do much work. We go to the fields around nine in the morning; lunch break begins at eleven-thirty; work resumes at two and stops around five.   Nobody puts any heart in the work. We enjoy the relaxed atmosphere in addition to the fresh open air. Someone calculated that the rice we produce is five yuan a pound, not including labor. If our salary is taken into account, the price would be more like twenty. We sell the rice to the state at fifteen fen a pound. You see, how much we lose running that farm!"

"You look darker but healthier," Mrs. Yin commented.

"Life is much easier there," Shalin said. "There is not as much pressure as there is in Beijing. Two-thirds are considered counterrevolutionaries or their sympathizers. We are the majority, you see. We enjoy the time. I've been thinking about having our family move there. The air and open fields will be good for our son."

"That's a good idea," Mr. Yin said. "Get away from this troublesome place in the city. Longsen can't live like this. Long periods of depression will ruin his health. But I don't think they will let him go down there. They take Longsen as the 'brain' of the counterrevolutionaries. They won't release the tiger into the mountains to stir up trouble."

Since our family was reunited, I went about the preparations for the five-day holiday, standing in the queues to buy our rationed meat and groceries, and cooking and cleaning the room, which was a mess after Shalin's four-month absence.

Without Dian Wen and Mr. Chang, the courtyard spent the holiday in desolation. Two rooms were dark—Erfeng staying at her parents' house, Guangfen's room locked up. On the eve of the previous Spring Festival, we had visited each other in every home. Our card club played through the night. On this eve, it was as if someone dear to all the families had died and lay in state. Shalin and I spent a little while in the Yins' room. They were making dumplings for a midnight snack, as old custom called for. We helped and around eleven o'clock went to bed, not waiting for the hour of Spring's arrival.

Around six the next morning, Driver Wong set off a string of firecrackers to "chase away bad luck." We remained in bed, each pretending to sleep, drifting in our own thoughts.

Shalin did not return to the farm after the five day holiday. She got in touch with a group of wives of counterrevolutionaries who were appealing to the top leaders to have verdicts reversed. I did not interfere, but thought it would not be of much use. I was afraid if Chan Kui learned about their activities, he would retaliate.

"The top leaders are busy," Mr. Yin observed. "Shalin and her group won't get any response, but it won't hurt anyone either. The other day Big Sister came. She had learned from some source that the people the Bureau sent to prison have not had a formal trial. They are 'entrusted to the care of the prison,' she said."

"But yesterday," I said, "all the departments were required to discuss what sentences should be given to Hu Bon and other ringleaders. The Military Control Group has suggested Hu Bon be sentenced to death and Dian Wen be given twenty years."

"Bluff," Mr. Yin sneered. "If it were last year, half of them would be shot. But not this year. Things are different."

My spirits rose. Though my mother's death seemed to have left me unconcerned about my future, I realized that if things turned for the better, I would still want to live a normal and fruitful life.

Driver Wong walked in. We had seen him slip out of Muchun's room with a bowl. Mr. Yin had quipped, "He feeds her at both ends." Recently Driver Wong had been going out of his way to be nice to Mr. Yin. He dropped in more frequently to have a chat. Perhaps he was courting Mr. Yin's favor so that the older man would feel obliged to refrain from talking about him in nasty words. But Mrs. Yin did not like him to be in her room. She would say, "Go to your room to play chess. Our room is too crowded."

"Oh, Longsen is here," Driver Wong said by way of greeting. "I got some fresh sheep tripe and made a stew. Come over and have a drink."

I did not want to go. Shalin had not come back from their "Liaison Office" in one of the rooms in the dormitory. I had cooked supper and was waiting for her.

"Why not," Mr. Yin said, his cynicism obviously meaning, "It's a fool to let a free meal pass."

We went to Driver Wong's room which, after sundown, was darker than mine, with a single bare bulb. It was like a prison cell.

Driver Wong was quick to lay out dinner. In ten minutes, four dishes appeared on the low table; two hot and two cold. "You try the cold crumbled beancurd first," he suggested. Mr. Yin and I each picked up a clump from the white porcelain bowl with our chopsticks and shoveled it into our mouths. Beancurd used to be plentiful at Beijing markets. Like everything else, it was in short supply now. "Isn't it delicious?" Driver Wong asked. "I got the beancurd directly from the workshop and the young shallots from the hothouse. Even the Beijing Hotel can't get such things so fresh. The sesame oil is special too. Someone brought it to me from Shandong Province."

"Ah, delicious," Mr. Yin said, clicking his tongue as he munched. I responded with equal exaggeration. Sheep tripe stew was a Beijing specialty. Diluted sesame butter and chopped coriander were added to the stock. Hot pepper oil was optional. I came to love it the first time my father took me to the Great White Pagoda temple fair after we came to Beijing.

"Have you heard that Hu Bon has escaped?" Driver Wong said. Both Mr. Yin and I realized that he had invited us over for more than a snack. We looked at him expectantly.

"From where?" I stumbled, knowing perfectly well what Driver Wong meant.

"From prison, of course. Beijing Public Security Bureau has issued a circular all over the country with his photo on it. Many people guess he is on his way to Guangzhou, from there to Hong Kong."

"That's stupid," I said anxiously. "Doesn't he know the consequence? He'll be charged with treason and sentenced to death." I suddenly remembered he was already as if dead.

"He is not stupid," Mr. Yin said. "People like him have no way out here. If he can get over to Hong Kong, he might live. Hundreds of Red Guards have gone over, some swimming across the water and some paying Yellow Cows to smuggle them across. The British are worried about the huge influx and have erected electric wire over the narrow strip between Kowloon and Shenzhen. A girl trying to climb over the wire got stuck and died."

I did not want to talk about Hu Bon any more and concentrated on the stew. The Erguotou was warm and soothing to my gullet.

I began to worry about Shalin. If it were true that Hu Bon had escaped from the prison and was trying to cross to Hong Kong, the situation for the counterrevolutionaries would become worse. The Military Control Group would have stronger leverage to crush any attempt to reverse the verdict, because Hu Bon's escape would prove him guilty.

I told Shalin that I thought it best to stop meddling with other counterrevolutionaries.

"Meddling?" she snapped, arching her brows that used to be very attractive. "We are fighting for truth, to bring the facts into the open. Hu Bon is Hu Bon. His escape has nothing to do with us!"

I knew it would be useless to argue with her and fell silent in resignation. Perhaps it would be good for her to divorce me, as Big Beauty had done with Hu Bon. I had despised Big Beauty for abandoning her husband in his difficult times. Now I thought she had done the right thing, so neither had to worry because of the other.

I had never known Shalin could be so stubborn. I gave up hope of her hearing my advice. Even Mr. Yin said to me in private, "She is impossible and will eventually get in trouble. The best way to survive a political campaign is to go along with the tide. It's very simple: you read the *People's Daily* and at meetings you say what it says. You're safe. Shalin takes things too seriously."

Shalin's department chief had talked with her twice to urge her to return to the farm. She had refused. Then the accounting office stopped her pay. "I'm not going to yield to blackmail," Shalin said to the Yins, who were persuading her to compromise.

"A hero has to learn to be flexible, to bide his time," Granny Yin said. "You are only bringing unnecessary suffering on yourself."

———
202

Shalin stuck to her guns. So three of us had to live on my salary of forty-nine yuan a month. Shalin did not allow me to tell my father. "We're not going to ask help from anybody," she said firmly. "We'll use our savings. What's money for? We won't let the cost bind our hands, will we?"

"Of course, we won't," I replied inanely.

With Sui in kindergarten, his expenses alone came to thirty yuan a month. We had only twenty left to live on. No matter how thrifty we tried to be, it would be necessary to draw thirty yuan each month from our savings. Our total savings were six hundred, which would last more than a year. I just could not see Shalin's victory in the near future.

I continued to swim in the icy water at August First Lake. The feeling of numbness was good; the undefiled snow that met the water's edge covered all the ugliness of the world. My capacity for alcohol kept increasing. "You can compete with my husband now." Mrs. Yin commented as Mr. Yin and I drank Erguotou over a dish of hot peppers.

32 · I Walk out on a Limb

On September 13, 1971, Lin Biao died in a plane crash as he
fled China. He was accused of conspiring to usurp power from
Chairman Mao. A severe purge at the top was carried out. Important military men fell. There had been rumors about his
death. His betrayal of the Chairman, his mentor, was a heavy
blow to the Communist Party's credibility, which had already
fallen dramatically during the Cultural Revolution. Only a year
earlier, Lin Biao had been claimed as the closest comrade-in-
arms of Chairman Mao, and his name was entered into the
1970 National Constitution as the immediate successor.

Suddenly, according to the official version, he became a traitor,
trying to grab the supreme position. He was sixty-three and
Chairman Mao was seventy-eight—so the official reason that
he had become impatient waiting for his turn at the top—was
flabby. We speculated that there must be other reasons, which
would not be revealed for another half-century when those deeply
involved in the most inner circle of the Communist Party had
died.

The event much boosted the morale of the counterrevolutionaries in the Bureau. They were hoping for another shift of power
that might reverse their luck. I was not so optimistic. I didn't
hope at all. I just waited. I had learned not to confront authority,
no matter how wrongly I was dealt with. I had developed a
strategy for treating the people around me—keep a respectful
distance; think twice before saying anything; and refrain from
telling the whole truth.

I became more and more concerned about Shalin's involve-

204

ment with the group writing appeals to the central authorities. It had expanded from four wives of confirmed 5/16 elements to fifteen, including those whose cases were not serious enough to send them to prison. The young counterrevolutionaries, though having been cowed enough to make false accusations, resumed their defiance of the Military Control Group's absolute power. First in private, then openly, they expressed their enmity to the army officers.

They hung criticism posters in the Bureau dining hall. The campaign against 5/16 elements had been unfairly executed, they declared, and as a consequence many innocent people had been wrongly accused. I agreed with the content; however, my apprehension increased. I feared that the present relaxed period was a twilight glow in the small hours. Before dawn still lay the darkest moment of the whole night. I did not want to be a martyr to herald the dawn. But Shalin was deeply involved.

Our little room had become a rendezvous for the group. They talked about which Party leader they should write to and through whom he could be reached. Some letters were delivered through personal contacts, others by friends of friends. When they sat and argued in an atmosphere of comradeship and conspiracy, I wondered how long such make-believe optimism would last. Since there was nothing I could do to prevent them, I would join them in card games, to laugh and relax. Sometimes our hysterical laughter kept the neighbors awake.

For two months Chan Kui and the other officers kept quiet. Counterrevolutionaries were jubilantly writing more letters to the leaders. Some provoked the officers directly. One rash young man pushed an officer off his bike on the street. I sensed the time for the Military Control Group to renew its attack was coming and I warned Shalin one night, as she sat down to draft another poster to denounce Chan Kui's "atrocities."

"Please stop writing criticisms against the Military Control Group," I pleaded with her.

"Why?" she asked and didn't raise her head. I heard that

sharp edge in her voice whenever I expressed disagreement with the posters she wrote against the authorities.

"Because if you continue you'll drag me into more serious trouble."

"Why?" she asked absent-mindedly. She knitted her brows, which meant she was not listening.

"How can I make you see reason?" I felt the tense frustration in the depth of my stomach. "Chan Kui has the power. He can send people to prison at whim. We can't provoke him further. Yes, at present he's cornered. That will only make him more dangerous. If we push him still harder, he will take harsher measures to suppress us. He has reported to Premier Zhou Enlai that the seven deaths were not suicides but murders and the premier has directed him to find the culprits. Chan Kui can't back out and dares not withdraw his words. He will stake everything he has in a single strike. He will smash those who stick their heads out against him. Understand?"

"But he has wrongly condemned so many people as counter-revolutionaries and murderers. If nobody stands up to stop him, still more people will suffer. We can't let him deceive Premier Zhou Enlai. You don't have to be afraid. Times are different. Chan Kui can't send us to prison."

"Listen," I said desperately. "He can't send all of us to prison. But he will pick out those who lead the appeal drive."

"I've done no wrong. How can he send me to prison?"

I was irritated with her naiveté in politics: there was no reason, no truth; power was the truth. Your superior's watch was always more accurate than yours. You just listened.

"He won't send you to prison, but he will send me!" And I felt so bitter. I was afraid of arguing with Shalin. To a degree I was ashamed of arguing with her. During my detention I had lied about myself. I made up a confession in order to please the power. Shalin stuck to the truth from beginning to end. Although she had not been detained, the pressure from the Military Control Group was no less than it was on me. I believed if she were detained, she would still adhere to the facts. She did not know how to lie. This virtue kept her blind to the nature of politics.

"I assure you," I tried a milder approach, "Chan Kui will find fault with me if you persist in putting out criticisms against him. Yes, theoretically we should stand out and speak the truth. As Chairman Mao says, 'A true Communist should not fear telling the truth. He should not fear even losing his head to tell the truth.' But we must learn how to protect ourselves first."

"We have not violated the law, have we?" Shalin demanded, her expression very solemn. She could be a political commissar in the army. "The Constitution stipulates that we have freedom of speech, and Chairman Mao also said we have the freedom to put up posters to expose wrongdoing. The Military Control Group has to abide by the law."

The words sounded hypocritical to me. If only those who made the Constitution abided by it!

"Well . . ." I still wanted to explain, to put in her obstinate head a little wisdom about political treachery. "You need to understand Chinese history before you get involved in politics. Intrigue is essential for anyone who wants to succeed. Politicians never blush when they lie in the name of so-called national interest. You know what Americans say about politicians? They say there are three kinds of people in the world you cannot trust—lawyers, doctors and politicians. There is the law, the Constitution, all in black ink on white paper. There have always been laws and constitutions. But how many people have been wrongly condemned in the previous political campaigns? How many have spent years in prison for mere political disagreement with some authority? How many have died for doing nothing wrong at all? There was an officer in my unit, the radio expert of my regiment. During the campaign against Rightist trends, he was accused of having Rightist thoughts. The charge against him was that he said the communes were hurting the peasants' initiative. He was expelled from the Party and the army and was sent to a state farm in the wild northeast. He spoke the truth and lost his career. Even if his criticisms prove right, who will remember him? He is lost forever."

"Things are different now," Shalin snapped. She might be thinking I had become a coward. "Can't you see, Chan Kui and his men are so quiet? They don't even dare hold criticism meetings any more."

"Please," I said. "Things always change. But the small fish like us are just left when the pond dries out. In 1919 a few intellectuals started a Cultural Revolution that showed the Chinese people the darkness of feudalism. Today we are having another Cultural Revolution, but who knows what it aims at? Three years ago, a group of people were brought down as feudal remnants; two years ago another group were brought down as Capitalist Roaders among the Communists themselves; and this year those who brought the first two groups down are being condemned as counterrevolutionaries. The question is too complicated and confusing for us ordinary people to figure out. Please, let's keep away from all this. From the beginning of the Cultural Revolution I have been trying not to be involved. And still I did not escape. As Chairman Mao predicted, the Cultural Revolution will touch the soul of everybody. I have had my share, and I take it as my fate. Now I want to wait and watch until the storm is over."

"The storm won't be over so easily if we don't fight," Shalin said. "You're scared. I'm not. I have no tail in their hands."

"You forget the saying, 'There is always evidence for any charge.' Perhaps they won't touch you, but they can make your life difficult."

After supper Shalin continued working on the poster. I went to bed early. When I awoke around midnight, she was still sitting at the table. The stove was burning high, but the room was chilly. She had pinned a piece of newspaper on one side of the bulb to block the light toward the bed. A piece of old cloth hung over the window curtain to reduce the draft. Her quilted coat was tightly tucked around her waist. I was angry with her and her accomplices. Why couldn't others make the posters? They

208

talked so bravely at their gatherings. When it came to writing criticisms, they became very modest, saying Shalin was the best writer among them. Only the honest and simple Shalin did not realize they were afraid of bearing the consequences; no matter how many signed the poster, the Military Control Group would eventually find out who had written it and pick that one out for punishment.

"All right," I thought to myself, "if I am to suffer more, I can't avoid it. Let it be!"

I dressed quickly and said to Shalin, "You go to bed. Let me finish the poster."

She looked up and yawned. She was about to tell me where she had left off, but I stopped her. "Go to bed. It's cold in here."

The next morning the poster was copied onto large pieces of yellow paper and hung at the entrance to the dining hall. Quickly a crowd gathered to read the shocking title, "What is Fascism?" I wrote that what Chan Kui had done in the Bureau could be compared with Hitler's persecution of his political rivals. His frame-up of so many counterrevolutionaries was no less criminal than Hitler's creation of the Reichstag Fire.

Two young trustees of the Military Control Group came to take photos and copied down the text. I watched from a distance and knew I had made my bed. I was ready to lie in it.

A month passed and Chan Kui did not move. Emboldened, others put up a few more posters demanding reexamination of all the cases. Rumors had it that Chan Kui had asked the Beijing Public Security Bureau for my incarceration but was refused on the excuse that the prison had taken in too many from the Bureau already. Shalin's group grew swiftly, and the original members became the core for a drive to reverse the verdicts. My apprehension was mounting, however.

33 · The Courtyard Is Falling Apart

Without Dian Wen and Mr. Chang to care about community welfare, our courtyard was falling apart. The outdoor bulb burned out and no one bothered to change it. I bought a flashlight to use after dark when I had to go to the toilet or fetch water. The toilets were filthy. Several families sent their children to just sweep away the soiled paper. Muchun and Aunt Kang did not take their turns at all. The stove was not lit very often. Pipes froze. The bowls filled and froze. At first I would light the stove to warm the pipe. Later I preferred to walk down the alley to the public lavatory.

But we had to get drinking water from the tap. I bought a big bucket and filled it with water whenever the pipe in the toilet was defrosted. Sometimes I wondered how much patience a human being could have. We would live on with the pipes frozen for days. And finally when one family had indeed run out of drinking water and could not wait any longer, one of them would go to the toilet, light a pile of kindling at the base of the pipe and old newspapers around the faucet to melt the ice inside the pipe. Then we would have running water for a day or two, depending on how cold it was outside. On Sundays, the courtyard felt dead as a ghost town. Each family was cooped up in its tiny world, hugging the stove. Occasionally Muchun's sighs and squeals would stir the stagnancy.

"Ha, with Driver Wong she's making up the loss of all the years," Mr. Yin remarked, not without jealousy. "Mr. Chang is a bag of bones—just can't satisfy her."

Finally the winter was over. I tore down the sunflower stalk and plastic sheet shelter in front of the door and moved the stove out under the eaves. Shalin and I cleaned the grease off the table and cupboard with washing soda and rearranged the furniture. On a fine day we hung all the clothes and bed linens in the courtyard, letting the sun drive out the clamminess, mold and mildew that had accumulated through the long winter.

It seemed that Chan Kui was at a loss for what to do with those noisy wives. On the other hand, left alone and having no other central leaders to send their appeal letters to, Shalin's group had fallen into a stupor. Shalin went to the office regularly, though there was no work for her. "I don't want to give them any excuse," she said. I thought that was stupid. No one would care. The accounting office had orders not to pay her unless she returned to the farm. Meanwhile our bank account was shrinking rapidly. Shalin began to feel restless.

One Sunday afternoon Sui ran back from outside, crying bitterly. "Sanpan made Latai hit me," he told his mother. "I was playing ball and they came up and beat me."

I had told Shalin not to let the boy play in the alley. Not only because I was a counterrevolutionary and the children in the neighborhood would pick on Sui, but also because I did not want him to mix with those boys. Ours was a poor neighborhood inhabited mainly by uneducated laborers. Muchun's two sons, Sanpan and Sanpu, played with them. Muchun had to give something to Latai, the gang leader, so her sons would not be bullied. Now with her sons under Driver Wong's patronage, Latai and the other boys were soft-soaping them instead. Latai and his brothers were sons of a scavenger who supported his family by selling the neighborhood garbage to the recycling shops. They often skipped school to rummage through the piles at collection points in the street.

"I've told you again and again not to play with those filthy dung beetles," Shalin yelled at Sui. Shalin's temper was getting short and she had picked up coarse language. I remembered the boyish yellow-haired kid. It had been twelve years. Was her upbringing showing its true colors?

"You play with them and you grow up a street hooligan!" She spanked him and he wailed.

Muchun was washing clothes at the tap near the entranceway. It was a fine afternoon. The sun was slanting down over the Great White Pagoda whose shadow fell heavily on our roof. But the north row was dazzling with sunshine. Muchun wore only a knit top and thin pants, showing off her slim limbs and sturdy breasts. Soapsuds on her hands, she turned to Shalin demanding, "Who are filthy beetles? You'd better name them!"

Sui wailed louder and Shalin was seething with anger.

"You want me to name them?" Shalin hissed. "All right. They are whoever pick up my words."

Muchun stalked over, her breasts quivering under the thin layer of cloth. "My sons are filthy beetles then," she said menacingly. "How about your son? He's a bastard of a counterrevolutionary!" She suddenly flicked her delicate arm.

Shalin wiped the soapsuds off her face and stared at Muchun in disbelief for a moment. She moved one step to the left, stretched her right leg forward and brought it back in an outward hook. Thump, Muchun was down on the ground. Shalin bent over and slapped her on the face with measured deliberation, once, but hard.

Muchun screamed, thrusting her arms and legs upward frantically, her buttocks and back smeared with dirt. I glanced up. Driver Wong had disappeared into his room with his tea mug. I did not know what I would have done if he had intervened on the side of Muchun. I might have killed him. I caught myself grasping the kindling axe, the knuckles of my left hand white.

In the evening, Kang Ping and the Yin girls came over to congratulate Shalin for her heroic deed. "I didn't know you could do kungfu," Kang Ping said admiringly.

"That's not kungfu," Shalin explained. "That's a routine from military wrestling I learned in the army."

"Served her right!" Kang Ping said, and the others nodded in agreement. "See how pompous she is these days. She doesn't even try to be inconspicuous with Driver Wong. The other day my brother and Shen Qu climbed up on the roof of the south row to pick up a ball. You know what they saw? Ugh! they saw Driver Wong and Muchun . . . they have become so bold they don't even bother to close the curtain."

"Did you see them too?" Shalin was concerned, knowing what a naughty girl Kang Ping could be. She often climbed on the roof to play with the boys.

"She did," Yin Ying said quietly. "And she told us about it. Shameless! Oh! not her—I mean *them!*"

"Never do that again," Shalin admonished. "That's not the thing for a girl to do. You are twelve. You should know better."

The Yins were full of praise for Shalin. Muchun had become intolerable. She got a new radio and played it loud and very late. In the morning she would get up around six when everyone was still in bed, and bang pots and pans, cooking in the court-yard. "She is overflowing with pep," Mr. Yin winked at me. "She and Driver Wong are a match."

Mr. Chang came back from the farm and stayed a month. He brought back three hens that began laying eggs. Muchun never went to work in all that time, staying at Mr. Chang's side, seeing he had his comforts. Driver Wong went out of his way to please Mr. Chang. He bought pork liver, fresh fish, sugar and eggs through back door contacts. Mr. Chang thanked him for his concern for his family. "Pah! Concern indeed!" Jinli said to the Yins, twitching her mouth in contempt. "Driver Wong takes care of Mr. Chang's wife all right."

That very night, after Driver Wong drove Mr. Chang to the railway station to return to the farm, Muchun slipped over to Driver Wong's room. Jinli hurried over to inform the Yins, say-ing, "Those two were as restless as ants on a heated wok during the entire month. They couldn't wait a moment longer. Now they are making up for it."

Muchun did not kill the hens but kept them for the eggs. Beijing did not allow people to raise poultry inside the city for sanitary reasons. The Neighborhood Committee came several times to urge Muchun to kill the birds. She refused. The committee was not as powerful as it used to be. They dared pick only on those people with political flaws. Fortunately, Mrs. Yu was on the committee, which protected me from their general harassment.

When the weather turned warm, Muchun left the hens out to roam the courtyard, leaving droppings everywhere. One day a hen flew onto the Yins' supper table. Mr. Yin grabbed the bird and threw it onto the ground. For five minutes the bird didn't stir, only her claws twitching spasmodically. We thought it was dead. Mr. Yin kicked it across the courtyard and shouted he would kill another if it was near his door. Afterwards Muchun kept her hens in the coop which Driver Wong had built. When the weather was hot, Driver Wong killed them one by one. The smell from the coop must have bothered Muchun too.

The happiest person in the courtyard was Suyan, happier than Muchun. Her husband, Gu Fu, finally had the opportunity to study in West Germany. She laughed loudly.

Like millions of families, our nice neighbors in 6 Tanyin Alley had changed. Relations had become rigid and selfish, neighbors indifferent to each other. I wondered if the happy days of the past would ever come back.

34 · I Am Sent to a Labor Farm

After Lin Biao's death, China was plunged into further chaos. Rumors were many. One was that while Lin Biao was fleeing China with his wife, son and several staunch followers, the central authorities ordered the plane shot down before it crossed into Mongolia. The official version was that it crashed by itself. Since Lin Biao was defense minister and general commander of the army, its reputation plummeted further. Resentment against military control was rising. In the Bureau, things had been quiet for several months. Political study sessions were reduced to mere formality and the frequency dropped to one or two evenings a week. The officers confined themselves most of the time to their rooms. The printing house workers stopped swaggering in the corridor, some drooping like hens caught in a downpour and some asking to return to their workshop.

Chan Kui visited his family at the army base more frequently. The counterrevolutionaries believed their liberation would come soon. I remained cautious and skeptical.

I jerked awake. The window paper was washed white by moonlight. I peered at the alarm on the table as I urinated into the chamber pot—three o'clock. I returned to bed. Shalin shifted her position. I lay down. Usually the early morning was the best part of the whole night's sleep—no horrible dreams of jet planes crashing or fleeing among rugged mountains. But I could not fall asleep again this time, nor was I anxious to. I was becoming more and more superstitious and trusted more in fate than in man's ability to deal with fate. There must be something other than reason and logic that guides people's lives. Several times my intuition had proved right. Once a truck rushed past me very close on a rainy day. I sensed something would happen. I got off my bike and waited only a few seconds until the truck sent a cyclist in a green plastic raincoat onto the curb. Intuition told me that something was impending this day, something no good for me.

But I was not worried, and didn't care. I looked at the ceiling. The old piece of cardboard over the hole in the ceiling had warped awkwardly. Several thumb tacks had been pulled loose by the force. Dust fell onto the wooden trunks when the mice played around the hole. I should have replaced it. I had become lazy, in no mood to do anything.

I heard the creak of the Yins' door and the cautious sound of Mr. Yin taking his bicycle out. Then the sound of his door closing and the clattering of the bicycle crossing the courtyard toward the gate. The sound was sad, like weeping, suitable to blend with a dirge.

If only one could think a step backward. What would be left in one's life if he relinquished all ambition and desire? Is there anything so fine in the world for one to suffer so much for? How many hours were left to enjoy one's life deducting all the time of worry, anxiety, jealousy, quarreling, suspicion and competition. Does everyone live on ideals he can never achieve? Mr. Yin is dissatisfied with his life. Why does he still get up early to work with rotten plumbing all day? Only for a cup of the fiery Erguotou at the end of it? Why can't he just quit and find something he likes to do?

Well, how about myself? Why should I worry so much, care so much? What is the difference in life whether one is a big shot or a minnow? Everyone has to end up in a cold porcelain jar like Mother did. Would a top official or famous dignitary want his title and privileges hung on the jar of ashes?

The mice scurried and squeaked in the space above the ceiling. Their noise was not so irritating now. Old people said mice were the most forgetful creatures in the world. They were clever when they stood on their hind legs. But as soon as they set down their forelegs, they would forget all the smart things they had figured out. They were happy as long as they were not caught in a trap.

I wished I could be as transcendent as the mice so I could forget unhappy things when I was not in the trap.

Suyan and Muchun were chatting merrily at their doors; Aunt Kang yelled at Kang Ping, for the girl had not washed her face and would be late for school; Granny Yin quietly prepared breakfast next door. I knew Mrs. Yin was still in bed. She never helped Granny Yin cook. Shalin was up and making breakfast outside. She did not have to get up early. She continued to go to the office, though there was still no work for her.

My mind wandered at a slower pace and it was detached, as if all the activity had nothing to do with me. Passion, affection, love, hatred, none of them. In *A Dream of the Red Mansions*, the master of a noble house felt the same way before he left home to become a Buddhist monk. Ah, I was emancipated from the earthly world!

But I could not forget. I had a sense that after brooding for six months, Chan Kui would strike and I would bear the brunt.

I was reading in the office while the others were having a meeting. I was called to the meeting hall. Chan Kui read from a document: I had been given punishment of three years in a labor reformation farm. It was not a shock to me. My mind was cool, thinking nothing. I had become tired, waiting so long for this. I even felt relieved, as I had felt when I was finally detained.

I was not allowed to go home to say good-bye to my family or get my things. I was taken immediately to a detention center in the southern outskirts of Beijing.

A political counterrevolutionary, with no real criminal action, I was given only an administrative penalty, though the severest. I was treated with more decency than a criminal—not dumped on the floor of a police jeep with four policemen's feet on my back. Instead, a Bureau car and two of my case members sent me on my way. July breezes from the open fields along the

217

highway were comforting; the luxuriant green of trees, grass and rows of vegetables were pleasant to the eye.

Almost all my friends were either in prison or at the Bureau farm working under supervision. I had had uneasy feelings being outside with my family, as if I had let my friends down. Now my position was in between, better than prison and worse than the farm. I could put my conscience at rest.

I was confident I would be able to cope with the three years of hard labor. How would Shalin live? Oddly, I found that I was not concerned. My mind dwelt far beyond the Western Hills, on a broad horizon which was clean of all debris. All difficult things were underground on that side of the Western Hills.

35 · The Labor Reform Farm

Chadian Labor Reformation Farm was two hundred miles northeast of Beijing on the Bohai Sea. The land, bleached by alkali, was sparsely populated. The barrack-like row houses in a dozen compounds were scattered desolately amid immense stretches of fields. The new Communist government built them in 1951 to hold the thousands of secret agents, militia and officials of the former Kuomintang regime. In 1957, Rightists were sent there to be reeducated through labor along with minor lawbreakers. I was to spend three years with pickpockets, rapists, burglars and a few political prisoners like myself.

With several years of experience hanging out with the wild boys near the city wall, I got along well with my fellow inmates. But the work was heavy and the food poor and inadequate. The police guards were suspicious of me because I was not only a political counterrevolutionary, but also a stinking intellectual. So they were stricter and sterner with me. I laughed bitterly. To those real intellectuals in the office I was a contemptible bumpkin, and among the uneducated I had become a parasitic intellectual who ate off the socialist society where only the working class created wealth.

During the first six months I was given the hardest work to do—submerged in mud, digging ditches; weeding fields; shouldering fertilizer to the fields until I wished I would fall in a ditch and break my leg. Twelve people slept on a platform bed, a bare light bulb like a ghost glaring down from the ceiling throughout the night, so the duty officer could count heads.

Team Leader Nu, an army veteran in his late forties, was sent to Chadian Farm with his regiment in 1951. Gradually I found out that he shared my views of the Cultural Revolution and did not believe that I was as bad as my file described. He actually suggested to other officers that I might be wrongly accused. He never checked the packages Shalin sent, even though there was food in them, prohibited by regulations; we were here to be reformed through hard living conditions.

"You're lucky," he said to me. "Half a year ago, people with your record wouldn't be comfortable. An officer could bind and beat a man or hang him from a tree." I began to imagine how uncomfortable it could be.

I was assigned to tend the rice fields, a privileged job. It offered relative freedom because the rice needed attention throughout the day. I could leave the barbed wire barracks and spend a few hours on my own, away from the obscene gossiping, quarreling, and boasting of the other inmates.

Shalin visited me on major holidays. She had finally come to see it was she who was to blame for my being in a labor farm. "Don't mention that any more," I said, smiling genuinely. "The labor farm will be a valuable experience in my life. Not everyone can be in such a place, even if he wants to. I might write a book about it someday."

"Writing a book?" Shalin twitched her mouth to smile. "Forget it. I would be satisfied if we could be left alone after you are released. Your labor reformation farm record will affect our son's life. He may not even get into college because of it."

"Ha," I laughed. "You worry too soon about that. Who knows what it will be like when he grows up. Sui was growing quickly, sturdy and handsome, but was estranged from me.

"You'd better not come here so often," I told Shalin.

"You don't want to see us?" she searched my face, her expression more wronged than resentful.

"Not that," I said, finding it difficult to explain. I didn't want her to see how humble I had to act in this damn place, how wretched my appearance must be. In the small reception room, there was always an officer supervising the meeting, and four or five other families would be visiting as well. He watched us closely to see if any visitor passed a package of food or cash to the inmates. The feeling of humiliation was so overwhelming that I often failed to come up with the right words.

"Sui is too young," I said. "He must be a heavy burden for you to carry all the way here. And you have to change trains in Tianjin."

Shalin bent her shoulders and drew Sui away from me. I saw tears coming up to her eyes. I didn't know how to comfort her. If I did I wouldn't dare to say it out in front of all the others and the hawk-like officer.

"All right," I said, infusing my voice with cheerfulness. "What is good news?"

"I have been assigned work in the library again."

"Chan Kui must be afraid that he's made too many enemies," I answered. "He must be loosening up his control a bit. How's Granny Yin? Is her health still good? Do the girls help her at home?" I waited anxiously for her to say something. If she decided to keep silent as she would often do at home when she was angry, I would feel even more awkward.

"Granny Yin wants me to say hello to you," Shalin said. I breathed out the air I had held for a long minute. "She still does all the house chores. The girls don't do anything at all, spoiled by their mother. Granny Yin is still in good health, but her spirit seems to be failing. When the coalman makes his delivery, she can't calculate as fast as she used to. Since you left, she has given me much help. Every time I come here, she helps me cook some food to bring. And when we get home, she will have cooked a pot of noodles for us and filled the thermos bottles with hot water, since the train gets in so late."

"How about the others?"

"The Yus, Changs and Shens were very afraid of talking to me after you were taken away. But now Mrs. Yu even offers to look after Sui when I have to go out alone. Mr. Chang is still in the Cadres School. And Muchun and Driver Wong have not changed. Mr. Yin has stopped playing chess with him. Now the courtyard seems haunted in the evening."

Shalin's weary face brightened up a little bit. "Longsen," she lowered her voice, realizing she had talked too loudly in this hush-hush room. "Take good care of yourself. Remember 'As long as the mountain is green, there's no worry about firewood.' We have much to look forward to."

I nodded my head, but was not so sure at heart. I might end up in an ashes jar with a label of counterrevolutionary. I looked at Sui and smiled. He looked at me, cowering closer to his mother. I took Sui's hand in my hand, feeling the coarseness of mine. "Mother told me you've learned to play chess. We'll play together when I get home."

Sui looked at me, his eyes big and bright like mine. "When?" he asked.

"Very soon," I said and my heart began to bleed.

Living without freedom was intolerable. I suffered more from the hurt to my self-esteem than from heavy labor and poor food. I endured, often wondering why I couldn't end it all. Human weakness for living? Or desire for revenge?

Hot summer and cold winter alternated three times. My police friend worried about my mood. "You've become very cynical. You are not coming to hate the whole society, are you?" I smiled faintly. "That's very dangerous. You should have faith in the Communist Party. Your case will be redressed sooner or later."

I really didn't care. He might be right that the Communist Party would change its policy; it had changed so often during the Cultural Revolution. But how long should I wait? In 1957, during a political campaign against "Rightists," thousands of university students and educated professionals were branded. Many of them were sent to Chadian to be reformed through hard labor. Beijing wouldn't take them back. Here on the Farm, they were given twenty-three yuan a month, barely enough for three simple meals a day. They did not have families because they did not see a future. Would I be able to live like them year in and year out after I was released? I doubted it.

Thanks to a new Communist Party policy, those released from the Farm in 1975 were allowed to go back to their original work units in Beijing. "You're lucky again," my police friend was saying good-bye to me. "The policy may change back next year and all those released would either be kept on at the Farm as laborers like those Rightists, or resettled in remote regions."

Shalin brought Sui to meet me at the railway station in Beijing. We hired a taxi to carry us all and the luggage. Only Granny Yin was at home. She greeted me wholeheartedly and with tears. "Poor child," she wiped her eyes with the sleeve of her blue jacket. "You're thin, only bones left. You didn't have enough to eat, did you?"

I smiled. "I'm all right. What I've lost in meat I've gained in bones. You see, my eyes are larger than before."

Granny Yin brought over a thermos bottle so I could wash.

The courtyard had changed. For each room there was a tiny kitchen of red brick and corrugated asbestos tile. They formed a small square block in the middle of the courtyard. It was obvious they had not been built at the same time. Their size and height were slightly different and each was separated from the next by a narrow strip of space, just wide enough for a cat to pass through. Many bricks could have been saved if the kitchens were built with an overall plan. They could have shared walls. The Yins had their kitchen too, although smaller. Perhaps Driver Wong had exerted his influence in the Housing Office to get it built for them. I wanted to ask Granny Yin if she had entertained Driver Wong for dinner, as she promised three-and-a-half years ago. But I changed my mind—I should not be humorous. I felt I was still in mourning.

No one had taken over the corner room after Guangfen left. In 1968, Red Guards from the local middle school had helped the Neighborhood Committee search the houses of bad elements and confiscate many things. And those families who were ordered to return to their native villages left many things behind.

The Neighborhood Committee turned in valuable things such as jewelry, porcelain antiques, gold and money to the higher authorities, but was asked to store books, clothes and furniture. They had moved these things over to the vacant room. It must have become a merry-go-round for the mice.

Erfeng still kept her room clean and neat, but seldom slept in it. Dian Wen's mother had died the year before in Big Sister's home. Dian Wen was not permitted to return for the funeral—there wasn't one anyway. The old woman was put in a raw wood box and loaded into a truck. Big Sister and her husband escorted the body to the crematorium.

Big Sister had found out about the shameful affair between Big Brother and his sister-in-law and refused to talk to him. Erfeng spent most of the weekdays at her mother's home. She returned to her own place on Sunday for her day off. Every time she came back, Big Brother would come. I had never expected Erfeng to be so brazen. In broad daylight she could spend an hour with Big Brother inside with the curtains pulled closed, and still have the grace to greet the neighbors when they came out! I felt ashamed for Dian Wen.

Mr. Chang had returned from the May Seventh Cadres School. He came back without permission, as many had done. The Military Control Group pretended not to know, following the proverb, "keeping an eye only half open."

Muchun had become very cool toward Driver Wong. "It is not because Mr. Chang is now home," Mr. Yin explained to me. "Muchun is not afraid of her husband a bit. She could easily find a way to make a tryst. But she got bored with Driver Wong. He is too coarse for her. She tired of playing with him and cut him out. That's all."

He chuckled. I was alienated by his sarcastic chuckle.

"You know what," he lowered his voice, looking toward where Shalin and Mrs. Yin were chatting, "Skinny women are more lustful. Erfeng and Muchun are skinny. Jiang Qing is skinny." I had heard rumors about Jiang Qing but did not believe them. She was hated and people made up stories to defile her name.

Muchun still dressed scantily. Even in the cool morning she would walk out of her room with a pair of pink underpants and a knit top showing half of her breasts and a strip of belly. She really had more heat than other women. She would speak to Driver Wong as if nothing had ever happened between them. He, however, tried hard to keep his eyes away from the flesh which was now beyond his reach.

36 · The Girls Have Grown Up

Kang Feng, Shen Yuo and Shen Chiu had grown up fine young men. The girls had grown into pretty young women. I felt self-conscious when they addressed me "Uncle Longsen" the way they used to. They were as tall as Shalin. I could not possibly imagine how they had ever climbed up my back to play. I felt aged.

Yin Ru and Yu Min had graduated from junior middle school. Mrs. Yu had got permission for her daughter to remain in Beijing to wait for a job assignment. Yin Ru had been notified to go to either an army factory in the mountains of Guizhou Province or to work in a village for two years in one of Beijing's outlying communities. The government had abandoned the policy of sending youngsters to live permanently in a remote provincial village.

Mrs. Yin announced gallantly that the present world was filled with injustice. "It is only because we don't have back door connections," she complained loudly, "our daughter must be banished a thousand miles away in the mountains. Ru is only fifteen. I'm worried just thinking she will be alone so far from home. I would like to let her live in a village near Beijing. Then she can come home on holidays. But go to Guizhou Province . . ."

"Here you go again," Mr. Yin said impatiently. "Ru wants to start working right away instead of waiting two years in a village. I agree with her. Children grow up and leave their parents. We can't keep them with us all our lives. So let her go. I started working at thirteen. Why can't our children?"

226

"You are a man," Mrs. Yin retorted. "Our Ru will be able to come to visit us at most once every two or three years. I would prefer to keep her at home and feed her. But they won't let us. They say children are the property of the country. But it is us parents who have to take care of them! Mrs. Yu has connections, so Yu Min can stay in Beijing. Is it fair?"

"What kind of connections does Mrs. Yu have?" Mr. Yin said. "If she had real connections, she would send Yu Min either to the army or directly to a factory in Beijing. But she doesn't. She has only succeeded in keeping Yu Min at home. How long might it be until she finds a job? I've told you many times it is no good for a grown child in Beijing to have no job. You should be grateful for the present policy.

"A factory worker automatically becomes a government employee," Mr. Yin was trying hard to convince his wife about the advantages of letting Yin Ru go to Guizhou. "She will get medical care, regular raises, paid home visits, and many other benefits, since all the factories belong to the government. And sometime in the future she may be able to transfer to Beijing. But to stay home or go to live in a country village near Beijing? Well, she'll lose all that.

"Tong Hua has been living in the countryside for—how long? Seven years? She has no vacation, no medical care, no guaranteed pay. When she returns to Beijing, if she can at all, she will be stuck at the beginning. She has to look for a job and when she gets one, she'll get the lowest pay. By then Ru will be getting fifty yuan a month."

"You talk so lightheartedly," Mrs. Yin lamented. "Ru is a piece of my flesh. Of course I'm worried about her. If only you could be more useful than a mere plumber!"

Shalin and I felt uneasy sitting there. Mr. Yin hated to be looked down on. I was about to say something to cool down the atmosphere. But Mr. Yin said calmly, with a tone of resignation, "You always pick at me for this. I tell you I'm much more capable than many a big official. Only the times didn't give me a chance."

"Shame on you!" Mrs. Yin hissed. "I've waited for seventeen years and seen many chances gone to others." She turned to me and added, "I ask him to talk to his factory for an official letter so we can appeal to the authorities to have Ru stay in Beijing. He said he doesn't beg favors. Can we live on pride?"

"I won't have anything to do with officials," Mr. Yin said, getting angry. "In this world the most honest and decent people are the common people. Though you may say some are loose, like Big Brother, Erfeng, Muchun and Driver Wong, they are much cleaner than those big shots. Power poisons the mind. We all complain that big officials abuse their positions. But if you had that kind of power, you wouldn't be much better than them. That's why they say, 'when you have power, take advantage of it. If you don't, you're a fool.' Mrs. Yu could only manage to keep her daughter in Beijing, but can't get a job for her. That's because Mr. Yu's position is not high enough. If I were a bureau chief or something, I would certainly send our daughter to study abroad. We are common folks. Be content with what we are given."

"All right!"

Mrs. Yin said angrily. "Ru is not only my daughter. She's yours too. If you don't worry, why should I?" She fell silent, seething inside.

"Well, to tell the truth, Longsen," Mr. Yin said to me, "I've given a lot of thought to the future of Ru. I believe it is very good for her to go to a factory, even though it is far from home. In two or three years she'll be a skilled worker. By that time, those who stay in a village near Beijing will be just beginning a job. Beijing is very crowded, and there are too many young people without jobs. Who knows how long Yu Min would have to wait. Three years? Five? Young people who have been sent to Shaanxi Province are coming back. They need jobs too. Besides those who have recently graduated and will graduate, there will be several tens of thousands more waiting. There won't be enough jobs for everyone here, and they won't be good jobs."

I agreed with Mr. Yin's argument and said to Mrs. Yin, "I think Mr. Yin has a point. Children have to make their own lives. Yin Ru will have a secure job. It is better this way for her future."

"You might be right," she sighed heavily. "I talked with the person from that factory who was here enlisting. He said Yin Ru will work as a typist. So she won't have to work in a shop or be exposed to wind and rain. If only she were a boy!"

Kang Ping had become the prettiest girl in Tanyin Alley. Her face, neck, body and limbs had filled out nicely. Her arms and legs were slim, no trace of the thinness of several years ago. While other girls were shy of their breasts, Kang Ping raised hers higher with a bra. Young girls nowadays had larger and higher breasts than formerly, thanks to good nutrition. Shalin did not approve of Kang Ping's behavior. Only fourteen, she began to mimic Muchun's walk. She was intelligent, but didn't like school.

"You should put more heart in your school work," Shalin admonished her. They had remained good friends through all the years. Even if the girl had picked up some bad habits, she was still genuine.

What's the use of good grades?" Kang Ping said. "No matter how hard you study, you end up laboring in one of the villages or in a remote factory in the mountains. Tong Hua was a good student. Then what? She is now suffering in a poor village in Shaanxi along with those who didn't do well in school."

"Knowledge will be useful in the future," Shalin argued patiently. "Tong Yi is your age. His elder sister and two brothers have all gone to the countryside. Does he know if he will have a good job waiting for him after graduation? But he still studies. Have you ever seen him play cards or stay out late? No. He reads, and reads alot. I tell you China will need many people with knowledge. You study hard now, and you won't regret it."

Kang Ping did not seem convinced. She envied and at the

same time resented two of her classmates whose fathers were big officials. They had their own rooms at home. They would all go to the army next year to avoid working in a village or a mountain factory. They had plenty of clothes and their fathers were known to the teachers. Her mother was illiterate and had bound feet to display her village background. Her father, a cook, had only one eye. She was ashamed of her parents.

"You're very pretty," Shalin looked at Kang Ping closely, examining her delicate features. Her fingers were soft and long. Kang Ping smiled shyly, lowering her head. Her hair was much longer than was fashionable. "But a pretty face is not enough. Learn something and you will have more independence in your life."

Kang Ping looked up, her face pink with a blush, and smiled sweetly. "I'll remember your advice," she said.

37 · The Tongs' First Visit to My Room

Two weeks after I returned from the Farm, Mr. and Mrs. Tong came to visit. They came very late, around ten-thirty, knocking at the door tentatively and asking, "Have you gone to bed yet?"

Before opening the door, Shalin looked at me, puzzled. Why are they here? her eyes asked me. They stood there, their smiles awkward and self-conscious. They had never stepped across our threshold since we had moved to 6 Tanyin Alley, nor had we talked much in the courtyard either. The visit was very formal.

"We won't be long," Mrs. Tong said apologetically, as Shalin ushered them in. Shalin led Mrs. Tong to the bed and I offered her husband the only chair. "We were out the whole day and had no time to tidy the room," Shalin acknowledged the messiness.

Mrs. Tong had aged a lot. I would believe she was the same age as Granny Yin if I didn't know she was just fifty. I poured tea into glasses for them. "Don't bother. We won't be long," Mr. Tong said politely.

Mrs. Tong bent over to look at Sui sleeping in bed and said, "Is the boy running a fever?"

"He must have got chilled yesterday when we took him to Beihai Park," Shalin said. "We took him to the clinic this afternoon for an injection."

Mrs. Tong felt the boy's forehead. "The temperature is high. You mustn't be careless. In summer a cold is even more difficult to get over." She smiled at him and turned to Shalin. "The boy is as bright as his father." Looking at me, she continued, "I'm not flattering you, Mr. Huang. Although we have little contact,

Mr. Tong and I often talk about you. Mr. Tong respects diligent people. He often tells our Tong Yi to follow your example. Others in the courtyard might not have noticed that you listen to the English broadcast from abroad, but Mr. Tong did."

Mr. Tong gave his wife a warning glance. Listening to programs from either the Soviet Union or the United States was unofficially illegal—there had been no public statement on the matter, but there would be trouble if officals found out. Mrs. Tong did not catch her husband's meaning and went on, "Sui will do well when he grows up."

"I dare not expect too much for the boy's future," Shalin said. "Now that his father is a counterrevolutionary . . ."

"Things will change," Mr. Tong said. His hair had become grayer and thinner. "You can't lose heart. I know we haven't spoken much. As a matter of fact, I have never had a long conversation with anyone in the courtyard. The neighbors are all good people, but the person I admire is Mr. Huang." Mr. Tong flushed, embarrassed for praising someone openly.

"Do you know Banti?" he asked me.

"Yes," I said, remembering that delicate elderly woman who had been sent with us to the Huairo Mountains in the autumn of 1969 to help with the millet and chestnut harvest. It had been sheer nonsense to take her along. She, already over sixty and in poor health, could hardly walk on the mountain slopes. She was, however, a bad element and had been ordered to learn from manual labor.

"She's the Party secretary in the Bureau now," Mr. Tong said. "It was she who advised the Military Control Group not to send you to your native village. She said it would be too harsh a punishment. They compromised by sending you to the labor reformation farm."

I shuddered, imagining what a life that would have been. Me, forced to work from early dawn to dusk in the fields, with peasant militia guarding me . . .

Mr. Tong was not used to long conversations and tonight he

seemed to have overexerted himself. He fell silent. Mrs. Tong examined the flushed face of Sui and said, "How time flies. He is already six. He's growing up handsome."

Shalin and I were proud of our son. He was indeed pretty. Sanpan and Sanpu, Muchun's boys, were growing more and more ugly. Especially Sanpu, six months older than Sui. His small eyes were becoming like those of a mouse. Secretly I felt gratified, though "to take pleasure in others' misfortune" was disrespectful. Mrs. Yin was sure that the ugliness of the Chang boys revealed their mother's inner evil disguised behind a pretty face.

"He's reached school age, hasn't he?" Mrs. Tong asked. Perhaps she was thinking it would be impolite to leave us so quickly.

"He will start school in September," Shalin answered. We all felt a little awkward now that we had to look for something to say. I asked Mrs. Tong, "How is Tong Hua? Any letters from her recently?"

Mrs. Tong sighed. She liked to find a person to talk with about her beloved daughter, although talking of her always made her heart ache. "She used to send us two letters a month. Not that often now. There are only three Beijing students left in her village. The others have all come back. I've been running my legs off, begging here and there to get her back. They have set up a new program, the Young People's Reestablishment Office. It is in charge of youngsters who have returned from the country villages but can't find work. I go there almost every day. They always say, 'Be patient. There are too many people for us to handle. We have to do things one by one, and first is first.' Then who should be first? We don't have official connections and have no money to buy gifts. I asked my old man . . ." She glanced at her husband who was flipping through my son's picture book. "I asked him to get an official letter from his office. He wouldn't do it, as if his words were made of gold and he couldn't give them out carelessly."

Mr. Tong was a proud man, I mused, and would not beg

favors. "Hua is twenty-three this year," Mrs. Tong continued. "It's already late for a girl to start a career. If we can't get her back soon, she will have difficulty finding a husband . . ."

I tried to say something sympathetic, but failed to come up with any idea that might sound at all practical. I looked up at Mr. Tong and said instead, "Want more tea?" Immediately I realized I was implying that they should leave.

"Oh, no," Mr. Tong said, standing up. "It's late, and you must be tired. We are leaving."

"Please come over more often," Shalin saw them to the door.

When it was closed, she blamed me for my untimely offer of tea. "You must have forgotten how to be civilized in the labor reformation farm."

"How can I remember how to deal with civilized people," I teased, "when I have spent three years in a jungle of savages. They would come up behind you and crack your head open with a brick. I had to squat before I could talk to the guard."

Sensing the bitterness in my humor, Shalin changed the subject quickly. "Poor Mrs. Tong," she said. "Three of her four children are in the countryside. The family has to send them money to buy grain. On their production teams they can't earn enough workpoints to live."

By the end of 1975, twelve million middle school graduates from the cities had been sent to settle in remote regions. The first batch, inspired with revolutionary ideals, went off to the villages of their own accord. They wanted to do something to help poor dirt farmers live better. They had seen the poverty in most of China's rural areas when they were traveling nationwide to "exchange revolutionary ideas" in the winter of 1966. Tong Hua was among the first who volunteered to go to one of the poorest regions, Shaanxi Province, in the north. She set off in September, 1967 with a dozen classmates, all eager to contribute their share to building a modern socialist countryside.

"I'm not going to die," Tong Hua had said to her weeping mother cheerfully. "Everyone is going to the countryside. We are determined to change the backward situation there. We'll wipe out illiteracy first and then poverty, all over China."

She was seventeen and had graduated from high school the previous year. Her teachers had promised to see that she got into the best university in Beijing.

She had not allowed her mother to see her off at the railway station. The staunch Red Guards would be embarrassed by their sobbing mothers. She left, with 170 others from several schools, on a train bound for the loess plateau a thousand miles due north of Beijing.

Her early letters were happy ones, describing in poetic narration all the curiosities the city youngsters encountered in a small village. The local inhabitants loved vinegar dearly, she told her anxious mother; they drank it like water. The fields rolled on and on over the yellow earth, endlessly. Some flood-eroded gullies could match in beauty the great limestone sculptures in Guilin. Everything was exciting. Sleeping on an earthen platform with six other girls was itself a novelty. The platform-bed was heated from below with crop stalks, they were told, and were waiting eagerly for winter to come so they could try it. The air in the vast open fields was refreshing. The Beijing graduates were confident that their rich store of knowledge and steel-hard determination could "pull the village out of poverty in two or three years."

After several months, the letters sounded less and less romantic and more practical. She asked her mother to send some soap, toilet paper and even thread. They could not find these things at the county market town. Then rumors began to circulate widely in Beijing. There were horrible stories about the city youth in the villages—girls being abused by local cadres, raped, forced to marry the cadres' sons; boys being beaten up. Shanghai students sent to live in Yunnan Province revolted. They returned to Shanghai to stage a protest demonstration. Despite great efforts, Tong Hua's group were not accepted by the villagers, except for one who had married the son of the village Party secretary, after two-and-a-half years. To the villagers, the spoiled city young-sters were nothing more than extra mouths to feed, a heavy strain on the limited local grain resource. Furthermore, they tried too hard to be smart about everything and gave too much advice.

Tong Chen and Tong Chu, the two older sons, went to live in Shaanxi villages, first one, then the other. Mrs. Tong dared not tell her husband she was sending money to them.

38 · Tong Chu Breaks His Neck

Another dry summer in Beijing. The ground was parched and smoked at noon. The red tiles of the north row roof and gray asbestos boards of the tiny kitchens shimmered under the brilliant sun. The leaves of the jujubes drooped as if depressed. There was not much fruit. Sanpan brought the street boys to the courtyard and with sticks they knocked them down unripe. When Mr. Yin happened to return home early and see them, he yelled, "You turtle eggs! Get out of the courtyard. Or I'll break your legs!" The boys scurried down the other side of the house and fled.

I was lying on a reed mat in the shade of the eaves, shifting position restlessly to escape the sweat-wet spots. My sinuses always gave me trouble in this season. Granny Yin was dozing on a chair at her door. She was not as energetic as she used to be.

Old Huang, the postman, walked into the courtyard. His green uniform had wet patches on the shoulders and under the armpits. While all public service people missed their schedules, Old Huang was never late with a delivery. I stood up to greet him. "There's a pot of cold tea here," I invited. "Sit down and cool yourself a little while."

He sat down on a stool and waved the fan I offered. Granny Yin opened her eyes and said, "So here you are again." She and Old Huang were great friends. "Still able to run around, I see."

"Not that fast any more," he smiled. "My bones are falling apart. Here's a telegram for the Tongs."

I took it and read to Granny Yin: "Tong Chu broke his neck swimming. Will arrive Beijing by train on the thirteenth."

I hurried to a public telephone and called Mr. and Mrs. Tong at their offices. According to the telegram, the train would arrive at three this afternoon. I called Driver Wong and asked him if he could get a minibus.

As soon as we had rushed through lunch, the Tongs, Mr. Chang and I rode in the minibus over to the station. Driver Wong negotiated with the station master and got permission to bring the bus onto the platform. Mr. Tong sat there showing neither worry nor sorrow. Mrs. Tong wept quietly. We did not know how to comfort her, and sat in silence.

"His neck broken!" Mrs. Tong sobbed. We waited, hating the clock for ticking off the seconds too slowly. We were anxious to know how seriously the boy was injured. All the Tong children were nice kids. They respected elders and were friendly with other children. And they did well at school. Mr. Yin had commented, not without jealousy, "The Tong boys could make it big."

Tong Chu was the brightest of the three. He was fourteen when he went to join his elder brother Tong Chen in the village two years earlier, a few months before the government decided Beijing graduates could stay in a village near the capital. "If only he had graduated one year later," Mrs. Tong said with great remorse. "He could have stayed in Beijing. Why has all the bad luck fallen on my family?"

The train slowed down and we saw Tong Chen's head stretching out a window. We ran over. Passengers were swarming out and we waited. When the car was empty, we went in and carried Tong Chu out on a stretcher. His face was deathly pale.

Tong Chu spent a month in the hospital with his neck in traction. His mother went to wait on him as soon as she was off work. Mr. Tong did not go to the hospital. Tong Chen went back to the village immediately because a factory from Taiyuan City was there enlisting Beijing students. He didn't want to miss the chance.

Tong Chu's head tilted slightly to the right after his recovery. He carried himself erect, however. He was the most handsome among the brothers, half a head taller than the eldest, and athletic looking.

He refused to go back to the village after the recuperation. Mr. Tong became even colder to him. Beijing was flooded with jobless young people. The tumult of the Cultural Revolution had disrupted normal life, as well as production. The city could not provide jobs to half a million people at once. For many years China had been telling the world that there was no unemployment. To save face, a term was invented to define the loafing city youngsters: "Educated Youth Waiting for Job Assignments." So China still did not have unemployment. Beijing residents joked bitterly about such cleverness.

Mr. Tong, the gentleman, did not like those young people who were wiling away time in the streets. Thousands of them were coming back from Shaanxi Province without official permission. Since their residence permits were still for Shaanxi, they were not issued grain or other ration coupons. Indulgent mothers had to think of ways to feed them, and face the wrath of their husbands.

A great number of pickpockets and burglars had been brewed. Street brawls had become a common scene. They were not young political radicals beating up former landlords or store owners. They were uncivilized hooligans killing each other with knives. They bullied common folk. In the early fifties, I had admired the gallant street fighters. They would negotiate and select a quiet spot outside the city to fight among themselves. In 1957, a thorough drive had sent all the ringleaders either to prison or the Chadian Labor Reformation Farm.

I despised these new street brawlers. They had no respect for fraternity and did not abide by rules and codes. They did not practice marital arts. They would creep up on a rival and knife him in the back, and cheat their friends of money.

Having nothing to do, and chilled by his father's cold stares at home, Tong Chu sought human warmth from his old classmates who were in the same situation, roaming streets and public parks. He learned to drink and smoke. In the courtyard

---

239

he remained respectful to the neighbors. He liked to have a chat with me. I was amazed by his broad knowledge and wondered where and when he had read so much.

Again Mrs. Tong pleaded with her husband. "We only want an official letter to prove Tong Chu has returned because of his injury, so we can get his residence permit back."

Mr. Tong said nothing. His nostrils flared and his breath was harsh. Mrs. Tong dared not ask whether he was angry with her, their son, or the situation.

Tong Chu stayed out later and later, skipping supper at home. When he came home, he would slip into the room he shared with his youngest brother and go to sleep silently. We never saw the light turned on. Sometimes we could hear the muffled sobbing of Mrs. Tong talking with him.

39 · Tong Hua Returns Home, Tong Chu Leaves

Mrs. Tong worried more about her beloved daughter. Tong Hua's letters were less and less frequent, but more and more disturbing. She told her mother which friends had gone back to Beijing; which to the army through a connected relative; and which was almost forced to marry a young man in a nearby village. "There are only three of us left in the village," Tong Hua wrote in a recent letter. "The parents of the other two are working on connections. I don't know how I can stay here alone after they leave."

Mrs. Tong showed the letters to us. Mr. Tong would give her no comfort. We all knew he loved his only daughter and once had high hopes for her. But he hated begging favors. He could only sigh, and his sighs made Mrs. Tong more desperate. At least Mr. Yin and I would tell her to go the Youth Reestablishment Office more often and we gave her a few pointers she might use to convince the officials that Tong Hua should be allowed to come back, though we all knew our words were useless.

After Mrs. Tong received the news that her daughter's last two companions were leaving the village, she plucked up her courage, like a hen whose chicks were about to be snatched by a hawk, and shouted at her husband. To the neighbors' amusement Mr. Tong, the family tyrant, listened patiently and went to his office to demand an official letter addressed to the Western District Youth Reestablishment Office. The political department of the Bureau, in charge of such matters, had pity on this good old gentleman and willingly extended their help.

Tong Hua returned in early October, a woman of twenty-four, unmarried, and without a job. Mrs. Tong ran around, getting a letter from the Neighborhood Committee, another from the local police station, and talking humbly to the impatient officials at the Youth Reestablishment Office. The girl's school records were excellent. She was given a temporary job teaching at a primary school.

With three grown children, including a young woman, crowded into two small rooms, Mr. Tong became more short-tempered. Most of his colleagues with equal seniority had been given more spacious living quarters. For his family's size, he was entitled to a three bedroom apartment. But he did not send in an application for a change. "They won't give me a larger place whether I apply or not," he told Mrs. Tong impatiently. "As long as we don't sleep in the open, it's all right with them."

The only comfort for the Tongs was their youngest son, Yi. He was short for a boy of fourteen, but he had a precocious mind. He observed coolly the happenings at home and in the society, and took his classes earnestly while many students had lost interest in learning. To the neighbors he was polite. In his family tradition, or at least his father's, he seldom talked with anyone in the courtyard. Occasionally he would play cards or chat with the other boys his age. He was sympathetic with his elder brother, Tong Chu. Quietly he kept an eye on what his brother was doing, knowing when he started to smoke, to drink, to have girlfriends. He did not tell his mother, afraid of worrying her more, and dared not tell his father, to whom he had very little to say anyway. And it would be improper for a younger brother to talk to his elder brother about such matters.

Tong Chu returned home only once or twice a week now. Tong Yi comforted his mother saying, "It's not all his fault. He's almost twenty-one and there is no hope of him finding work soon. He's too depressed. You know he was not like this before. The world has made him what he is."

In this, Mrs. Tong agreed. She had a special love for Tong Chu.

"When things turn better . . ." Tong Yi said. "Things will definitely turn better. Otherwise China can't survive. Then my brother will become a useful person. Have a good talk with him, reason with him, and make him see the brighter side of himself."

"Your father doesn't allow me to talk to him," Mrs. Tong said. "No sooner do I mention his name, than your father yells at me. Besides, Tong Chu is very pigheaded. He won't listen to me."

What Tong Yi worried about the most was his premonition that his brother was going to tangle with the law one of these days. He had tried to hint to Tong Chu to be patient and wait for his chance. His brother only smiled and patted his little brother on the shoulder. His smile, so sarcastic, drove a spike into Tong Yi's heart.

Cynicism had become a fad plaguing the entire younger generation. They felt they had been used and let down by the authorities. They had fought vigorously as Red Guards and helped begin the Cultural Revolution. But the reward was several years in dirty villages far from home. Now they had struggled back to Beijing. There were no jobs for them. They did not believe those beautiful words of revolution anymore. Facts were truer than dogma. Disillusioned, many did not care what became of them.

However, there were some far-sighted people. They tried to look for a way for themselves and for the future of China. A number of intelligent youth began writing short stories and poems both to denounce the evils of the society and to vent their frustration and sorrow. They called their writings "literature of the wounded." No one, of course, dared publish any of their work. They would gather in out-of-the-way places to read their pieces and exhibit their paintings. They passed around hand-copied poems and short stories among themselves.

Tong Yi, in defiance of his father's severity in such political matters, would sneak out to one of the rebellious young writers' gatherings by August First Lake. He loved those poems which brimmed with compassion and bitter lament against the injustice done to the youth. He copied them down in a notebook and kept it with him all the time. August First Lake could be reached easily by bicycle and the place had very few visitors during cold days except the few winter swimmers. Tong Yi was especially moved when a girl around twenty recited this poem:

Last night I dreamed of my mother calling.
She was standing by my bed,
Touching my emaciated face.
"What a lovely face you once had,"
Mother said.
"Now it's wrinkled and cracked by wind."
I wanted to say something but couldn't.
Awake, I cried in the dark and cold.
Through shattered window panes,
A frigid moon shone.
Cocks crowing,
I dragged my aching body to the field once more.

Tong Yi went up to the girl and asked her name. She gave him a cold stare and walked away, accompanied by two other girls. Later he learned that nobody at the gatherings was supposed to ask names. They would come, read a poem or an article, listen to others, then leave. Some would pass out manuscripts, unsigned. He hoped to see his elder brother there. He should make his life as meaningful as these young, daring men and women.

One day Tong Yi came home from school and found the house in chaos. His father was standing among an overturned table and fallen chairs, the wash basin dumped. Water was all over the floor. Mr. Tong quivered in great fury. He hissed in low, controlled anger, "I'll kill you and get rid of my trouble once and for all! I don't want to suffer for you!"

His mother and sister were shielding Tong Chu. Crying silently, Tong Chu said through gritted teeth, "Let him beat me to death. Why should I live? There's no place for me at home or in the world. Death would be better than living!"

Mrs. Tong pleaded with them both. "Please ask your father's forgiveness!"

Tong Yi stood by the door for a moment, looking pitiful and helpless. The neighbors knew better than to interfere. We listened from our rooms but could not determine what had caused this violent eruption.

Finally Tong Yi went over and pulled his mother and sister up. With his body between his father and brother, he dragged Tong Chu out of the room and into the alley. I went over to join them. I liked the two boys very much and they trusted me.

"You'd better stay away for a couple of days to let things calm down," Tong Yi suggested. "Father will have a stroke if he is angered again."

"I hate this world!" Tong Chu said vehemently. "I'm no more stupid than anyone else. Look at those bastard big shots. When we were being sent to the countryside, their fathers got them into the army. Now that the universities have opened again their fathers can get them in there. Stupid, good-for-nothing playboys. If the school enrolled by academic standards, there wouldn't be a place for any of them. Where is justice? In the hands of those in power."

We had walked out of the west end of Tanyin Alley. Tong Chu said to us, "You go back and have supper. Tong Yi, you can find me at Shi Shen's home." He turned to me and said, "Don't worry, Uncle Longsen, I'm all right."

Tong Yi wanted to say something, but swallowed it back. "Take care of yourself," he said, sounding older than his elder brother. Taking out a five yuan note from his pocket, he gave it to Tong Chu who took it, saying nothing.

It was growing dark. Street lights came on, shedding a jaundiced glow. Tong Chu turned north, toward the High Wall. I went into the store to buy toilet paper—old newspaper and school pads were too coarse for my hemorrhoids.

The store was busy with late customers and the assistants were getting impatient. Two stood by the door to stop anyone from entering. It was twenty minutes before closing time.

Shalin and Sui had gone to her father's home. They must have stayed for supper, since they were not back. There was a piece of steamed bread and some salted turnip slices at home. That did not appeal to me. The weather had settled down after a whole day of dust storms and it was not cold. I might as well go over to the High Wall for a stroll.

The street lights around the High Wall were much more powerful than the dim bulbs in nearby alleys and side streets. I did not think it wise to use strong lights in this area, if the compound was indeed Jiang Qing's residence as Driver Wong said. Seen from the air, this place must be very bright, like the halo around the Buddha's head in a dim temple. The young poplar trees, grown tall through the years, quivered in the silvery light. I made out the silhouette of Tong Chu and hurried over, worried.

"You are still here?" I asked.

"It's quiet here," he said.

We walked along the vacant road. Tong Chu pointed at the gray wall and said, full of bitterness, "Look at this huge place. Every time I come here I want to tear it to pieces."

Many neighbors around the High Wall harbored strong resentment against this elegant sprawling compound.

"That evil woman lives like Dowager Empress Ci Xi of the Qing Dynasty," Tong Chu continued. "But Ci Xi did not have a wall with tunnels inside to guard her summer palace. That woman should be sent to the most remote and poorest village in Shaanxi Province where people live in pigsties and chicken coops and don't have enough coarse grain to carry them through the year. They say that woman has her bodyguards bring along her personal chamber pot when she goes to the countryside. Here in Beijing she has this huge mansion for herself. Big enough to house two or three villages. Those big shots, they speak beautiful words. They urge the common people to live simply and work hard for the revolution, to spread Chairman Mao's ideas throughout the world. They remind us of the hardships they endured on the Long March. But who knows what they fought for? To serve the People? Pah! To serve themselves!"

Tong Chu's outburst scared me. As outspoken as I was, I would not dare make such remarks to anyone, though I might agree with what he said. I wanted to leave him. "You'd better go to your friend's place," I said. "It's getting late."

Tong Chu gave a vicious kick at a bush; the bare branches crashed. The armed guard turned in our direction, his bayonet shining devilishly.

We separated, he going west beyond the city, I returning home to have my cold meal.

A week later, 6 Tanyin Alley learned that Tong Chu had been arrested for stealing. Policemen began to visit the Tongs in the company of Neighborhood Committee members. They would talk to Mrs. Tong for half an hour, her door closed. When she came back from seeing them out the gate, her eyes would be red and swollen.

When Mrs. Tong realized she could no longer conceal her family shame, she went over to have a talk with Granny Yin.

"I've let my Tong Chu down," she began. "You all know how nice a boy he used to be. He has changed so much. I can't blame him for all this mess. January fourteenth he'll be twenty-one, but he doesn't have a job. His father yells at him every time he comes home. We have pushed him into the abyss. Yesterday I went to the police station to see him. I told him not to hate his father. His father has never hurt anyone in his life; at the office he does what he is told, never argues or complains. You know, Mr. Tong has ideas and aspirations. He has to restrain himself and obey others. That's why he's so short-tempered at home. He's only letting it out on us. We let him. Otherwise he would be ruined. Mr. Tong used to have high hopes for Tong Chu. Now the boy is finished."

Granny Yin poured a cup of tea for Mrs. Tong. "We all know Tong Chu is a good boy," the old woman comforted her. "He has a warm heart. I remember him helping me carry coal cakes.

He was at most seven then. He tumbled over the steps at the gate and broke three cakes. He didn't cry, but said to me, 'Granny Yin, I'll buy three cakes to repay you. I have five fen in my pocket.' How time flies. Fourteen years have gone by. If the times were not so chaotic, he'd be in college. How many years did you say his sentence is?"

"Three years on a labor reformation farm," Mrs. Tong said. "The police told me if he behaves well he can be released earlier."

"He'll get out earlier," Granny Yin said earnestly. "It's a pity that so many good children have gone astray. The Fang girl and her younger brother in Number Nine courtyard, you know, were involved in a street gang when their parents were away in a May Seventh Cadres School. Both of their parents are professors and have raised the children properly. But several years ago the children became wild. They fought in the street and had all sorts of young men and girls at their house. Early this year their parents' names were cleared. So the sister and brother have become good again. Sister Tong, don't be too hard on yourself. Tong Chu will return to you a good boy."

The next day, the Neighborhood Committee officially notified the neighbors that Tong Chu had been sent to Chadian Labor Reformation Farm. Since I had been there, I might give him some advice, but changed my mind. It would not do for me to go to talk to him at the police station which had my own file.

40 · It Snows on a Sunday

The winter of 1975 set in earlier than usual. In late November, Driver Wong and I shut off the water faucet at the entranceway and moved the other into the toilet. The Housing Office delivered a truckful of coal balls to the east end of the alley. Boys were mobilized to carry the coal into a corner in front of the toilet under the big locust. I remembered the lively, noisy scene when Dian Wen was home.

Families in the colder south and east rows replaced the old window paper. Under Shalin's surveillance I tore away the blackened paper, washed the thick layer of dust off the frame and pasted fresh paper on. I sealed off all the cracks I could find around the door and window frames. Shalin swept the walls and ceiling. The room seemed brighter. We also moved the stove into our bedroom—now I could call it that since we had a kitchen. I again built a closet-like shelter in front of the door with sunflower stalks and plastic and stored our pile of cabbage there, which every family bought in great quantity when the price was low as the harvest came in. There was just enough heat from the room to keep them from freezing. We were ready for winter hibernation.

A snowfall came on a Sunday, one week before New Year's Day. It came stealthily during the night. I woke earlier than usual, my bladder full, which meant it was colder tonight. The pale reflection was certainly not that of the moon. I was delighted, realizing it was snowing. I wanted to have a look out of the window. I love snow or rain, or any kind of bad weather. It is poetic to walk out then; the world does not seem so crowded.

I put out one arm to try the air. Goosebumps flashed down it. Hastily I retrieved it back into the warm quilt. I heard a door creak. Mr. Yin was pushing his bicycle out of his room. Then his steps crunched on the snow. The crunching steps and clicking wheels went out of the courtyard. My expanded bladder refused to wait any longer. I threw a quilted jacket over my shoulders and rushed to turn up the stove. By the time I had relieved myself, I was shivering. The chill penetrated to the marrow. I crawled under the quilt, my teeth chattering, and rubbed my arms and legs to regain warmth. Ten minutes later I could feel the air warming in the room. I made up my mind to get up early to enjoy the pure whiteness of the snow before it was spoiled.

A jet-black semi-transparent icicle had formed at the exhaust end of the stove pipe which protruded two feet beyond the window. Directly below it was a similar stalagmite, thicker and shorter. Of frozen coal gas, they looked striking against the whiteness. The air was fresh without that pungent smell which a few years later we identified as pollution.

Konni, Dian Wen's son, ran out. He was five years old, lean and energetic, a year younger than Sui, but as tall. The boy was restless like his father, skipping in and out from door to door. He taught himself to do somersaults. When Big Sister learned about the shameful affair between Erfeng and Big Brother, she took the boy in herself, not trusting Erfeng with Dian Wen's son. Her health was not so good since Granny Dian's death, which had affected her deeply. Konni was too active for her to run after. With Erfeng's second sister married and unable to find a place to live, their mother's house was too crowded. So Erfeng came back with the boy to live at 6 Tanyin Alley.

Beijing residents had a glorious tradition of being very considerate, to save face for themselves and for others. As they said, "A tree must have bark to live, a man must have face." In the courtyard we talked about Erfeng and Big Brother behind their backs, though we greeted them and chatted with Erfeng as if we knew nothing of their unusual relationship.

250

Erfeng did not sniff around, poking her nose into the business of others. She had never asked Dian Wen what he was doing late at night, but had waited patiently for him to come home, with supper and hot water ready for him. She didn't gossip, while almost all Beijingers made it their hobby. So she had no enemies, nor close friends either. The neighbors began to be conscious of her presence only after the affair had become an open secret. The Yins and I agreed it was all Big Brother's fault.

Konni jumped over to me and called out, "Uncle Longsen, I'll help you sweep the snow and we'll build a snowman." I often wondered where this boy got so much energy. "He doesn't use brains," Granny Yin said. "So he doesn't need much rest. Like father, like son."

"We will make a snowman," I said, liking the boy. "But we'll get Sui up first and we'll all make the snowman together."

Konni followed me into our room. A foul smell assaulted my nostrils. Sui was sound asleep under the heap of quilts and blankets. Konni put a cold hand into the quilt which made Sui shrink further under the covers. I coaxed him saying, "You need more oxygen. Our room is very smelly. The coal stove gives off too much carbon monoxide and if you breathe too much of it you will die. Little Tiger in Number Thirteen died of carbon monoxide poisoning last week. Don't you remember?"

Sui reluctantly came out of the covers and Shalin opened the door to change the air. Shalin had such a fear of gas poisoning that she insisted on keeping the door open for at least five minutes before we went to bed, no matter how cold it was outside. Every room in the courtyard had a ventilation hole in the window. Even so, cases of gas poisoning happened from time to time.

Snowflakes were still flying. It must be very nice in Beihai Park. The lake would be all white. There would be very few people. I suggested we go there, but Shalin said there was a lot of laundry to do. I suggested we have Mongolian hot pot for lunch. She agreed. I set out to find the right piece of mutton.

As I returned from my hunt at the butcher's, I saw Konni running out of Jinli's room and she following, flourishing a ladle, shouting "Oh, you naughty boy!"

Erfeng hurried out of her room and inquired anxiously, "Has he been into mischief again?"

"Mischief?" Jinli seemed to be on the brink of exploding, but seeing the pitiful expression on the younger woman's face said instead, "Nothing serious, Sister Erfeng. The boy poured a full jar of salt in my pot of beef stew."

"Oh, that wretch!" Erfeng exclaimed. Konni was standing at the Yus' door, looking curiously at his mother talking with Jinli. Yu Min motioned him to run. But the boy was too slow to comprehend the serious consequence of what he had done. Erfeng turned and rushed at him. He was amused at the scene, as if he were merely an onlooker. Until his mother had grabbed him by the arm he didn't realize he was going to be beaten. Erfeng flailed her thin arm and her delicate hand thup-thupped on the boy's buttocks. He whimpered.

"Sister Erfeng," Jinli came over and intervened. Her anger had vanished. "Don't beat the boy. He was just trying to be funny." Jinli by now must have remembered how much willing help she had gotten from the boy's father several years ago. Erfeng gave a few more swats. Jinli held her arm and said, "That's enough. If you keep beating him, I'll feel guilty."

Tears streamed down Erfeng's face. Jinli led her by the arm to her room. I walked over to Konni and asked, "Did it hurt?"

The boy looked up at me and grinned. There were no tears in his eyes. "Hurt? Not a bit."

"Then come play with Sui. I bought two strings of candied haw apples. You and he will each have one."

The boy smiled, so much like Dian Wen. Sui was lured out into the courtyard by the candied fruit. Shalin and I started tidying up the room so we could have space to prepare lunch.

"Big Brother hasn't come to the courtyard since National Day," Shalin remarked. "Perhaps he's afraid Dian Wen may be released one of these days, now the Military Control Group allows relatives of those in prison to visit them there."

I was busy cutting the mutton. It demanded patience, skill

and concentration to cut the slices as thin as paper. I wouldn't dare shift my attention to Erfeng and Big Brother now.

"They say that some people sent to prison by the Military Control Group may have been falsely accused. Do you think Dian Wen is one of them?"

"Who knows," I answered. I did not want to guess and didn't care. Nowadays things went along like making a pancake—one side up, up side down; the cook doesn't care which side is which.

That evening Shalin decided we should go over to talk to Erfeng.

I felt strange in Dian Wen's room. I had not been in it for at least four years. The furniture was still spotless and bedcovers clean. The window sill was covered with durable white paper. The stove pipe shone from constant swabbing. But the room felt empty. Erfeng must be cold sleeping alone in it. Her fragile body would not generate much warmth. She needed heat from the outside. Big Brother was strong and full of energy. He could give her warmth. As a matter of fact, I didn't despise her as I did Muchun. It was not only because Erfeng was my best friend's wife, it was because she was different from that beastly woman. Muchun played with men as she would a cat. Driver Wong had been a fool; he must have forgotten Muchun by now. If I were him . . . Well, Muchun had a way of enchanting men.

Konni jumped up on my knees and demanded we play cards. Sui was not very happy seeing him so close to me. I put my arm around Sui's neck.

Mrs. Yu came over too. Recently, like the other neighbors, she had become friendly toward Erfeng. Perhaps she wanted to make up for her coldness in the past. Mrs. Yu had been very cautious toward families of all 5/16 elements.

"Life for a woman is never easy," Mrs. Yu said. "For all these years you both have suffered much. Any woman with a weaker mind would have collapsed." Erfeng and Shalin listened with gratitude. "Have you heard any news from Dian Wen recently?"

"Now he is allowed to write us once a month and Big Sister and I can visit him in prison. A policeman there told us Dian

Wen has not been formally indicted. They keep him there at the request of the Military Control Group. We are not allowed to see him without their written permission, though there is no problem whenever we ask."

"Humph!" Mrs. Yu felt indignant. "The Military Control Group said all those sent to prison had been tried in court. They lied to us!"

"No. There has been no trial," Erfeng said in her mild tone. "The prison police assured us of that."

"No wonder Mr. Yu told me many people in the Bureau are beginning to suspect all the murder cases. From the beginning I didn't believe Dian Wen would kill anyone. We all know Dian Wen is a good man." She turned her head to Shalin and me, saying, "Things will clear up. We've lived in this courtyard together so long, we of course know Dian Wen wouldn't kill people. Good people will eventually be rewarded."

"I don't expect any reward," Erfeng said quietly. "I only hope that his name will be cleared as soon as possible, so he can come home. It's really hard to be the wife of a counterrevolutionary, especially of one in prison. Even the kids at Konni's kindergarten call him names." Tears brimmed in her eyes and she dabbed them away with a towel.

"Did the prison police tell you how long Dian Wen will be kept there?" Mrs. Yu asked.

"No."

"That's bad," Mrs. Yu commented. "A sentence has a fixed period. No matter how long it is, you know when he can come back. Longsen had three years and served it. Now he's home."

Erfeng sighed, Mrs. Yu sighed. Shalin and I said to Erfeng, "Talk to you another time," and left. We wanted to take a walk around the High Wall.

The snow in the alley had been tramped into dirty mud, as gray as the sky hanging around the Great White Pagoda. The snow around the High Wall would still be pure and white.

41 · Pretty Kang Ping Changes —for the Worse

My generation was brought up in a tradition of obedience at home and an orthodox Communist doctrine at school. We were trained to follow, to endure wrongs done to us with submission. The Chinese had always been known for their great ability to tolerate. Historically, only when authority became rotten through and through and there was also great starvation, would the peasants finally revolt. Otherwise they endured and waited. The Cultural Revolution had unintentionally brought up a very rebellious generation. They listened to no one's orders without asking why, and they asked too many disturbing questions.

Kang Ping was one of the youngsters who grew up in the worst turmoil years of the Cultural Revolution. She was too young to have fought for Chairman Mao's revolutionary line as a Red Guard. She belonged to another group known as the "ruined generation," those younger than the staunch Red Guards who were regarded now as the "wounded generation." But they had similarities—cynical toward life, suspicious of the world, and rebellious against their elders.

"I've seen through the hypocrisy of the nice preachers," Kang Ping said to Shalin. She must have encountered another dispute at school or in the family. I listened, pretending not to. "The school is asking us graduates to fill in a questionnaire. Only a few wrote down the cliche, 'I'll go wherever the country needs me the most.' Who believes their high-sounding words? They want to please the school authorities so they have a good chance of going on to high school. You know, only a small number can go. Most of us have either to go to a village or stay at home waiting for a job assignment. I refuse to go to a village and live in a pigsty."

"You should go on with school," Shalin said. "You are very intelligent. It will be a pity if you can't continue. Don't neglect your school work. With a little more effort, you'll make it."

"What's the use of spending more years at school?" Kang Ping sneered. My father is only a cook and Mother's illiterate. Haven't you heard people say that 'a good education is not as useful as an influential father'? You don't have to learn anything in school if you have a father who can get you into a university or find you a good job. These years have taught us something. We are not so easily deceived by nice talk."

"You're too young to say such words," Shalin lectured her. "You're only fourteen. The most important thing for you is to learn. Your brother told me you failed most of your courses. If Yin Ying did, I wouldn't be surprised. She's not as intelligent as you are. You shouldn't do so badly. Knowledge is always useful. Tong Yi is your age. He doesn't skip classes. Doesn't he know that his chance for college is very slight because of his family background? Still he keeps learning. Longsen likes to quote a line from Li Bo, the great Tang Dynasty poet, who said, 'My heaven-bestowed talents will be put to use one day.'"

"Now you are talking about Longsen," Kang Ping looked in my direction and said, "What has he achieved from hard learning? He read and read, didn't go to films. You complained that he even stayed at the office when Sui was born. Then what? He was sent to a labor reformation farm for three years! I believe life is to be enjoyed! Whenever I can afford to, I'll enjoy it. I don't want to worry. Fate will take care of itself."

The girl was silent for awhile and continued, "People gain by being hypocritical. They say 'for the revolution' but in their heads they think only of themselves. We are selfish creatures, the most selfish of all living things. When the Housing Office was rebuilding the Yus' house, at night I watched Gu Fu and Driver Wong take armfuls of the wood to their rooms. Later they used it to build furniture. You see, Gu Fu has been rising fast. Longsen is a good man. But he has been in disgrace for six years. There are no standards of right and wrong, white or black, good or bad. Now I'm young, I want to take advantage of it and enjoy life as much as I can."

The girl sounded too philosophical. I hadn't expected her to think so like a grownup.

"But you are not really enjoying life," Shalin said patiently. "You are ruining yourself. Your mother recently told me you often come home very late at night. That's very dangerous for you as a young girl. You even bring boys home when your parents are away. The neighbors are talking about you."

"I know," Kang Ping murmured. "I can't help it. I can forget all my worries only when I'm with friends in the same situation. We laugh, joke and argue. That's fun."

Shalin could say no more. I felt a pang in my heart. Kang Ping was no longer that little innocent girl who would pester me for stories. She was jaded. Now she would politely decline our invitations for supper, while not so long ago she had shouted with joy. She still came to talk with Shalin in the evenings because she thought Shalin would understand her and be sympathetic. In private, Shalin and I thought she had become vain, cheaply vain. She imitated Muchun in walk and gesture. She put her intelligence in the wrong place, spending hours exploring the pages of foreign fashion magazines. We didn't know where she found them, since publications from the West were guarded by trustworthy people in the office. She saved pocket money to buy fabric and cut patterns which she worked out herself. She could knit beautiful woolen sweaters by using worn out yarn she collected from friends and from Shalin.

By the middle of the year, it was definite Kang Ping could not go to high school. She refused to go to the countryside. And she spent days and days at home. Occasionally she went out to meet friends in the same plight. Out of school, she became more cynical. She seemed not to worry about her future despite her mother's constant lamentation and urging to talk to the Neighborhood Committee about a job. "Yu Min has taken a sparetime job," Aunt Kang pleaded with her daughter.

"That is not a job," she retorted. "She does piecework embroidery. I want a real job in a factory."

"But Yu Min is earning money for the family."

"Money! You only care about money! She works from dawn to dusk. She's ruining her eyesight. Do you want me to be blind for one yuan a day?"

Kang Ping complained to Shalin, "My parents talk only about how much a pound of cabbage costs or a bottle of soy sauce. Every night they prattle on. It's so irritating that I can't sleep."

"Your parents have to worry about every penny. I have to worry too. Otherwise we can't make ends meet."

"But you and Longsen don't gossip about other people. My parents take pleasure in passing the gossip around—who is having an affair, who had a deformed baby. It's really disgusting!"

Shalin had a hard time explaining to her that people with different educational backgrounds had different interests and that Kang Ping should try to understand her parents.

Shalin's words failed. Next Sunday afternoon Kang Ping and her mother had a big row in the courtyard. Kang Ping had bought a bottle of shampoo. Aunt Kang was furious. "Two yuan and twenty-five fen for a bottle of sticky water!" she exploded outside her door. "You really know how to squander money, don't you?"

Kang Ping was smiling. "It's more economical than soap. A few drops will be enough to wash my hair. This is a new invention. You should try it."

Aunt Kang would not listen. She yelled—she seemed always to yell these days when she meant to talk. "What's wrong with soap? A cake of the best soap costs only forty-five fen and you can use it for a month? Two yuan and twenty-five fen can buy five cakes, and you say using that stuff saves money! When I was your age, I didn't have fragrant soap at all. We used soda to wash our hair. We didn't die of it, did we? Now you are dissatisfied with fragrant soap. How much do you think your hair is worth? I don't know what will become of you even if you find a job and earn your own money!"

The last remark hurt too much. Kang Ping began to sob, her hair, long and shiny, cascaded down her shoulders, the new style of the bolder girls.

"Yes, I'm not making money for you yet!" she sobbed loudly, feeling very wronged. "I'm wasting your money, right? I'll pay you back for all you have spent on me."

"Ah, you ungrateful girl," Aunt Kang rushed toward her daughter, a broom in her hand. Jinli and Shalin ran over, Jinli trying to calm Aunt Kang down and Shalin dragging Kang Ping to our room. Kang Ping threw the plastic bottle on the ground.

"You see how damned arrogant my daughter has become!" Aunt Kang wailed. "Nowadays young people don't think twice about spending money!" She picked up the plastic bottle and showed it to the gathering of neighbors. "You see, this little bottle costs two yuan and twenty-five fen. I have never heard of washing hair with this sticky water!"

Kang Feng took the bottle and said to his mother, "You haven't heard of a lot of things. You'd better come inside and stop howling in the courtyard."

"Oh, you bastard!" Aunt Kang pointed the broom at her son. "You have all grown up and can bully your mother!" She stood there, her legs straight and her bound feet apart, grinding the earth. It took Jinli and Mrs. Yu some effort to drag her over to the Yus' room.

"What's the meaning of life?" Kang Ping sobbed. Yu Min and Yin Ying had joined Shalin in comforting her. "I can't get a job and don't want to go live in a village. I have nothing to do and don't want to beg the Neighborhood Committee for an official recommendation for a job. What a life this is!"

The other two girls sat quietly with her, saying nothing. They were not as quick-witted as Kang Ping and they took life in a much simpler way: go along with what comes along.

Aunt Kang was still lamenting in the Yus' room. "I had expected they would support me in my old age," she said in her hoarse loud voice. "But both of them are good for nothing. Now I only hope that they can keep themselves alive after my old man and I are dead. It's my fault! I didn't have any schooling and can't teach them proper manners. My two children are driving me crazy!"

Jinli and Mrs. Yu tried to put in a few consoling words, but Aunt Kang offered them no chance. "What do I live for?" she wailed. "I eat simple, dress simple, so she can have better clothes. But she complains the fish I buy is smelly and the pork has too much fat. I don't know what evil things I did in my former life to deserve this retribution! I shouldn't have spoiled her so much!"

Jinli finally got a chance to say, "Don't be so upset over such a trifling matter. Every mother in this neighborhood envies you for having such a pretty daughter. She's like a water lily. You should be proud of her."

"What's the use of only having a pretty face?" Aunt Kang said, her voice softening. "You can't live off a pretty face. I only hope she will find a job soon. It's not for her income—I can feed her for a few years more. But I hope the leaders of her work unit can tame her."

"Nowadays the leaders dare not say too much to young people," Mrs. Yu said. "Young people do what they want. They come to work late or don't come at all. Soong Cheng, the young man in Number Nine courtyard, goes to work three days a week, and then for only half a day. He knows a doctor who gives him sick leave every time he asks for it. He and his wife take turns staying home to take care of their baby. They still get full pay. It's no good for young people to be idling at home. They learn bad things."

Jinli said, "Your Ping is a pretty girl. She'll find a husband from a big official's family. Aunt Kang, don't worry yourself. You'll have good days ahead."

"To tell the truth, I don't expect to benefit from her," Aunt Kang smiled. "I would be content if she could just stop making trouble for me."

Mrs. Yu and Jinli knew the crisis was over. Jinli picked up the bottle of shampoo and looked at it against the window. "How pretty it is," she exclaimed. "Transparent red. It'll make Kang Ping's hair soft and shiny. I wish Kang Ping had an eye on my Ron. I would like her to be my daughter-in-law."

"All right," Aunt Kang said, "I'm fed up with her. You take over so I can have a few days in peace."

All laughed. Shalin and the girls in my room heard the conversation clearly. They smiled at Kang Ping, whose face was flushed. She had quieted down. "Your mother has seen hard times," Shalin said. "She came from a very poor village. You can't expect her to agree with your fashionable ways. To tell you the truth, I can understand you, but don't agree either. I can assure you, Tong Yi and Shen Ron will be able to do something one day. You're no less intelligent than they are. Learn something while you wait for a job."

Kang Ping sat there, twisting her long hair tenderly. "Ours is a socialist country. It is supposed to feed and clothe anyone who lives in it. Isn't that right?"

I wanted to say something, but did not know how to begin.

"A socialist country is supposed to give each person a job. Isn't that right?" she persisted; sarcasm or genuine belief, I wasn't sure. "But they didn't give me a job when they drove me out of school. Is it my fault that I'm not working or studying? They should feed me and clothe me. It's the right of a citizen of a socialist country."

I finally came up with something. "There is the question of a person's obligation to society. I think one is born to contribute something to society in his life. What's the meaning of living if a person is born only to eat and dress? I'm not saying that everyone should make a name in the world. But at least we should not lay aside our conscience. We should do our share for society."

"Conscience!" Kang Ping murmured bitterly and fell silent. I suspected she had to swallow hard to suppress another argument. This word had become as distasteful to young people as "feudal ways" had to the Red Guards.

"I know you might not agree with me," I continued, "but I still want to tell you. One should do something good for society. You feel let down by it—it has let too many people down. If we keep blaming it, we will only ruin our own lives."

Kang Ping did not look up at me. I knew my words sounded too nice to ring true to her. I wished I could believe them myself. I was now living in a paradox. Cynicism could ruin the lives of youngsters like Kang Ping. It would ruin mine as well. I had no right to lecture Kang Ping.

"You're growing prettier and prettier, you know," I said, wanting to end the talk in a more relaxed atmosphere. Aunt Kang had finished lamenting and was laughing heartily in the Yus' room.

Kang Ping smiled at me self-consciously.

42 · Premier Zhou Enlai Is Dead

On Thursday, January 6, 1976, around ten, I was taking my daily walk near the office during morning break. A radio in a shop cracked alive. I had never heard mourning music broadcast over national radio before. I felt seized and wondered why. The dirge, which was to be heard again that year, was sad in the dusty, windy day.

I lingered in the street. My colleagues would be talking about it. I did not want to be among them. More radios had been turned on. People stopped to listen for details. The announcer only repeated the same terse information: "Premier Zhou Enlai died at 09:57 hours this morning."

The street was full of Bureau people using the morning break to shop. They hurried back to the office. I returned a bit later and met Shalin at the gate.

"Premier Zhou Enlai is dead." Her voice was full of pain.

"I heard the news," I said flatly.

"Many are crying over his death," she noticed my coldness and spoke reproachfully.

"So what?" I demanded.

"Aren't you moved?"

"Why should I be?"

"He was the best leader in China."

"I'm not sure." I was getting impatient.

"You'd better watch what you say." Shalin looked around.

"He sent me and my friends to prison!"

"He did not!"Shalin was angry. "He was deceived by Chan Kui and the Military Control Group."

"But he sent Chan Kui to the Bureau and approved the arrests."

"I've said many times he was deceived by Chan Kui. Can't you see the difference?"

I couldn't. If the premier was as wise as the world claimed, how could he be so easily deceived by a mere army officer? I didn't want to argue with Shalin at the moment. I had suffered humiliation for a long six years and still didn't see any chance of getting out of it. I might live in shame all my life. Nobody cared if I died or lived. Nor could I care who was dead or alive.

I did not join my colleagues in the outburst of sorrow. Many were reluctant to go home. They waited in the office for further news. They waited to see if the central authorities would call for a demonstration in honor of the late premier. There was no further news, only the music playing again and again and the deep, sad voice repeating the same message. As soon as I felt it was appropriate, I left for home.

In the courtyard the men were gathered in front of the Yins' room chatting. It would be impolite not to join them. Also, I wanted to hear the speculations.

"We'll see what China will become," Mr. Yin was saying. He, so cynical, was solemn at the moment. "Something will definitely happen."

"There will be new shuffling at the top," Mr. Chang commented. "Chairman Mao doesn't have many trusted people now. That's why he relies on his wife, Jiang Qing, so much. After Lin Biao's death, his men were out. The top army commanders now are all the premier's men. I'm sure Zhou Enlai must have told them how to deal with the situation."

"I don't think they can last long." Driver Wong said, referring to Jiang Qing and her people as "they." "All day I drove the new Bureau chief around to meetings concerning Zhou Enlai's death. I overheard them talking. Those at the top are very busy. They hear that a couple of military commanders might make trouble. They're worried about Xu Shiyou the most. He is the chief of the Guangzhou Command, with nearly a million men under him. He's tough. They say he could scale walls with one jump in his young days and that once he shot an aide who entered his office without knocking. If he brought his troops north, Beijing would tremble."

"I don't think any of the military men dares move right now," Mr. Yin said. "Chairman Mao is still alive."

Driver Wong lowered his voice and said, "He hasn't been in very good health lately. Have you noticed how thin he has become? In a film I saw, he was supported by a nurse when he met the president of Sao Tome. He can't even talk clearly now."

"The Chairman's health has been ruined by the Cultural Revolution," Mr. Yu said. Although he had begun to take part in the courtyard chatter, most of the time Mr. Yu was a listener. As a Party official, he had to be cautious about what he said, so we gave special attention when he spoke. His opinions were more authentic than Driver Wong's. "He was in good shape three years ago. But his health has been waning since last year. He didn't expect the situation to run so wild that it would get beyond his control. He supported the Red Guards routing out Capitalist Roaders within the Party. But the Red Guards literally dismantled the whole Party structure. Then he sent the army to government offices and factories to put the situation back to normal.

"The army itself was fighting factional wars. In some cities army units supplied guns so civilian factions they supported could fight against each other. In Sheyang, factory workers used big guns and tanks in street fighting! Consequently, the reputation of the army is ruined, too. Look at the army officers at the Bureau—they don't show up at meetings or even in the corridors any more. I've heard they will be withdrawn soon."

"They should have gone back to their barracks long ago," I pitched in. "They haven't done a bit of good since they came. They have only split the Bureau further. The only thing they have given us is twenty-three people in prison and two hundred labeled 5/16 counterrevolutionary elements!"

"I heard that the cases were approved by Premier Zhou Enlai himself. Is that so?" Mr. Yin asked Mr. Yu.

———

265

"No," Mr. Yu answered. "Chan Kui reported that some young radicals in the Bureau had used torture and electric shock on people under investigation and several had died. The Premier was very angry and said something like, 'These young people have no respect for the law. They must be disciplined.' The Premier hadn't meant those in the Bureau specifically. But Chan Kui told us in a way that implied the Premier had condemned the people here. Also using the same trick, he forced the prison to accept the people he sent. Chan Kui is now sitting on the back of a tiger. The only solution is for him to be withdrawn from the unit."

"But I don't think the Bureau will let him get away so easily," I said, having learned that confirmed 5/16 elements had sent an appeal to Chan Kui's commander that he stay at the Bureau until all the cases were cleared.

"I'm afraid there's not much to do about it," Mr. Yin said. "During this Cultural Revolution, too many people have been wrongly accused and not a few have died. Also as an old Chinese custom goes, people can be wrongly arrested but they can never be lightly released. You will be lucky if you are ever exonerated."

On January 11, the office building was emptied after lunch. It was said Premier Zhou's body was being delivered to the crematorium at Babaoshan in the western suburbs. A strong Siberian wind was blowing. Shalin left for Chang'an Boulevard. She gave me a stern stare when I said, "You needn't go there in this chill to show your respect for him." She left on her bicycle. I returned home.

The courtyard was deserted. There was an order from the city government that no factory stop working that day. Students were kept in school. The central authorities did not like Premier Zhou's popularity and were trying to minimize his glory. Granny Yin was dozing off on a chair by her stove. I lit mine.

The wind was whipping at the paper and whistling through the spaces around the window. I found some old newspaper and pasted another layer over the cracks. The fire was spritely but didn't give much heat. There was always that queer smell as the room was heating up. I opened the door to invite in a cold current of air, which carried some dried leaves of the jujubes. I hated to stay in the room during the day. Two hours would make me dizzy and nauseous from inhaling the bad air. I took a book and a stool and went over to the northern row. All the doors were locked. I set the stool against the Kangs'. It was warmer in the inset of the doorframe, in the sunshine, than it was in my room. The wind sounded faintly overhead, only stray drafts whirling at my feet.

Around half past three Driver Wong came back, carrying a net bag with pigs feet. He offered me some. They were nice, clean and succulent—not easy to find these days. I politely declined. "Then have a beer with me after I put them on to cook."

I returned to my room and added another cake to the stove. I sat by the window to read. Driver Wong went to the toilet to fetch water. It would take an hour to scrape the pigs feet with an electrician's knife.

At a quarter to five Mr. Yu and Mr. Yin came back, their bicycles rattling down the steps at the gate. Mr. Yu was never interested in public events such as parades and meetings. He went because he had to. He was not a hero worshiper. Having stayed in the courtyard three hours without anything to do, I wanted to talk to someone. I was annoyed with Shalin. She would be exposed to the wind all those hours and might catch cold. Then I'd have to wait on her!

"Hasn't Shalin come back yet?" Mr. Yin asked. He understood his neighbors and knew Shalin must have gone to Chang'an Boulevard.

"My wife must have gone there too," he said lightheartedly. "I rode down a section of Chang'an Boulevard. The sidewalks were packed with weeping people. This is the first time I can remember so many people out on their own free will, and even with the central authorities discouraging such a show of feelings. People's will cannot be bullied, aha."

Mr. Yin chuckled, resuming his tone of cynicism. "Ha, we common people still have enough conscience to take things seriously. There are at least a million people in the street to see the premier off. That's worth living for, to be respected by so many. By the way, Longsen, you'd better prepare some hot soup for Shalin. She must be freezing, standing in the wind."

Shalin didn't return until six, her face flushed from cold and excitement. "You should have seen it," she said, holding the soup bowl in two hands for warmth and sipping at it. I should be thankful to Mr. Yin for his good advice. Without the hot soup to show my concern, Shalin would be angry with me for not having gone to pay respect to her most worshiped man. "You really should have gone," she said. "You would surely have been moved. People wept and cried as the hearse went by. Many ran after the cortege."

I refilled her bowl from the pot on the stove and urged her to drink more. "This will chase the chill from your body," I said solicitously. "I don't want you to catch cold."

43 · Tong Yi Is Arrested in Tiananmen Square

Every year in early April when the ground was thoroughly thawed and the grass green and flowers budding in sunny spots, people would go the graveyards to pay respect to the dead. This was the Qingming Festival. Folks in my native village would be very serious on this occasion and we children looked forward to it. In early morning the boys and grownups would go out to gather in their clan's burial ground. Girls were not allowed because they would take another name at marriage.

We would ride in ox-drawn carts with the women and offerings. We kowtowed first to the highest mound in the northernmost tip of the graveyard in which the clan's earliest ancestor was buried, and then to the smaller and smaller graves that fanned out southwards as the clan was divided into successive family units. The grownups burned ghost money—gold paper cut like coins to help the ancestors make their way in the nether world—and covered each grave with a layer of fresh earth from a nearby pit. Then the time came when the clan elder distributed roasted cakes and fried rolls, first to us children. Besides Spring Festival, this was our favorite occasion, though our mothers' stern stares kept us from cheering and shouting. This was a time of mourning, they would say.

When Beijing became the national capital in 1949, it exploded with inhabitants. Burial ground became very expensive. The city government began to urge residents to cremate their dead. Then the land became state property. Few people could afford to bury their dead any more. During the Cultural Revolution, cremation became literally compulsory. In the countryside, graves were either dug up or leveled to make room for crops. The festival was branded as feudal and superstitious, and was no longer observed.

In 1976, the Qingming Festival would have fallen on the fifth of April. Since the end of March, Tong Yi and Driver Wong had been supplying daily news about what was happening at Tiananmen Square. Wreaths and white paper flowers of mourning were being delivered there in great numbers by college students and young factory and office workers. Ribbons bore messages and poems of tribute to the late Premier Zhou Enlai. But restlessness and uneasiness were rippling in the atmosphere of Beijing.

"Some people are really brave," Tong Yi told us. His childish face and small stature did not suggest the rebellious young generation. He tried, or genuinely had, a reserved, mature expression on his face. "One poem reads," he said as he fished out a notebook from his blue jacket pocket and flipped to a page, "Listen, it reads,

"In my grief I hear demons shriek;
I weep while wolves and jackals laugh.
Though tears I shed to mourn a hero,
With head raised high, I draw my sword.
China is no longer the China of yore,
And the people are no longer wrapped in ignorance;
Gone for good is Chin Shi Huang's feudal society.
We believe in Marxism-Leninism, we fear not
Shedding our blood and laying down our lives;
The day modernization in four fields is realized,
We will come back to offer libation and sacrifice."

The boy's face was getting even redder. "There is no misunderstanding who Chin Shi Huang symbolizes," he said. "The Chinese people won't tolerate tyranny of Chin Shi Huang's type."

I was amused. In politics his father was timid. Yet the son was unusually brave. He read a lot, like his father in this aspect.

Also like his father, he seldom talked to the neighbors. He was too outspoken today.

"Chairman Mao praised Chin Shi Huang for his burning of books and burying scholars alive . . ." the young man rambled on.

"Are there still so many people at Tiananmen Square?" Mr. Yu cut in sharply.

I got his message and said, "There was a notice at the office that no one should go to Tiananmen Square." We were trying to stop Tong Yi lest he blurt out more unseemly words.

Mrs. Tong called him in for supper. "Young people are young people after all," Mr. Yu said. "They dare say what they want to say."

"A newborn calf has no fear of tigers," Mr. Yin commented. "After it has been chased by a tiger, if not devoured it will become smart. Longsen learned his lesson. Three years in a labor reformation farm is enough to dissuade anyone from being brave. Isn't that true, Longsen?"

I smiled.

"Well," Mr. Yu said. "That may not be true for everyone. Some can learn and some cannot."

"I bet you Dian Wen won't learn his lesson," Driver Wong put in. "He won't have changed a bit if he is released. He will still be a leaf in any wind."

"Well . . . that might be," Mr. Yu said.

Beijing, capital of two dynasties for the six hundred years before 1911, was a regular square surrounded by a wall ten feet thick at top and eighteen feet high. Nine gates were located on four sides—two on each side and an extra one, Qianmen gate, directly in front of Tiananmen, the south facing palace gate. In the center of the city was another walled city, the Imperial Palace, or Forbidden City. In front of Tiananmen Gate was an open space, used as a buffer to keep people from being too near the palace. In the last period of the Qing Dynasty, Beijing expanded southward forming what came to be known as "the outer city." Tiananmen Square gradually become the center of Beijing.

On May 4, 1919, several dozen college students gathered in Tiananmen Square for a rally to denounce the humiliating treaty of Twenty-One Demands, the one of the most crucial political events in modern Chinese history. The First World War had ended and the Paris Conference convened. The world powers would not allow China to take back Shandong Province from Japanese occupation. The students used the slogan, "Fight for national sovereignty. Down with domestic traitors."

On January 19, 1935, Beijing students demonstrated at Tiananmen Square against the Japanese invasion of China's northeast. Either because it was the largest open space inside the city or because it was the center of the city, when the Japanese took the capital they also used it to hold parades to celebrate their victories in China and Asia. But Beijing people hated to talk of this blaspheming of their beloved sacred place. Tiananmen Square should be the symbol of glorious deeds and heroic feats.

On October 1, 1949, Chairman Mao Zedong stood on the repainted Tiananmen gate tower to announce the founding of the People's Republic of China. Every year that followed, the new government held parades on May Day, and National Day. Great rallies were held here to denounce imperialist Americans in the early 1950s during the Korean War, and revisionist Russians in the late 1960s during the military threat to China's borders. In the 1970s the Square became the ground where Red Guards displayed their might and support for Chairman Mao against Capitalist Roaders within the Communist Party.

In 1959, in preparation for the grand celebrations of New China's tenth anniversary, ten major construction projects were carried out in Beijing, two located in front of Tiananmen Gate— The Great Hall of the People on the west of the square and the Museums of Chinese History and the Chinese Revolution on the east. Old houses were torn down, as well as the two majestic archways on either side of the square. The square was enlarged on both sides and southward. Chinese leaders were proud of huge rallies to show the world. Every event in Tiananmen Square should involve one million people, one-eighth of Beijing's residents, a quarter of the population, excluding the old and very young.

Tiananmen Square had witnessed many parades and demonstrations during the twenty-six years of Communist rule. This was the first time Beijing residents had come to demonstrate their sentiments without official organization. The target was Jiang Qing, and everyone was aware that behind her was her husband. Going there to present a wreath or a flower in loving memory of the late Premier Zhou Enlai was a statement against the central authority. The danger was great.

Police were dispatched to pull down the wreaths and sweep away the flowers. Crowds protested. Factory militia were sent on the fifth of April. Soldiers formed a cordon around the square. A car with a loudspeaker circled and urged the crowds to go home, warning that those who refused to leave would be dealt with as counterrevolutionaries. At seven in the evening, factory workers in safety helmets with wooden clubs rushed out of the palace gates. Backed by uniformed police, they began to beat people and drag them to waiting vans and trucks. A car was overturned and burned, to create evidence of counterrevolutionary sabotage.

Tong Yi did not come home that night. At midnight the Tongs' light was still on. Mr. Tong said savagely in the quietness, "I knew that boy would get in trouble one day. He's been getting more and more restless. I told him not to go to Tiananmen Square but he wouldn't listen. He must've been arrested."

Mrs. Tong was desperate but helpless. It seemed there was no hope of her precious son's return. Twice that night Mrs. Yu had gone to the policeman in charge of the neighborhood. He told her, "The thing is just too hot for me to go asking around." Driver Wong and I went over to the Square. A curfew had been imposed around the area. It was deadly quiet there. Only street cleaners, sweeping away the litter of torn paper, orphaned shoes, hats and kerchiefs. We dared not stop. We all liked Tong Yi and wanted to help. As the policeman said, the matter was too hot for us to do anything but wait.

Tong Yi came home at dusk the next day. The Yus were in the Tongs' room, and the Shens and Kangs went over too. "We don't have to go over right now," Shalin said, "since there are already many people there." Sometimes I was irritated by her common sense attitude toward everything. One was supposed to do things for appearance's sake, such as being the first to send congratulations or condolences. I was dumb at socializing; she was worse.

Suyan had joined the consolation, her voice the loudest. She had no real affection for anyone so she could extend any feelings in the most moving and profound words. These days she laughed more often. Everything she did or saw seemed worthy of laughing about. Gu Fu had been in West Germany for nearly a year now. Suyan said proudly he had bought a color TV, and announced generously that she would let us watch it. It would be the first TV in Tanyin Alley and would surely be a grand event. I could see in my mind's eye how Suyan would laugh then.

Now she was not laughing, her voice was permeated with concern. Mrs. Tong was thanking her profusely.

When I came home the next day, I saw Tong Yi reading a book by their door. He looked up and greeted me with a smile and began to tell me what had happened.

"Were you beaten?" I asked.

"No," he said, "but many were."

"Perhaps they took you for a child because you are so small. Why didn't you leave earlier since they had already given warnings?"

"I went with three of my schoolmates. They wanted to stick it out."

"So you suffered from being unyielding."

"We didn't really suffer much. Except a few who were interrogated by the police, most of us were left alone in the front yard of the Forbidden City. The worst was the cold and having no food."

I laughed and went back to my room to prepare supper.

44 · Granny Yin Is Dead

The earth is *yin*, or female, according to Chinese philosophy, and the sky is *yang*, or male. The earth is activated in early spring after a winter of inertness. Thus *yin qi*, or earth energy, rises to push *yang qi*, heavenly energy, up. *Yang* is life and *yin* is death, in another interpretation. When *yin qi* dominates the atmosphere just above the ground, many deaths occur.

After Spring Festival, Granny Yin had fallen ill several times and looked more frail each day. "It's her age," Mrs. Yin told the concerned neighbors. "But she can still eat a big bowl of noodles."

Old age it might be, but we didn't like the way Mrs. Yin treated her mother-in-law. At least she should take her to a hospital for a checkup.

After April, Granny Yin seldom came out of her house. She seemed shrunken. Her eyes, once alert, had become misty. Her cheeks sank, but not like those of old toothless women; she still had her teeth and could eat anything. But Granny Yin's spirit was obviously short. As she went outdoors to fetch a kettle of water from the tap, her protruding shoulder blades quivered and her stick-like arms shook. She could no longer take in the laundry for her neighbors. When the coal man came she would shuffle out to direct him to arrange the coal cakes, supporting herself against the door frame.

According to one belief, old people had to pass through two crucial times: one was at seventy-three, the other at eighty-four. Granny Yin would be seventy-three this year and it seemed her health would not carry her over the threshold. The neighbors were whispering it.

"I asked Mr. Yin why he didn't take his mother to see a doctor," Shalin said, knitting a sweater for me. I was reading *On the Beach* and picking at the dirty threads of the frayed cuffs of my quilted jacket. How would I feel when the world was about to perish in a nuclear war, I wondered. "What did he say?"

"He said he couldn't afford to take a day off from work. 'The family has to eat,' is what he said. You see, what's the use of raising children? Granny Yin has spent her whole life bringing up Mr. Yin, and at her age she's still laboring for him. The other day when I was home looking after Sui, I heard a crash on the floor next door. I ran over. Granny Yin was on the ground. I took her to her bed. She had fallen asleep and slipped off the chair. Yin Ying is fourteen. She can come home earlier to prepare supper. But she doesn't. She has just recently begun doing dishes. We shouldn't spoil Sui like that. Granny Yin wouldn't let Mr. Yin do a single chore when he was young. He never learned to care about others."

I laughed and Shalin asked me why. "It's you who's spoiling our son."

On April 16 Granny Yin died, alone at home, crumpled in bed, fully dressed in her old blue cotton jacket. Shalin was home and had gone over to see if Granny Yin needed anything and found her. A pot of red beans was on the stove, simmering. Mrs. Yin had left word she wanted to have steamed buns with bean paste filling for supper.

Mr. Chang was home too. He called the Yins at their work and told me the news on the phone. I found Driver Wong at the garage and Mr. Yu in his office. We came back in Driver Wong's car.

Mr. Yin had not yet returned from his factory across the city. Without the son, there was no one to take responsibility. Even Mrs. Yin who had returned did not know what to do. Mr. Chang took charge of the situation. Mrs. Yu suggested Granny Yin's clothes be changed before her body became too stiff. So Mr. Chang gave the order to go ahead. Mrs. Yin took out a pair of trousers and a jacket, neither new. I suddenly remembered Granny Yin had given her deathbed clothes to my mother and she had never prepared another set for herself.

By the time we had laid Granny Yin out properly on the single bed, Mr. Yin arrived. He shed a few tears. We hadn't seen Mrs. Yin shed any.

Shalin and I had wondered if the Yins would be willing to spend fifty yuan to hire a hearse. "He might ask Driver Wong to take the old woman on a pickup truck to the crematorium," I predicted. Actually that would be better than the open truck the government would send.

Mr. Yin decided to call the crematorium after all. A van came instead of a truck. They were improving service. The two vicious looking men in their late fifties complained about carrying the coffin from the end of the alley where they had to park. Having experience with undertakers from my mother's death, I handed them two bottles of Ergoutuo. "Just for cleaning your hands," I used the traditional phrase. I added two cartons of Qianmen cigarettes.

Mr. Chang and I went with Mr. Yin in the van, and Driver Wong drove Mrs. Yin and Yin Ying along to the crematorium at Babaoshan.

"One should visit a crematorium once in awhile," I told Shalin after we returned. Shalin felt very sad about the death of Granny Yin. "Whenever I come back from there, I feel free of my mundane worries. Most people can live sixty or seventy years. Compared with the life of the earth, or the solar system, or the Milky Way, man's life is a moment. People die just like that. During your seventy years you spend one-third of the time sleeping. Before fifteen or sixteen you are in school, knowing nothing of the world. When you begin to know things, trouble begins. You worry about pleasing your superiors, about a job, and about money. Before you know it, you are old and dying. Think about it; how much time is there to enjoy life? You laugh when you listen to a comedian, you smile when something funny happens.

You put all these moments together; how many hours do they come to? A hundred in your whole life? No more than that, I bet. I give you a piece of advice: enjoy life when you can."

Shalin looked at me strangely, her knitting needles poised in mid-air, as if I had returned from Hell with ghosts dominating my soul. I smiled sheepishly.

I had been trying to forget, forget everything; forget the humiliation I had been subjected to all these years. But I couldn't. I wanted to fight with someone, winning or beaten I didn't care, just to get it out. In the beginning I hated Chan Kui and wanted to kill him right away. Now I hated no one in particular. To me, even Chan Kui was merely a pawn on a chess board. There were millions in China like him. Some were worse. At least Chan Kui was in the open. Anyone who was ambitious and who had power would do the same thing under the same circumstances. Many hid themselves in the dark and shot poisoned arrows at others from behind.

There had been too many betrayals of friendship, of brotherhood and of kinship. The Cultural Revolution had destroyed all the traditions of two thousand years, good and bad together. I had become suspicious of everyone around me. In the labor reformation farm as I was lying squeezed in a corner on the cold or steaming-hot bed with eleven others, my stomach aching from hunger, or as I stared at the sky during my breaks in the fields, I had thought hard.

I knew perfectly well I wouldn't have a chance to wash away my shame. Even if I were exonerated, as my friend Officer Nu had assured me as I was leaving Chadian Farm, I could never erase the shame I had brought upon myself.

I had yielded to coercion. I had made a false confession in order to get myself out of confinement. I would not have the courage to defend myself in the future. Who would trust someone who had made false confessions? A liar! I would have to live in shame the rest of my life, my tail tucked between my legs. I wouldn't dare speak loudly, lest I remind others of how cowardly I had once behaved.

Officer Nu had been wise. "The best way to deal with people around you," he had said to me, "is to keep a respectful distance from them. You smile at them, greet them pleasantly, but never get too close."

My weakness was, however, the feeling of loneliness in the absence of friendship. I needed someone to pour out my heart to. I could speak half my truth to Mr. Yin. But I had to be careful. Anyone might betray me when the situation required it of them. Even your best, most trusted friend might, when he had his own neck to think about.

I felt more frustrated now that I had no one in particular to hate. I hated the world in general.

I wanted desperately to extricate myself from this predicament. Why should I hate so intensely when everyone, big or small, had to end up in that mouth of fire at Babaoshan?

45 · An Earthquake

In 1969, an editorial jointly put out by *People's Daily*, *Red Flag* magazine and *People's Liberation Army Daily*, the three most powerful official publications in China, carried Mao Zedong's latest statement: "The next fifty to one hundred years, beginning now, will be a great era of radical change in social systems throughout the world, an earth-shaking era without equal in any previous historical period."

Zhou Enlai's death left a forlorn country behind. More rumors, always demoralizing, ran rampant. People had become bolder and bolder in their complaints. There were too many counterrevolutionaries. No family had escaped having a reactionary relative or friend. Reactionary, once such a horrifying term, had become worn out by overuse. People were waiting for something big to happen.

On July 26, 1976, at the still night hour of 3:43, a tremendous earthquake in twenty-three seconds totally demolished Tangshan, a city of one million people, officially taking the lives of a quarter of them. Many believed there were more dead. Chairman Mao's wise prophecy of a coming earth-shaking era began only eight years after he made it. Beijing, only a hundred and twenty miles from the epicenter, was thrown into panic.

I could not remember feeling the quake, but found myself crouching on the floor by the bed. Shalin was frantically gathering Sui in her arms and rolling under the bed. Now I felt the house shaking and swinging. I rushed to the door, pulled it open and jumped out. Shalin was slow with the burden of the child. "Earthquake!" I heard Mr. Yin shouting outside in the dark. "Get down!"

We all squatted down. Low rumbling sounds seemed to roll from deep within the earth and from some great distance. The houses quivered and heaved threateningly. The dark silhouettes of the jujube trees made a weird noise, less the rustling of wind than a shivering in fear. Bricks near the eaves of the Tongs' room came loose and some were falling. A house somewhere collapsed—even that sound was muffled, as if afraid of provoking more evil by falling with a clear howl.

All the men were in shorts, the women with thin sleeveless tops. Although it was in the hottest part of Beijing summer, the night air was cold, made colder by fear. Shalin was holding Sui tightly in her arms, trying to wrap him up with the bath towel she had snatched from the bed. I realized I had been selfish. She had remembered the child; I had cared only for myself. "I'll go in to get some clothes," I offered.

"Don't!" Shalin stopped me urgently. "The house may fall at any moment."

I waited five long minutes, the sense of guilt torturing me. Mrs. Yin and Yin Ying needed decent cover too. Mr. Yin and I, deciding the house would not collapse immediately, ran in and out in three seconds, grasping whatever lay on the bed. Other men did the same for their families.

Dawn broke to a pelting rain. Several walls that had been loosened by the aftershocks crashed down, blocking half the alley. The office notified us to send people to fetch a tent for temporary shelter. Driver Wong, Mr. Chang, Mr. Yu, the boys and I went, and brought it back in Driver Wong's truck.

The police station and Neighborhood Committee had allocated a space in front of the High Wall for each courtyard. The wide road and sidewalks there were the largest open place available for several thousand families nearby.

We worked in the torrent of rain, digging holes in the meticulously paved sidewalk to erect poles, and tying coarse rope around the young poplar trees. The armed guards of the High Wall mansion did not interfere, nor was this much of a gesture of hospitality from whoever lived inside.

We left enough space in the center for young children and divided the rest into halves for the women and the men. There was only enough space for each of us to sit out of the rain. Some families brought their stoves to cook meals. We from 6 Tanyin Alley went back to cook in the courtyard. Though there were kitchens in the middle, our courtyard was still the largest in the alley, so we could stand without fear of a wall collapsing on us. Despite the heavy rain, the air was stifling. Many sat out in the road with umbrellas.

In the afternoon, the Bureau Earthquake Office, set up in the morning, told us to come fetch poles, tar paper and other materials for building individual shelters.

I brought two rolls of tar paper and a dozen poles. Mr. Yin took some plastic sheets and wooden poles from his factory. We decided to pool our resources for a shelter in the open space in front of our two kitchens. We put two beds together and tied the poles onto the bed legs to form a frame, over which we first stretched the plastic sheets and on top the tar paper. Mrs. Yin, Yin Yang, Shalin and Sui slept in it while Mr. Yin and I slept on three chairs put together, exposed to the night air. Most people of other courtyards stayed on in the roadside shelters at the High Wall. Mr. Tong did not sleep a single night in the open. He used his wooden poles to build a scaffold over two double beds in his house and let his family sleep under it. He himself sat dozing under the eaves, a bath towel over his shoulders.

All government departments and organizations were already swollen with surplus manpower. For a good half of the office staff, going to work had meant drinking tea and reading newspapers. Now one-third of the usual staff was enough to carry on the office work. The rest were covertly encouraged to stay home. In our courtyard, only Mr. Yin and Cook Kang continued to work five or six hours a day. The rest of us sometimes dropped in at the office to get news as a distraction from the boredom. As soon as Mr. Yin came home, the card game began. It would last until six, to be resumed after supper. It wouldn't end until eleven. No womenfolk protested. I joined the playing every day.

It was as if the world was nearing its end. People were trying to savor a little bit more of what it had left.

The women chatted to pass the time. Shalin and Mrs. Yin were knitting in the shelter. Mr. Yin and I were playing chess under the eaves. The rain slanted down. The weather was getting cool as July approached its end. Aunt Kang swaggered on her bound feet over to the shelter.

"A retribution!" she said to the two women. "I had sensed an ill-omen for a long time. Think about all these years. Everywhere people lunging at each others' throats. Nobody putting any heart in their work. Wild kids saying 'awesome' and 'shake' instead of a simple 'good.' So the earth shook. They don't say 'shake' any more.

"Wasn't that an omen? Man cannot cross certain boundaries. Remember the Great Leap Forward? Everyone was in a frenzy. Making steel by melting down pots and pans. Free meals by the roadside. Communism had arrived, they said. In my village you could gather basketfuls of potatoes without using a spade. All left there to rot. My cousin was feeding wheat bread to her pigs. In October the cotton fields were still white—just too much to pick it all. Then the next three years there were droughts, floods and all kinds of calamities. Fifty people in my village died. In Beijing we were luckier, but we were hungry all the time.

"Heaven's retribution!" Aunt Kang continued, moving further inside the shelter. A gust of wind blew the rain onto the bedcover. "Things were beginning to get better in '66 when they started the Cultural Revolution. Perhaps the Chinese were born to suffer. We're not allowed to enjoy a decent life for very long! Last year so many people died in the floods in the south. From the beginning of this year, things have been going from bad to worse. First Premier Zhou Enlai dies, then General Zhu De, and now the earthquake. All these ill omens. It has not come to its end yet!"

Aunt Kang looked around mysteriously and sat on the edge of the bed to rest her little feet. Only then did Mrs. Yin remember she had not invited her to sit down yet. "Please sit down," she said, moving further toward the center. "I wonder when the rain will stop."

"You know," Aunt Kang refused to be distracted, "people are saying that Premier Zhou Enlai was the slops; General Zhu the hog feeding. Chairman Mao is the hair on the hog. Now Slops is gone, Hog is dead, how can the bristle last long?"

Mrs. Yin was horrified by Aunt Kang's statement, which came from puns on the names of the three leaders. "Oh, please don't talk like that. You'll get us all in trouble!"

Mr. Yin raised his eyes from the chess board and said to his wife, "You don't have to worry. After this earthquake and so many deaths, the authorities won't bother with us for passing rumors. Perhaps all of them have left Beijing for safer places."

"I won't say these words to anyone else," Aunt Kang spoke hastily. Mrs. Yin was not so sure about that. "Anyway I'm not the only one talking. The people at the High Wall are all saying so." The Kangs were sharing the tent there with the Yus and the Shens.

After a week, people's fear of aftershocks had greatly subsided. As July slipped into August, it began to get chilly during the night. Mr. Tong's method of protection became the best example for all of us. We built scaffolds over our beds and moved inside to sleep. Even those living in apartment buildings moved inside and slept under a canopy of wood sticks. I wondered how much protection the scaffolds might provide if an earthquake occurred again. A concrete slab floor would kill anyone in the room below. "When you are destined to die tomorrow, you won't live to the day after," Mr. Yin said courageously. The earthquake had revived the sense of superstition.

The Chinese government refused to accept international aid. "Vanity at the expense of the common people!" Driver Wong said to the card players. The survivors were living in sheds of cardboards and tarpaper and the weather would turn cold soon.

An army engineering corps worked on the highway and railroad to Tangshan day and night. Army and civilian rescue workers sent in relief materials and brought out those seriously injured. We had learned that my second brother was dead. His wife would give birth in a month, so my father and I decided to bring her to Beijing.

The Civil Construction Ministry was sending out an investigation team to Tangshan and my other brother and I managed to get a ride with one of their buses.

It had been raining heavily since the quake and the highway was jammed with all sorts of transport including animal carts, push carts and occasionally the car of an official directing the rescue work. And the uninterrupted torrent of bicycles loaded with household belongings, children and the injured. Nearby counties and cities were setting up refugee camps to lighten the disaster area's burden. More than half a million injured people were being shipped out.

More and more crumpled houses indicated that we were approaching the epicenter area. Rifts in the road had been filled, uprooted trees pushed out of the way. Frequently we saw only rubble where a village of several hundred families once stood, and we saw several corpses lying uncared for. Perhaps they belonged to families whose members were dead or injured. Rescue efforts were concentrated in the city. Outlying villages had to take care of themselves. Our driver said several days ago villagers swarmed to the city to loot and many were shot. "Greed is human nature, isn't it? Loot at such a time, pumph! I'm not a Communist Party member, but when they asked me to come to transport the injured, I didn't even go back home first. Some doctors who are Party members refused to come. Gold can be tested only in a crucible!" The driver was obviously proud of his sense of humantarianism.

When we stopped at the roadside to stretch our legs, an old villager squatting there was glad of the chance to rehearse his story. "I was on night watch on the threshing ground," he said. "It was stifling, so I was outside the shed. There were flashes of blue in the west and this low rumbling, way off, which rolled across the fields, very low but very scary. The air still as a tombstone. It was almost like I felt the houses and trees falling, since it was too dark to see, you know. Standing things just fell to the ground soundlessly, like soap bubbles exploding. I watched my village jump once and collapse. Only then did I feel the earth fall away from under me. I was knocked over. A quarter of my village is dead!"

In the city, rescue workers were still dragging bodies from the rubble and the air smelled terrible, a mixture of decay and disinfectant. We found Lian, our sister-in-law in a shed a mile from our village.

"I buried him myself," she told us, her voice rich with passion. "Third Uncle didn't immediately come to dig him out. I pleaded with him to help. 'He couldn't be alive anyway,' he told me. 'And why bother to dig in this rain?' He went off to rescue the things in his house!

"He might have lived, who knows. I dug, but how could I move those concrete slabs? After it was light, the neighbors came to help. He was already dead. I didn't go to Third Uncle for help again—I buried him myself. You want to see his grave?" No, I didn't think it would make any difference.

The village was riddled with pits. The ground had fallen into the thousands of coal mining tunnels under it. The mine administration had warned the villagers of this when I was a boy of five, I remembered. Several times the mine had paid the villagers to move. But country folks wouldn't move off their land as long as the fields were fertile. To move would mean to go begging.

We gathered Lian's things in a bundle and left for the highway. My father had wanted me to see how Third Uncle was getting on. Lian told us he had a shack in a village nearby, but my brother was too angry to go. Lian said little during the hours riding back. She looked old and exhausted. Her fingers were still raw and swollen.

Shalin offered to take care of her until the baby was born. We put a single bed in our small kitchen and built a safety scaffold over it. She joined the life of the courtyard, was modest and friendly toward the sympathetic neighbors. But Lian had witnessed too many deaths all at once; it had calloused her sense of sorrow. A month later, she gave birth to a lovely girl, whom we all adored.

46 · Chairman Mao Passes Away

It was as if the earth's tremendous jolt had awakened people from a dreadful hallucination. The force of nature showed them the insignificance and helplessness of their lives. After the panic was over, Beijing residents, old and young, resumed a docile life. The eight long years of struggling and quarreling seemed to be left in the remote past. Nevertheless, it was a bit too quiet, making us uneasy. It might be the heavy rains which followed the earthquake. Everything was damp, even our hearts. And our minds were foggy, too.

It might be something else.

Nature had not been kind to China since the Cultural Revolution began in 1966. If the deaths of Premier Zhou Enlai and General Zhu De had not placated the divine forces, a bigger sacrifice would have to be made. We were waiting for something. Something big enough to end the misfortunes of China, as the rumors predicted.

On September 9, 1976, Chairman Mao Zedong's death was announced. A dynasty would be leaving with him.

A million-strong funeral was held at Tiananmen Square. One-third of the office staff had gone there in the early morning. Those of us who didn't go watched the live broadcast in the meeting room. It lacked the drama of a film or the excitement of a ball game. I wondered how many were willing to go to the square or to watch such a dull event for two hours. Whether we liked it or not, we had to be there to demonstrate our sincere love to the late Chairman, the savior of the Chinese nation. Jiang Qing, now widowed, and her closest comrades-in-arms

Zhang Chunqiao, Yao Wenyuan and Wang Hongwen stood in the center of the Tiananmen Gate tower, a place reserved for the highest Party officials. They seemed self-conscious. Perhaps they had not got used to such prominence. Were they sure they could control the country? The generals and state and Party officials who had not been brought down or who had been re-established by the late Premier, kept an awkward distance from the upstarts. Chairman Mao once said, "All reactionary elements overestimate their own strength and underestimate that of the people." But by now many people had been confused in distinguishing revolutionary from counterrevolutionary elements. So this statement could be applied either way to anyone.

Wang Hongwen, youthful, handsome and taller than the average Chinese, appeared not bad for a state leader. Lin Biao would have been bad for the image of China if he had succeeded the late chairman. He conveyed a nasty feeling of conspiracy. Jiang Qing had aged too much. She had been a film star in the thirties, so she must have been pretty once. Otherwise the late chairman would not have chosen her to replace his former wife whom he had not had time to divorce. Well, actors and actresses can always remain attractive—that is their profession. But I did not like the idea of putting an actress at the helm of China. She might play at politics as she would the role of a pretty girl on the screen. Make-believe was her best virtue—if she had other virtues. But who knows, she might really believe she was representing the people's interest.

"Like a circus show, isn't it?" Mr. Yin commented.

"There you go again!" Mrs. Yin turned to her husband angrily. "Sooner or later you'll get us in trouble."

"Oh, don't worry," I said lightheartedly. "No one cares about how much people swear any more. The big shots are busy dividing the power."

"I don't talk to others this way," Mr. Yin chuckled. "I only say the weather is good, the cold is warm and the storm is refreshing. No talk about state affairs. Can you believe it, Longsen? Thirty years ago one dared not discuss them. In theaters and public teahouses there were notices forbidding customers to talk about state affairs. Now we are required to. Otherwise they will accuse us of being political loafers. But they don't allow us to say what's really on our minds. If we do, we're counterrevolutionary. They teach us how to lie."

"Brother Longsen," Mrs. Yin could not stop her husband, so she turned to me. "Don't listen to his nonsense. He started drinking as soon as he put down his bicycle. This month he has already gulped down two bottles of Ergoutuo. When he is half filled with that horse piss, he begins talking wild. I won't listen, so he takes you on."

"Madame," Mr. Yin took the cup from the table and made a gesture to tease his wife. "Dear wife, this cup is for your health. I wish you a hundred years of life."

Mrs. Yin stood up and stalked over to the table, snatched away the cup and pushed a bowl of rice over to him. "You'd better eat this to soak up the alcohol!"

"All right! All right!" Mr. Yin said and turned to me. "I'm forty-three this year. I would say I have seen a lot of the world. I have never been so confused as I am today. Now the Chairman is dead. Do you think the country will be better off, or worse? They say, in socialist China the workers are the masters of the country. But we have a special class, don't we? The other day I was on a street north of the department store on Wangfujing. You know, there is a special store supplying big officials. I talked with a driver there. He showed me the yellow croakers in a pickup truck. Fresh, refrigerated and big; fifty fen a pound. The price is the same as on the street. But the difference is quality. I have never seen such beautiful fish in all my life. We say capitalists in the West live extravagant lives. We denounce the Soviets for their privileged class. Which class do our big officials belong to? Every word they utter serves the people? Pure nonsense! In one respect I agree with the aim of the Cultural Revolution—to make the big shots suffer just a bit!"

Mrs. Yin urged him to finish his meal. "You'd better hurry. I have to do the dishes. After that I want to cook something for lunch tomorrow—it costs too much to eat in the factory canteen."

The great Chairman Mao had died. Yet we continued to live our simple lives, to worry about tomorrow's lunch.

News media under the control of Jiang Qing tried frantically to make Chairman Mao's death into an affair grander than Premier Zhou Enlai's nine months earlier. The public response was not as spontaneous. The mourning dirge that played continuously over the radio early on September ninth did not cause much weeping. Too many people had been made the fool by the Cultural Revolution he personally started. His staunch young Red Guards had been exiled to live among ignorant and often hostile villagers and they bore a huge grievance—they had been denied their college education, and thus their future.

The soldiers, no less the staunch supporters of Chairman Mao than the Red Guards, had lost their heroic image through their arrogant and tactless intervention in the civilian factional strife, which had plunged China into further chaos. Even government and Party officials, disgraced or not, were bitter.

Chairman Mao's death caused still more speculation on what China would be like. Disintegration? Unlikely. There were still many veteran Communists whose fate and personal gain depended on continued Communist rule of a united China.

Shalin and Yin Ying retreated to our room to knit. Mr. Yin talked on as his wife cleared the table and carried all the dishes outside to wash. "Hua Guofeng is a figurehead. And years ago the Chairman agreed that Jiang Qing would never be involved in leading the Party. Since then, she has harbored a grievance against those who opposed her, including Vice-Premier Deng Xiaoping. He was a sitting duck with his cover of Zhou Enlai in ashes.

"When Mao started the Cultural Revolution he had no strong backing from the Party. He realized too late that he had already lost it. The power was in fact in the hands of Liu Shaoqi's people, and Zhou Enlai's. Mao couldn't nudge these two away from the top, so he incited college students to do the job. And it worked in the beginning. But the Cultural Revolution ruined him in the end. Now the Chairman is dead. This will be a melodrama to enjoy!"

The kettle on the stove was whistling, emitting a shaft of white steam. Mrs. Yin shouted at her husband to refill it. Mr. Yin went out, taking a thermos bottle along. "Want to make a cup of tea? I brought some good tea leaves, sixty fen an ounce."

I went over to my room, brought my tea mug back. My forty-fen-an-ounce tea tasted flat. I didn't know whether it was because my tastes had refined or because the quality had gone down.

47 · Shalin and I Celebrate the Downfall of Jiang Qing

Six weeks later, one million again gathered in Tiananmen Square. The late Chairman must be turning in his crystal coffin—on display in the Great Hall of the People, awaiting construction of a mausoleum to match Lenin's. His suspended soul had to listen to the same voices that had pledged loyalty in carrying on his behests, now shout slogans supporting the arrests of Jiang Qing and her three cohorts. Marshal Ye Jianying had likened Chairman Mao to a valuable porcelain vase and Jiang Qing a mouse near it. "We didn't strike earlier because we didn't want to break the vase," he said.

Autumn is the best season in Beijing—the sky is high, the wind mild. I was glad I had not been asked to attend the gathering. Shalin and I decided to make an excursion out to Fragrance Hill. I had not been there since I left the language training program in 1966. I put Sui, now seven, on the cross bar of my bicycle and we rode out at dawn. The courtyard was quiet. As every Sunday, Chunlun, Driver Wong's eccentric wife, had hung out her mattresses and quilts, blocking the Tongs' doorway.

The streets were deserted. An occasional bus slid by. Red Flags over a number of houses and government buildings were fluttering limply in the breeze. Pieces and bits of red, green and yellow paper lay scattered, remnants of pennants with slogans like "Long Live Mao Zedong Thought!" and "Long Live the Proletarian Dictatorship!" The street cleaners did not seem anxious to sweep away the litter of this recent celebration. New slogans were painted on walls: "Down with the Gang of Four!" and "Down with Jiang Qing and Her Followers!"

We rode to the High Wall and then west along the wide road. I mused at the tranquility of Beijing after the drama of a coup d'etat, but did not share my thoughts with Shalin—no politics, just one entirely carefree day. I had a feeling that my case would be cleared soon, and I wanted to savor it.

Though the slogan "Long Live the Great Proletarian Cultural Revolution!" still echoed, with the downfall of Jiang Qing the Cultural Revolution would be less sacred. The new leadership would have to rehabilitate many veteran Party leaders who in turn would be looking for new supporters. They would find the greatest sympathy among those who had been persecuted during the Cultural Revolution. The future for me was not bad.

A clean name was not my great concern now, however. Through the seven years of disgrace, I had learned to see through the world. I was one of the first Young Pioneers, my political affiliation founded in the birth of the new China in 1949. I joined the Communist Youth League at fourteen, as early as I could. By nineteen I was a full member of the Communist Party.

I spent many evenings at the army library reading Marx, Engels, Feuerbach and Hegel to get a theoretical understanding of the Communism I believed in. I had, however, never read the history of the Chinese Communist Party, nor could I have found an authentic version, for all the political shifts. The Cultural Revolution had revealed too many contradictions, and the cruelties of the inner Party struggle were appalling. It was too confusing to want to think it through. At the labor reformation farm I made up my mind to abstain from political arguments—it was beyond me to figure out which was the right side to follow.

I thought about Mr. Yin's words of the night before. "Lu Xun said that the best way to kill a person is with over-praising," he had said. "You inflate him up to the sky, then let him go. Lin Biao as Deputy Supreme Commander had been riding as high 'as a heavenly horse,' as he himself boasted. Then he literally crashed to his death. Now Jiang Qing, our beloved Revolutionary Standard Bearer, is perhaps in prison. Ho! Who will be next?

"These years have taught me something: the self-proclaimed revolutionary officials are no different than the ministers of the feudal courts. The reason that so many bad things could have happened is that feudalistic traditions are still deeply rooted in China. Premier Zhou Enlai could have told Chairman Mao which parts of the Cultural Revolution were no good. But he didn't—because Chinese society is built on officials loyal to the emperor, not to the truth.

"Zhou Enlai knew this perfectly well. He himself led the rallies shouting 'Good health to our great Revolutionary Standard Bearer!' And we all knew he didn't like her. Who dared tell the Chairman what he did wrong? And the daring ones were purged and persecuted. That's the only way the Cultural Revolution could have come about."

If we hadn't had the Cultural Revolution, I mused as the buildings thinned, we would still believe officials live as simply as we do. One thing I had learned from it was that the common people will never again blindly follow orders from above.

When we had left the city behind, I began telling Sui stories. Bundled rice stalks were still in the dry paddies, ready for threshing. Jade Spring Hill glowed in the morning light. I told Sui that water from those springs had once been supplied exclusively to the royal family in the Forbidden City. Princes and dukes had to make do with water from the wells in Wangfujing, Prince Mansion Well, now the busiest shopping street in the eastern part of Beijing. The water from Jade Spring Hill was carried in wooden tanks on horse-drawn carts. Escorted by senior eunuchs leading the Imperial Guard, the caravan would strut through West Gate, then known as Water Gate, and rumble along the flagstones of Xisi Road to a side gate of the palace. With the Communist regime, Jade Spring Hill became the country residence of General Zhu De, who loved peaceful surroundings. Here he stayed more than half the year to avoid the political confrontations of Zhongnanhai, a wing of the former Imperial Palace, now used as residence and office by top Party and state leaders.

In 1965 when I first came to Fragrance Hill for my training, there were very few tourists. Those few who came would leave by four o'clock. The night was deadly quiet. Wind whistling through the pine woods was mysterious, almost frightening. When I was alone in the dormitory, I felt as if I were alone in the world.

In recent years, people had taken to traveling. There were many opportunities for office workers to include a sightseeing tour at their work unit's expense, as part of business.

Fragrance Hill was no longer an out-of-the-way park. Buses along two routes were crowded from early morning to dusk in the season of scarlet and crimson leaves. Beijing residents were learning to enjoy life and to relax. On this autumn Sunday, buses, cars and minibuses were backed up halfway to Jade Spring Hill. We congratulated ourselves for riding our bikes so we could thread our way through the traffic.

The park was packed and Shalin and I lost much of our enthusiasm. Broken windows and stripped interiors of the classrooms and dormitories were marks of the Cultural Revolution. The small pond was dry. Mirror Lake was a pool of dirty green sewage. We climbed Worrying Devil Peak. The small flat lawn on top was bare of grass and littered with bottles, bread wrappers and broken shrubbery. To the east, the city lay under a pall of dirty gray haze.

We rode back, feeling tired but refreshed, along a quiet road before we joined the human current near Purple Bamboo Park. We could feel the courtyard buzzing when we returned. The Yins came over to report that Gu Fu was back from Germany, but Suyan had not staged the grand reception for her husband which we had all predicted. According to Mr. Yin's calculation, Gu Fu had come back a month and a half early. That was unusual for any Chinese sent abroad officially.

"He was back at noon," Mrs. Yin said with an air of mystery. "Two men with him. Suyan didn't go to the airport but waited at home instead. I knew at once that something had gone wrong.

Suyan had a long face and Gu Fu kept his head bent. I didn't dare go over to greet him. Soon the two men left in the black car. Suyan and Gu Fu have not come out of their room since then. Isn't that strange?"

"Several people have defected to the West or the Soviet Union lately," Mr. Yin speculated. "The central authorities are mad about that. I wonder if Gu Fu was suspected of that as well. If he hadn't made political mistakes, they wouldn't have sent him back early—and with two escorts!""

"And he came back empty-handed," Mrs. Yin added.

"It doesn't seem likely he's back earlier for wrongdoing," Shalin said. Sometimes I liked her simplicity and kind intention. "Only yesterday Suyan was telling the children that Gu Fu would bring back a color TV. She should have known if something had gone wrong for her husband."

Driver Wong pushed the door open and slipped in, holding a bowl of noodles and a huge cucumber. Shalin stood up from the bed and greeted him; I gave him my stool.

"You're having supper late today," Mr. Yin said.

"Yeah," Driver Wong said. "We have a new Bureau chief. Feng Xuan has been transferred to the Liaison Department of the Party Central Committee. The new chief is younger, but has no clout with the top."

We were not interested in the new appointment—officials came and went, our lives remained the same.

"Gu Fu is back," Mrs. Yin said, knowing that Driver Wong would surely have a solution to the mysterious return of the aristocrat of our courtyard.

"I know," he answered with an air of authority. He shoveled a big mouthful of noodles and bit off a chunk of cucumber, munching with great content. We waited, watching his mouth work vigorously. The cheek muscles pouched and heaved. "He was escorted back by two embassy people," Mrs. Yin added, expectantly. Driver Wong filled his mouth again. This time Mr. Yin and I didn't watch.

"A young woman in my workshop cut a finger off on the lathe yesterday," Mr. Yin began a distraction and I immediately showed great interest and asked, "How come?"

Driver Wong swallowed the food in his mouth in one gulp. "Gu Fu was found sleeping with a woman from Taiwan. She works both for the Taiwan Secret Service and American CIA. Gu Fu was the leader of the Chinese students in Bonn, you know, and had the privilege of a room to himself. The woman was a student in disguise, but actively a professional spy. Gu Fu and she met and the woman offered to lend him her tape recorder and books and dictionaries. Each time, she would leave one or two ten-mark notes tucked in, as if my accident. Gu Fu kept the money."

Seeing he had gotten our attention back, he took a breath and another mouthful of noodles. "Chinese students there have only twenty marks a month for pocket money. They can't save enough in a year and a half to buy a color TV. But Gu Fu bought a TV, and a tape recorder and camera as well. How could he afford to buy these things without the Taiwanese woman?

"Gu Fu had built good relations with the Chinese embassy by reporting on other students. Of course the embassy didn't suspect anything. The students hated him and bided their time for retaliation. They had been aware of the affair, but said nothing.

"One evening the embassy tried to notify Gu Fu of a meeting, but couldn't find him. The students told them to look for him at a certain address. Two officials went there, but didn't ring. They waited. In the early morning when he came out, they brought him directly to the embassy. He was on a plane the following day and here he is."

"Sister Shalin, didn't I tell you Suyan laughed too loud and too often?" Mrs. Yin said, feeling proud of herself. "That was not a good way to laugh."

"Extreme pleasure begets sorrow," Mr. Yin quoted. I felt a twinge of satisfaction. All these years while my family was living in despair, Gu Fu and Suyan had been climbing high. I resented those who built their fortunes on the Cultural Revolution. They were fishing in troubled waters.

"Now Gu Fu has had it," Driver Wong said gleefully. "There is no doubt he is ruined. He will definitely be expelled from the Party. Suyan worked so hard to get in, only to exchange places with him. Wife gets in, husband gets out. One to one, no loss, no gain. Ha, ha!"

Muchun called from the courtyard, "Driver Wong, can I use your gas stove for awhile? My stove went out!"

Driver Wong stood up and hurried out, feeling flattered. "Of course, let me turn it on for you," he responded eagerly. He was the first in our courtyard to have a propane stove with a tank. He had the first black and white TV, too. Was that one reason he was pleased that all Gu Fu's treasures had been confiscated by the embassy?

"Retribution!" Mrs. Yin said as she and her husband stood up to leave. "One shouldn't crave too much!"

After they left Shalin said to me, "You go and have a few words with Gu Fu tomorrow. Don't let him feel that we drop stones on a man who has fallen into the well."

I agreed. Why should I make enemies? It didn't cost me anything to act concerned toward others.

I wondered about the same thing I'd been pondering for years: is one's destiny governed by some power that isn't known to man? It might have been known in remote antiquity. I had read speculation that there had been a long disruption in man's development. Many things we regarded with superstition today might have been understood by early man. UFOs might be their toys. Perhaps there was a God. Feeling that man had been too clever for Him to control, He might have decided to wipe out knowledge for a period of time. Wasn't He said to have destroyed the Tower of Babel? Were myths and fairy tales simply wild imaginings? There might have been a time when man could tell his own future. Fortune-tellers might be serious students of these mysteries. Who knows?

"Would you please re-tie the broom?" Shalin brought me back from my reveries.

"I told you to buy a new one," I said, irritated. "We have had it for over two years. We've had our money's worth."

"Forty fen are forty fen," she said. "You aren't a millionaire yet, saying 'buy this and buy that.' How many forty fen do you make every month?"

I made barely a hundred of them a month, which was enough to bring me back from my daydreaming.

48 · Winter Comes, the Thaw Begins

There was great jubilation over the downfall of Jiang Qing's Gang of Four, and the nation celebrated with genuine enthusiasm. Guo Xiaochuan, a renowned poet, who had been accused of writing bourgeois sentiments and was laboring at a farm, was over-excited. He had had too much to drink and died in flames when his cigarette ignited the mattress in his desolate room.

I held my optimism in reserve again. "Warlords who have been at each other's throats will have the grace to toast each other's health," I told Mr. Yin. "And thousands upon thousands have died fighting for them." I did not share with other counter-revolutionaries the thrill of expectation of a quick exoneration. It seemed that whatever happened to me had passed beyond my caring now.

Shalin was annoyed. "You should go to the investigation team and explain your case," she kept pestering me. "Others have talked with them and been assured that their cases will be re-examined. The new army officers made it very clear that Chan Kui committed grave mistakes during the campaign against 5/16 elements. If their names can be cleared, so can yours." Whenever Shalin mentioned appealing to the authorities, I felt the anger tighten my stomach. I still believed that if she had kept quiet after I was released from detention in the office, I would not have suffered at the labor reformation farm. I resolved to do everything Shalin wished; everything but one: never follow her advice where politics was involved.

This time I was determined to remain quiet.

Big Sister had come to visit and was talking with the Yins. Shalin and I went over to say hello to her. Erfeng was there too.

"Big Sister, you look much better," Shalin greeted the older woman, sitting next to her on the bed.

Big Sister laughed. "I'm retired, eat well and sleep well," she said patting Shalin on the arm. Her hands had regained some of their former plumpness. Shalin's showed strong blue veins. I remembered their smoothness during our courting. Erfeng had aged, too. Her cheeks were shallow and the color of wax. The vague grace of her fragile body had left no trace. The blue jacket hung loosely over her protruding shoulder blades and her hair was dull. I wondered if Big Brother still demanded too much from her.

"Officer Min from the investigation group called us to the office," Big Sister said for the benefit of Shalin and me. They must have been talking for quite awhile already. The tea in the glasses had turned dark brown; no steam came up from them. "They told us we could visit Dian Wen any time we want from now on, so we went this morning."

"How is he?" I asked, trying to imbue the question with more concern than I felt. I had to recapture my wandering mind from pursuing thoughts of Big Brother and Erfeng. "Is he in good health? Does he have to do hard labor?"

"He's well," I heard Big Sister saying. "He gets along well with the guards and they let him work in the sock knitting shop. The officer in charge told us Dian Wen is a good man. He never believed he had killed anyone. Of course, he said that in private." The officer must have been notified that Dian Wen's case was up for reexamination, so now he talked nicely.

I smiled. "That's good news. I mean it's good he doesn't suffer much."

No. He doesn't suffer at all," Big Sister said. "The officer took us to his dormitory and the workshop. Everything is neat and clean and they eat quite well too." I laughed. I didn't believe Big Sister had learned anything of prison life. At the labor reformation farm they fed us undercooked corn buns and raw salted vegetables and made us do heavy work in the fields. But they always served good meals on holidays which were the times when relatives came to visit. It might be that at a regular prison the conditions were better than the Farm, but I hoped not to find out.

"He performs during holiday celebrations," Big Sister said proudly.

"From what Big Sister says it won't be long before Dian Wen's case is resolved," Mr. Yin observed. He looked at Erfeng, and I looked at her too. Her face seldom showed her feelings, but the corners of her mouth twisted in response to Mr. Yin's stare. "Now that the Gang of Four are in prison themselves, Marshall Ye Jianying and his new leadership have to clear up the mess they have left. The Bureau is noticeably over the three percent quota of counterrevolutionaries. They have to do something. I feel Dian Wen will be released in two, at most three months."

"Big Sister, we miss Dian Wen," Mrs. Yin sounded genuine and I chorused, "Yes, indeed." Shalin turned toward me and glared.

"The courtyard has become dull since he left," Mrs. Yin continued. "He came to every table at supper. His jokes whetted my appetite. I could always eat an extra half bowl of rice. Also, without him no one wants to take the lead when something goes wrong in the courtyard. He is warmhearted!"

Big Sister sighed. "That was how he got in trouble. He's easily used by others."

"Ho, ho! That's Dian Wen all right," Mr. Yin added. "Hu Bon once said Dian Wen could serve any master well if the master knew how to manipulate him. The only thing needed is a few words of praise and a pat on the back. He would make a good valet."

Yes, I thought, if he had not been so eager to help the Military Control Group with false evidence, he perhaps would have been spared seven years in prison. I was not sure whether he was simple-minded or selfish. He and several others provided evidence against Hu Bon and some leaders of the Revolutionary Rebels. It was right that he spend the same length of time in prison as Hu Bon. If he'd been spared, how would those who had had to serve think of him? And I could stop hating him for reporting what I'd said to him, now that he had suffered more than I.

"You'll eat with us," Mrs. Yin announced to Big Sister. "I cooked some pigs feet yesterday. So there's no extra effort for supper."

"No, Sister Yin. Thank you, but I have to go back home. My old man is waiting for me. He won't eat without me. You see, we two old people can't be separated too long." She laughed heartily.

"We're good friends," Mrs. Yin said, seeing her out. "Although you don't come often, don't feel a stranger here."

"Not at all," Big Sister said. "I always think you're the best neighbors I've ever met." Her glance included Shalin and me.

Back in our room, Shalin said, "You should talk to the investigation group."

I didn't want to start another argument over the issue and went out to wash the tomatoes we had bought at a roadside stand. We would have noodles with tomato sauce.

"Murder cases are easy to clear up, Liang Sihuan told me yesterday." Shalin was being persistent in convincing me of her point. "Police coroners had confirmed them at the time as suicide. It was the Military Control Group which reversed the verdicts. Now the investigation group only needs to reconfirm the original verdicts. Also none of the people in prison have been formally tried. The prison can release them any time the Bureau wants.

"Your case is more complicated. You were accused of counter-revolutionary thoughts. There is no physical evidence, just your written confession. Liang Sihuan and the other murder suspects don't think your case can be easily settled. You should go to the investigation group to explain. Tell them you were forced to make a false confession."

"No. I didn't make a false confession," I told Shalin. "I wrote down many things I didn't say, if that is what you mean by 'forced.' But all of them were what I really thought. Shalin, listen to me this time. My name will be cleared sooner than theirs. I might even be made a hero for denouncing the Gang of Four in my confession." I did not laugh at my little joke because Shalin had not found it funny. She had a right to be worried.

The water was boiling on the stove. Shalin sat on the stool with no intention of moving. I put the noodles in the pot.

While the noodles were cooking, I poured Ergoutuo into a small cup and raised it toward Shalin and said, "Hey, have a taste of it." I wanted to cheer her up. I picked up a piece of sausage with my chopsticks and offered it to her mouth. She brushed it aside.

"Don't be angry with me, dear," I said soothingly. "If they don't clear my name before the others, I'll jump out the office window to let them see how wrongly I was treated." Shalin was very sensitive on that subject. Six of the ten so-called murder suspects had jumped from our office building. But she knew my weakness—I was unable to stand a gloomy atmosphere in my home. She cheered up, or pretended to. "You drink your poisonous water. I'll look after the pot."

49 · I Am Cleared

Almost everyone in Beijing accepted the political honor of working a day on the construction of Chairman Mao's mausoleum in Tiananmen Square. The stand of pine trees was dug up. The pit for the foundation was almost three stories deep. Work had never been done so fast. I was the last in my department to be sent there for a day's labor.

"You've behaved well," I was told. "The Political Department decided to let you go. You're the only counterrevolutionary from the Bureau to be permitted. Be careful."

My face showed a gratitude I did not feel.

I was surprised to see so much steel used for the reinforcement of the foundation. I heard it said that the steel was imported from Japan. Ten days after the excavation began, Beijing's first revolving-cylinder cement trucks arrived, and they poured day and night.

At the site I heard that a hoard of gold ingots had been found during the digging. "They say the place was once the secret treasury vault of Emperor Qian Long. He died mysteriously, telling no one about it. The gold is much more than enough to cover the cost of the mausoleum."

"So we shouldn't complain about the extravagance of our beloved leader for that."

"Perhaps the gold was buried here for this purpose."

"Chairman Mao must have cared about our welfare—he brought fortune to the country even after his death."

A few days later I was cleared.

"You're lucky, you know," Mr. Yin said that evening. From

his doorway I could see Shalin chatting with Mrs. Yin, Kang Ping and Mrs. Yu who had gone over to our room to extend their congratulations. At supper Shalin had allowed me to have as much Ergoutuo as I wanted.

"That's true," I said.

"The moment was right for you. There are thousands who were branded as Rightists in 1957 who are still living in disgrace."

"I know. I was exonerated because the central authorities needed it to prove that the Gang of Four, or Chairman Mao himself, was wrong and they were right. I'm a scapegoat one way or the other, but I'm glad I didn't have to carry the burden too many years. It's been so hard on Shalin and our son.

"I did ask the Bureau chief not to make a hero of me against the Gang of Four—I don't want to end up the scapegoat in the next tide. At the Chadian Farm I swore I would never get involved in politics again. My only desire then was to go back to my family and lead an uneventful life.

"I had met some ex-convicts there, all Rightists, who stayed on at the Farm to work. The outside world didn't want them. They spent their meager monthly allowance on cheap liquor.

"Now the new leaders are talking about redressing the wrongs done the Rightists. That's good, because they can't complain themselves—too scared, or too numbed toward life already."

I had noticed Mr. Yin was not very attentive. He sipped at his tea, picking at the chipped enamel of the mug, and staring at the crack in the table top, as if speculating how to seal it up. Enough dirt had accumulated to fill the gap. I remembered, when Granny Yin was alive, the table was always spotless. There was no dirt in the crack. I realized I had drunk too much at supper. The alcohol was advancing on my brain.

"You're lucky," Mr. Yin said. "You suffered only eight years. With your Party membership back in hand, you will be a success. I often told Shalin you had a destiny to work for."

I detected despondency in his voice.

"The moment was right for you," he repeated.

It came to me suddenly. Mr. Yin had been reassigned to manual labor in 1958. All the Rightists were sent to state-run farms or labor reformation farms in that year. Mr. Yin had not gotten an official brand as Rightist, for he had merely offended the Party secretary in his section. Though other young people had been branded for that.

"Yes, I'm lucky, I should say." I wanted to end the conversation. "I've been caught in the right moment."

Sunday Shalin insisted we go out for a celebration dinner. We took the bus to the Sichuan Restaurant. I felt awkward sitting inside a luxurious place, more because it was my first time eating out formally, than for the cost of twenty-four yuan.

Two months later the investigation group announced that all the murder cases were frame-ups. The original verdicts of suicide were upheld. The murder suspects who had not been sent to prison were wild with joy. They stalked around the corridors, gathering together to talk loudly and giving cold stares to those who had attacked them at meetings. I noticed the disdainful side glances from those who had managed to remain neutral through another episode.

Dian Wen came home, accompanied by Big Sister and Erfeng. We were not surprised Big Brother was not with them. Dian Wen seemed to be cheerful. Shalin and I went over to express our congratulations. I pretended not to see the flush of shame on his face and his lowered eyes when he shook my hand.

Everyone had been released from prison, even Hu Bon who spent his seven years in solitary confinement for attempting to escape to Hong Kong. I did not go to visit him right away. It would take some time before I was ready. I had made up a couplet for him: "Remember the early lesson of strife; Forego ambition for a peaceful life."

I returned to Chadian Labor Reformation Farm to clear my record with the police officers there. The Bureau offered to send a car but I declined. I didn't like that kind of display. Some people who had been imprisoned went back by car, accompanied by a senior official. The prison authorities received them with ceremony and even treated some to a celebration dinner. I went alone, on the same train which Shalin had ridden with our son two dozen times.

I walked the two miles from the station to the barracks where I had spent three years. First I looked up Officer Nu who had understood me and had tried to help. He accompanied me when I went to see the places where I'd worked. The rice in the paddies was two feet high. The luxuriant green was lovely. Days of weeding under a scorching sun in steaming water were faint memories shrouded in a delicate nostalgia.

I remembered the comparative freedom his friendship had allowed me. I had been free to escape the density and chatter of the barracks and find peace in the solitude.

During that time I had had the chance to see the plight of the peasants. In early spring there had been village girls cutting young reeds for fodder. The water in the drainage ditches where they stood for hours came to their chests. I could not have stood it for twenty minutes. Their lunch was sorghum buns, blackish and bitter, and a brine pickle. They earned twenty fen a day. Mistaking me for an officer, several peasants had asked me to let them live inside the walls. "We don't ask for pocket money," one said with the nod of the others. "We only want three meals of decent grain." I had wished for the power to stop all the nonsense of political campaigns so the Chinese nation would not waste its wealth and energy, but concentrate on building a better life.

I remembered the time, when the rice was ripening, and several of us had built small dams in the irrigation ditches to trap fish heading downstream. We cooked them in aluminum lunchboxes, with salt stolen from the horse stables.

I was amused to find that all my memories were not as bitter as I'd expected. I felt a great relief.

Officer Nu rode me on the back of his bicycle to the railway station and saw me off. I brought back to Beijing a large basket full of the grapes and pears which I had watched in the orchard with watering mouth a few years back.

Glossary

baozi—steamed buns stuffed with meat and vegetables.

Capitalist Roader—pejorative term for an official in a leading position who is believed to oppose socialism and favor capitalist strategies.

commune—in 1958, Communist Party Chairman Mao Zedong called on agricultural cooperatives to form communes in which the individual peasants' land and tools were all owned by the commune.

Cultural Revolution Leading Group—also called the Central Cultural Revolution Group, was organized by some officials of the Communist Party. This group included people like Jiang Qing (Mao Zedong's wife and member of the "Gang of Four"). It quickly became the most powerful group in China during the Cultural Revolution.

Eight Model Operas—operas on revolutionary subjects which Jiang Qing adapted and had performed in strict accordance with her directives.

fen—1/100 of a yuan.

5/16—refers to May 16, 1966, when a Chinese Communist Party circular was issued outlining the principles of the Cultural Revolution and calling on Party members to launch a strong attack on all "bourgeois" elements.

Great Leap Forward—a movement (1958-59) launched by the Chinese Communist Party to push China forward at great speed, but which instead caused economic dislocation and decline.

guiyuan—a date-like fruit, also called a *longan*, grown in southern China and thought to have medicinal value.

jiaozi—dumplings filled with meat and vegetables.

Kowloon—the area next to Hong Kong.

Kuomintang—originally the Chinese Nationalist Party, it became the Chinese "right wing" after a split in the party. The term also refers to the anti-revolutionary army headed by Chiang Kaishek, who officially ruled China from 1927 to 1949, when he was driven from the mainland.

mahjong—a Chinese gambling game, usually played by four people with 144 domino-like pieces marked in suits.

Manchu—Manchurians, a minority nationality of northeast China which established the Qing dynasty.

May Seventh Cadres School—communes where intellectuals and cadres were sent to be "reeducated" by the peasants through manual labor.

May 4th Movement—beginning on May 4, 1919 with student demonstrations in Beijing, the May 4th Movement grew into a nationwide anti-imperialist movement and a revolt against feudal ideology. It ushered in a new stage of the Chinese revolution, in which the working class and radical intellectuals took over leadership, culminating in the establishment of the People's Republic in 1949.

Military Control Group—formed with Chairman Mao Zedong's call for a "People's Liberation Army" to support the left, the workers and the peasants and to restore order in the chaotic situation of the Cultural Revolution. The group itself, however, was guilty of some of the excesses it was supposed to remedy.

Ming Dynasty—the dynasty which existed from 1368 to 1644, which had sixteen emperors spanning twelve generations.

National Day—October 1, 1949 was the day the People's Republic of China was officially established in Beijing.

Neighborhood Committee—a group of resident representatives that supervises community affairs of a neighborhood.

Qian Long—an emperor of the Qing dynasty (1644-1911), known for admiring and promoting Han (Chinese) culture.

Qing Dynasty—established by people of Manchurian nationality, it was the last imperial dynasty (1644-1911) in China.

qipao—a high-collared, sheath-like gown slitted at the bottom, of Mongolian origin.

Red Alliance—the name of one of the Red Guard factions in the Revolutionary Rebels.

Red Flag Detachment—a detachment of the Revolutionary Rebels.

Red Guard—a young person of worker, peasant or soldier background who, during the Cultural Revolution, became a self-styled "defender" of the proletarian revolution.

Revolutionary Rebels—the name of a major Red Guard group.

Shenzhen—an area of Kuangtong province bordering Kowloon, now known as a "special economic zone" in China.

Spring Festival—China's major holiday, the beginning of the new year according to the lunar calendar, usually occurring in early February of solar calendar.

Western Hills—hills west of Beijing, known for their beautiful autumn foliage.

workpoints—peasants in communes were paid in cash corresponding to the number of workpoints completed, with different jobs and individual performances valued at different workpoints.

Yellow Cows—a Hong Kong slang term for those who sell tickets at illegally high prices for a profit; the equivalent of "scalpers" in American English.

Young Pioneers—a children's organization led by the Communist Youth League of China.

yuan—the Chinese dollar, worth about 1/3 of a U.S. dollar.